THE GOOD

C000091755

MICHAEL DICKSON

THE
GOOD PRESENT
GUIDE

Pan Books
LONDON, SYDNEY AND AUCKLAND

First published 1993 by Pan Macmillan Ltd
Cavaye Place London SW10 9PG
and Basingstoke

Associated companies throughout the world

ISBN 0-330-33334-8

1 3 5 7 9 8 6 4 2

A CIP catalogue record for this book is available from the British Library.

Typeset by Spottiswoode Ballantyne Ltd
Printed by Cox & Wyman Ltd, Reading

FOR RACHAEL

CONTENTS

INTRODUCTION

'The excellence of a gift lies in its appropriateness rather than its value.'

Charles Dudley Warner

Throughout the year we have birthdays to remember, hospital visits to make, retirements to celebrate, christenings to attend, staff leaving, godchildren, thank yous, weddings – a seemingly ever-increasing number of special occasions, before we stop to consider ... Christmas. The ultimate gift ideas book has therefore been created: *The Good Present Guide*.

This Guide intends to solve forever the present-buyer's dilemma – how to buy the right present at the right price. It should also help if you frequently tear your hair out when people ask 'Well, what would *you* like?'

Selecting the right present

As an ideas book we've selected over 1500 imaginative, practical and original suggestions and categorized them according to interest and price. The idea is to make everything as easy as possible to find. However, as we all know, people refuse to be categorized, so whilst you might start with the Gardening chapter for the gardener, it's a good idea to check Country as well if you have time, then you could browse through DIY.

At the right price

Everything that's priceable is priced. That's not to say you might find a cheaper version elsewhere once we've planted the idea in your head. You must also expect variable prices from different retailers. We have selected quality products which also offer decent value; based on the philosophy that the best present doesn't disintegrate on Day Two. We've mentioned specific retailers and broad categories – depending on their efficiency you may have to shop around.

By mail if you wish

Small specialist suppliers are burgeoning and the quality of their products and produce is generally excellent; significantly above the mass market 'lowest common denominator'. There are also many retailers who offer a mail order service. For anyone tied to the office or home, or living at a distance from interesting shops this facility will save an enormous amount of time and effort. All mail order contact numbers have been included. Where they are excluded suppliers may not accept phone orders. There are also quite a selection of presents which you won't find in any High Street, but which are VERY GOOD IDEAS (and useful for giving to people who live at the other end of the country)! Finally, it's worth asking about postal orders even if mail order isn't an advertised service. Quite often charm will win the day.

A word about supply and demand

Some of the most original ideas are tucked away on bottom shelves – at least with *The Good Present Guide* at hand you'll know what to ask for. However, few stockists will put hand on heart and guarantee to stock permanently some of the more specialist items. What we've tried to do is point you in the right direction. Mail order companies, for example, often specialize in a range of like products, so whilst they won't always guarantee to continue with the precise items if demand slows, they may well have something similar. It pays to PERSEVERE! Armed with *The Good Present Guide* you may well be better informed than the shop assistant or the person answering the phone.

Irresponsibility is a good thing!

Amidst the serious business of day-to-day living, present-giving is an excuse to do something silly! The art of a good present must be that the recipient is delighted and the giver basks in the warm reflected glow! So no apologies are made for including balloon flights and fridge locks for failed dieters – just sit back and bask in the effect they cause!

My Best Present Ever

If it isn't included here, please let us know what it is – presents that you've enjoyed giving and receiving – the idea being to discover things that are slightly out of the ordinary in as many different areas as we can, as well as the classic gifts which are given year after year. Should you chose to take up the challenge, please be specific: accurate names of the goodie concerned and its manufacturer will be helpful – a 'nice blue jug' will not. Please contact us at The Good Present Guide, PO Box 1954, London W1 3ZS.

We've had enormous fun compiling the book. We hope you have fun using it.

CHAPTER ONE

BABIES 0–2

This year over 800,000 British babies will be born – over 90 every hour! Gone are the days when Mum was around to press linen and soak nappies – within three months one in two will be back at work. So today's babies are kitted out with both parents and child in mind, and you may well find baby cotton-buds and shampoos being used by the whole family. The emphasis is firmly on practicality and easy-care, combined with bold colours and fun.

UNDER £5

Baby Gro

Almost a uniform for the first six months – soft, stretchy and very washable. There is a quality difference between Baby Gro and own label – do you want it to survive for the next arrival?

PRICE: From £3.99.

AVAILABLE: Mothercare, M&S, Boots ... Universally.

'Baby on Board' Stickers

Mothercare's version has a reverse with 'Child on Board' so is actually an investment for the future.

PRICE: £1.99.

AVAILABLE: Mothercare branches nationwide; Cherry Tree Road, Watford WD2 5SH Tel: 0932 240365 (Mail Order).

Bath Products

Johnson's has become synonymous with the smell of 'baby', but there are ranges available including The Body Shop, Boots, Jeyes; all of which have a similar 'talcummy' cuddly smell.

PRICE: From 80p.

AVAILABLE: The Body Shop; Boots and all chemists.

Bath Toys

Pumps, fountains and bubble makers; lots of fish, ducks and frogs that swim and wiggle; or simply containers that you can pour from. Avoid anything too small so swallowing is impossible.

PRICE: From £1.75; e.g. £3 Suds Pal [Tomy].

AVAILABLE: All good toy shops; Mothercare.

Bibs

Small soft bibs for the tiny, to be replaced as soon as possible with wipeable plastic 'pelican' versions which catch the crumbs and reduce the washing mountain. Also 'Squeak-Me' Amish design bibs which feature squeaky lambs and pigs, etc.

PRICE: From £1.99 for pack of three terry bibs; £2.45 for plastic versions; £8.50 'Squeak-Me' bibs.

AVAILABLE: Mothercare, Boots, department stores and children's stores; Gallery Eurotas Ltd, Battle Hill, Elvendon Road, Goring-on-Thames, Oxfordshire RG8 0DT Tel: 0491 872123 (Mail Order).

BOOK CHOICE
The Hungry Caterpillar

Eric Carle's classic first book with holes in the pages for the caterpillar to crawl through.

PRICE: From £3.50 [Penguin].

AVAILABLE: All good bookshops.

BOOK CHOICE
The 'What' Books

First word and picture books based on objects a child will recognize – also what colour, what number and what shape. Babies will follow bright pictures but tear paper, so board books are preferable. Suitable from about three months upwards.

PRICE: From £2.95.

AVAILABLE: All good bookshops; The Early Learning Centre branches nationwide; South Marston, Swindon SN3 4TJ Tel: 0793 832832 (Mail Order).

Bowls, Beakers and Plates

Wedgwood's Peter Rabbit range of china is a children's classic – The Early Learning Centre have transposed the tale onto hardwearing and durable melamine, which although not as chic is much more practical. For the less classically-minded, Noddy and Postman Pat are equally popular.

PRICE: e.g. Melamine: divisioned plate £2.99, bowl £3.49, training beaker £1.55.

AVAILABLE: Chinacraft, department stores; The Early Learning Centre branches nationwide; South Marston, Swindon SN3 4TJ Tel: 0793 832832 (Mail Order); all children's specialists.

Cuddly Toys

It is a very important moment in anyone's life when they meet their first rabbit.

PRICE: From £3.

AVAILABLE: Almost everywhere.

Glostars

Enchanting star and moon-shaped stickers which are invisible until the lights are turned off, when they fluoresce and create the cosmos above the crib.

PRICE: £3.99.

AVAILABLE: Toy shops; Frog Hollow, 15 Victoria Grove, London W8 Tel: 071-581 5493; 21 High Street, Pewsey, Wiltshire SN9 5AF Tel: 0672 64222 (Mail Order).

Glow Lights/Night Lights

Plug these into a socket and they will emit a gentle glow, which not only comforts junior, but saves Mum from falling over in the dark. Also cot lights which turn off after ten minutes and glorious pottery night lights of snails, mushrooms, fairy caravans, etc, which fill the room with magic.

PRICE: From £4.25 (glow light); £8.99 (cot light); £29.00 (pottery night light).

AVAILABLE: Mothercare, BHS lighting, department stores.

Musical Brush and Comb Set

Music fascinates the very young, so here's a fun way of incorporating it.

PRICE: £3.49 [Tommee Tippee].

AVAILABLE: Department stores, children's specialists.

Nursery Thermometer

Easy-to-read thermometer which measures the temperature in terms of too hot, ideal or too cold. It is important to remember that the ideal nursery temperature is *not* tropical.

PRICE: £2.45.

AVAILABLE: Baby equipment stockists, department stores.

Paddies

Soft-lined cord booties which are the precursor of the first shoe. Not suitable for outdoor exploration.

PRICE: £2.99–£3.99.

AVAILABLE: Department stores, Mothercare (own label), Boots, etc.

Playsuits

The all-in-one totally practical coverall. For adult entertainment choose the Father Christmas, clown or dinner jacket versions (which often include matching hats) for seasonal and special occasions.

PRICE: From £3.99.

AVAILABLE: Most good childrenswear outlets.

Pram and Buggy Mobiles

A string of happy creatures to look at and ping when stuck in the queue at the supermarket.

PRICE: £4.49.

AVAILABLE: All children's stores and departments.

Rattles

Rattles have been with us since Egyptian times – because babies love them! In fact anything that makes a noise is going to be a great hit – whether a rattle, a ring, a hoot or a buzz.

PRICE: e.g. £3.99 Ball Roller [Ambi Toys].

AVAILABLE: Toy shops, department stores.

Spill-Proof Cup/Liquid Container

Parents realize that the beginning of the motorway triggers 'I'm thirsty'. All journeys, long or short, are improved with spill-proof beakers and containers.

PRICE: From £2.39; e.g. Save and Serve Travel Set £3.99 [Tommee Tippee].

AVAILABLE: All children's stores.

Sunhats/bobble hats

Protection from the sun or cold is essential – and transforms even the most roguish-looking face into a little cutey. Strawberry-style available.

PRICE: e.g. £1.75 (sailor hat), £1.95 (peaked cap).

AVAILABLE: Branches of John Lewis Partnership; all other children's clothes shops.

Teething Rings

Either medicinal versions which ooze soothing gel for teething babes – or a substitute for the jumper, necklace or finger that they would chew on anyway.

PRICE: From £3.25.

AVAILABLE: Chemists, children's shops.

Toiletries Travel Pack

It is amazing that such little people require such a lot of clobber – a travel pack including handy sizes of all toiletries will make the whole process more manageable.

PRICE: £4.49 (includes baby powder, lotion, bubblebath and shampoo in a PVC cosmetic purse).

AVAILABLE: Mothercare branches nationwide; Cherry Tree Road, Watford, WD2 5SH Tel: 0932 240365 (Mail Order).

BETWEEN £5–£10

BOOK CHOICE
Hugh Jolly Book of Childcare

For those who aren't Penelope Leach fans, Dr Jolly has an equally loyal following.

PRICE: £9.99 [Unwin].

AVAILABLE: All bookshops.

BOOK CHOICE
My Soft Story Books

Bright and bold picture books which are built to withstand chewing and throwing. My Soft Story books go hand in hand with the marvellous Activity Bear (see page 9) – the pages squeak, rattle, flap and fascinate young babies.

PRICE: £5.99 [Matchbox].

AVAILABLE: All good bookshops, toy shops and toy departments.

Chatter Telephone

When used as a telephone or a pull-along toy the Chatter Telephone continues to be extremely popular despite or possibly because of its familiar design.

PRICE: £5.99 [Fisher Price].

AVAILABLE: Most good toy shops.

Cologne

You may not believe it, but colognes exist specifically for sensitive young skin. The chocolate one is probably the most outrageous.

PRICE: £6 Abracadabra [Absorba].

AVAILABLE: Harrods; White House Ltd, 31 New Bond Street, London W1Y 0BY Tel: 071-629 3521.

Flying Toys

A range of wooden aviators which flap their wings with a natural movement when set in motion by a pull cord. Seagulls are the version most often seen but dragons, Pegasus and Dumbo are also available.

PRICE: 90p-£18.

AVAILABLE: Some toy shops and craft fairs; Humble Bee Toys, The Oaklands, Stroat, Nr Chepstow, Gwent NP6 7LR Tel: 0594 529237 (Mail Order).

Hammer Shapes

Small children haven't yet learned the adage about fitting square pegs into round holes – this is their chance. All the pieces have been safety-tested.

PRICE: £5.99.

AVAILABLE: The Early Learning Centre branches nationwide; South Marston, Swindon, SN3 4TJ Tel: 0793 832832 (Mail Order).

Nursery Frieze

Alphabet, animals or nursery rhymes – decorative and/or educational borders for nursery walls.

PRICE: From £8 for ten metres (Baer & Ingram's elephants and rabbits).

AVAILABLE: Baer & Ingram Wallpapers, 273 Wandsworth Bridge Road, London SW6 2TX Tel: 071-736 6111; also DIY stores, hardware shops, Mothercare.

Sponge Bricks

Covered foam bricks are quiet, easy for small hands to grasp and safe to throw and chew on.

PRICE: £6.99 for six.

AVAILABLE: Branches of Adams; Boots, department stores and toy shops.

Tape of Womb Sounds

Sweet Dreams is a compilation of 'straight womb sounds' which may prove restful for fractious newborns.

PRICE: £5.95.

AVAILABLE: Mysteries, New Age Centre of Covent Garden, 9-11 Monmouth Street, London WC2H 9DA Tel: 071-240 3688 (Mail Order available).

Walking Rein

As we are all too aware, a harness or strap is essential for all children as they are prone to go on the run – it will prevent them travelling too far and causing anxious moments. Adjustable straps and a back clasp which cannot be undone.

PRICE: £5.99.

AVAILABLE: All childrenswear shops.

BETWEEN £10–£20

Activity Bear

After ten years, the Activity Bear shows no signs of flagging in his mission to introduce babies to the fun of learning.

PRICE: £18.99 [Matchbox].

AVAILABLE: All good toy shops, department stores.

Baby Accessories Box

A large compartmentalized box which organizes the large amount of toiletries and accessories that accompany any baby. Particularly useful when travelling. Becomes a picnic or sewing box when no longer needed for the child.

PRICE: £16.99.

AVAILABLE: Mothercare branches nationwide; Cherry Tree Road, Watford WD2 5SH Tel: 0932 240365 (Mail Order).

Baby Change Bag

How to make the clobber look like a reasonably elegant shoulder-bag. Fold out to act as a waterproof changing mat.

PRICE: £17–£18.

AVAILABLE: Adams, Boots, department stores, etc.

Baby Shower

Prevents sudden hot and cold changes in temperature by recycling bath water. In the shape of a duck with wings that flap to keep everyone amused.

PRICE: £14.99 [Tomy].

AVAILABLE: For stockists contact: Tomy (UK) Ltd, Wells House, 231 High Street, Sutton, Surrey SM1 1LD Tel: 081-661 1547.

Birth Chart

A coloured chart wheel supplied with an in-depth analysis of the child's physical, emotional and mental characteristics – so parents can be prepared. All this is possible by supplying Chris Marshall with the baby's time, place and date of birth.

PRICE: £15.

AVAILABLE: Chris Marshall, c/o Mysteries Ltd, 9-11 Monmouth Street, London WC2H 9DA Tel: 071-240 3688 (Mail Order).

BOOK CHOICE
Baby and Child

Penelope Leach's sensible replacement to Dr Spock – the baby book written from the baby's point of view!

PRICE: £12.99 [Penguin].

AVAILABLE: All bookshops.

Cot Activity Centre

A cot-attachable gamesboard where pressing, pulling and spinning provide the requisite quota of rattles, squeaks and squeals of delight.

PRICE: From £9.99.

AVAILABLE: Most good toy shops, department stores.

Cot Bumper Set

Foam or quilted padding which prevents knocks into the side of a cot. Usually available to coordinate with cot quilt. A musical/activity bear version is also available.

PRICE: From £14.99.

AVAILABLE: Department stores and children's specialists.

Cot Sheets and Linen

These have to take a lot of washing, so look for quality to last. 100% cotton will ensure no allergic reactions from either sheets or blankets.

PRICE: e.g. flat 100% cotton sheet £5.99 (pack of two); fitted stretch terry sheet £6.99 (pack of two); cotton cellular blanket £5.99; brushed cotton blanket (with embroidered appliqué) £19.99.

AVAILABLE: Mothercare branches nationwide; Cherry Tree Road, Watford WD2 5SH Tel: 0932 210210 (Mail Order). Also department stores, children's specialists.

Crocheted Bootees

Absolutely charming, hand-crocheted cotton bootees in white. They are tied with ribbon and will last for generations. Perfect for special or display occasions.

PRICE: £18.95.

AVAILABLE: Past-Times branches nationwide; Witney, Oxford OX8 6BH Tel: 0993 779444 (Mail Order).

Cuddle and Dry Robes

A fluffy towelling bathrobe with a hood. Like the adult versions, the price increases as the towelling becomes thicker.

PRICE: From £13.99.

AVAILABLE: Mothercare branches nationwide; Cherry Tree Road, Watford WD2 5SH Tel: 0932 240365 (Mail Order). Department stores.

Discovery Mat

A quilted discovery mat to make life interesting within a three foot radius. It features 12 different textures and sounds including mirror, peekaboo flap and glove puppet.

PRICE: £11.99 [Fisher Price].

AVAILABLE: Most good toy shops and department stores; call Fisher Price direct for nearest stockist Tel: 091-518 0383.

Hanging Name

Handmade felt names to decorate nursery walls, doors or cots with either a clown or a teddy and balloon decoration (available in either primary or pastel colours).

PRICE: From £15.99 (0–5 letters).

AVAILABLE: Letterbox, P O Box 114, Truro, Cornwall TR1 1FZ Tel: 0872 580885 (Mail Order).

Jeans

For the youngest swinger in town – these are nappy-accommodating rather than hip-hugging.

PRICE: From £14.

AVAILABLE: Branches of The Gap nationwide.

MAGAZINE SUBSCRIPTION
Practical Parenting

Pregnancy and birth, baby and child care, health and education – covers all issues surrounding parenthood.

PRICE: £16.50 p.a. (monthly).

AVAILABLE: *Practical Parenting*, Kings Reach Tower, Stamford Street, London SE1 9LS Tel: 071-261 5058; Subscription Dept Tel: 0444 445522.

Microwave Bottle Sterilizer

No more overnight soaking – just pop it into the microwave with a little water and it sterilizes in ten minutes.

PRICE: £14.99 [Avent].

AVAILABLE: Children's specialists; Early Learning & Baby Centre, South Marston, Swindon SN3 4TJ Tel: 0793 832832 (Mail Order).

Mother's 'Comfitum' Seatbelt Guide

A guiding system designed specifically to make seatbelt wearing more comfortable by releasing pressure around the tum, either pregnant or convalescing.

PRICE: £14.99.

AVAILABLE: Early Learning & Baby Centre, South Marston, Swindon SN3 4TJ Tel: 0793 832832 (Mail Order).

Nursery Cutlery

Silver-plated spoon and pusher reproduced from an early nineteenth-century design. Could also be useful in adulthood to deal with the perennial problem of peas.

PRICE: £18.95.

AVAILABLE: Past-Times branches nationwide; Witney, Oxford OX8 6BH Tel: 0993 779444 (Mail Order).

Parasol

Protection for sensitive skin from the harmful sun's rays. As it is impossible to get a pair of sunglasses for a baby, a parasol will also protect his eyes.

PRICE: From £14.50.

AVAILABLE: Department stores, some toy shops.

Suncare Products

Very young skin is particularly sensitive. Most suncare ranges include a product for babies which is practically bullet-proof.

PRICE: From around £3 upwards e.g. £3.69 (Johnson's Baby Sun Protection Cream Factor 15, 75g).

AVAILABLE: All chemists.

Swim Seat

A Floatie swim seat is a flotation device specifically designed for babies. A double ring and integral back rest make it quite safe for baby to bounce about in complete safety – but always under parental supervision.

PRICE: £11.99 (3–12 months); £13.25 (10–18 months).

AVAILABLE: Selected children's shops and toy/sports shops; for nearest stockist contact: Sytrox (UK) Ltd, Unit 7, Mount Pleasant Road, Aldershot, Hampshire GU12 4NL Tel: 0252 316626.

BETWEEN £20–£50

Aran Sweater

Luxury handknitted Aran sweater in miniature form for snuggly warmth and rosy cheeks.

PRICE: £23 (22").

AVAILABLE: The Irish Shop, 14 King Street, London WC2. Tel: 071-379 3625 (Mail Order available).

Baby Bouncer

A good way of entertaining baby as frustration mounts pre-walking. Fits into most doorways and folds compactly. Can be used as soon as the head can support itself.

PRICE: £29.99 [Maclaren].

AVAILABLE: Baby equipment stockists; Early Learning & Baby Centre, South Marston, Swindon SN3 4TJ Tel: 0793 832832 (Mail Order).

Baby Monitors

A plug-in microphone and receiver device that allows parents to relax in front of the TV rather than leap up and down to listen for cries. With the new awareness of cot death there are also alarms which can detect if the child stops breathing for a period of time.

PRICE: e.g. £29.99 Tomy Walkabout 2000 (looped antenna for improved reception); £49.99 Tomy 2-Way (both units transmit).

AVAILABLE: Boots, Mothercare, Adams, baby equipment stockists, department stores; Early Learning & Baby Centre, South Marston, Swindon SN3 4TJ Tel: 0793 832832 (Mail Order).

Baby Walker

A solid wooden trolley (and brick carrier) which is essential for newly mobile toddlers as it instills confidence and helps balance. Can be used indoors and outside and is designed specifically not to tip over when young children pull themselves up by the handle.

PRICE: £29.99.

AVAILABLE: Toy shops; James Galt & Co Ltd, Brookfield Road, Cheadle, Cheshire SL8 2PN Tel: 061-428 8511 (Mail Order).

Back Pack/Front Pack

Body contact is back in favour and seems to help babies sleep happily. Front carriers are ideal for younger babies incorporating head supports and enabling sleeping or nursing; back carriers are more suitable for an older child.

PRICE: e.g. £27.99 Tomy Cradle Carrier; £22.50 Fisher Price Carrier (front carriers); £41 Tomy Dream Rider (back carrier with storage bag and adult lumbar support).

AVAILABLE: Children's shops, department stores.

Bike Seat

Special seats over the back wheel are available for babes in the fast lane. Pashley make traditionally styled hand-built bicycles which are incredibly sturdy and do a double-seater child-seat version for a family of twins or two young children.

PRICE: £48.74 [Pashley].

AVAILABLE: Cycle retailers, branches of Halfords; for nearest stockist contact: W R Pashley, Masons Road, Stratford-upon-Avon, Warwickshire CV37 9NL Tel: 0789 297044.

Foldaway High Chair

A robust little number which fits easily and securely on any table. Ideal for family visits to a non-child oriented location.

PRICE: £24.99 (tested to 5 stone); £29.99 (tested to 20 kilos).

AVAILABLE: Mothercare, department stores.

Liquidizer

By the time Mum's cooked and mashed a special meal and had it rejected several times over, she'll realize the sense of liquidizing non-seasoned versions of the normal family diet.

PRICE: From £22.75.

AVAILABLE: Electrical appliance shops.

Musical Mobiles/Other Mobiles

Mobiles are good for eye-movement development for cot-bound babes and gentle lullabies *do* help send them to sleep.

PRICE: £39.50 [Eden], £29.50 [Mothercare].

AVAILABLE: Most children's shops, department stores, toy shops.

Nappy Delivery Service

Disposable nappies are one of the most cumbersome consumables that anyone has ever had to struggle home with. Organize a nappy delivery service – Boots deliver nationwide free of charge for about a month's supply.

PRICE: From £17.94 (240 Boots compact disposable nappies); £27.96 (192 Pampers disposable nappies).

AVAILABLE: Boots Home Delivery Service, Boots the Chemists Ltd, Nottingham NG2 3AA Tel: 0800 622525.

'New Baby' Pillow

A frippery as pillows are not advised for infants. Embroidered pillow (with a pink or a blue trim) which includes two names and the date of birth.

PRICE: £29.99 (14″ x 14″).

AVAILABLE: Frog Hollow, 15 Victoria Grove, London W8 Tel: 071-581 5493; 21 High Street, Pewsey, Wiltshire SN9 5AF Tel: 0672 64222 (Mail Order).

Stair Gate

The best is the gate which opens for adults but remains firmly closed for the toddler.

PRICE: £22.99.

AVAILABLE: Mothercare, Adams, department stores.

Tiny Trike

Think of the trike you had as a child and it will probably be the same as this one! Galt have designed the Tiny Trike to go on and on forever. It has double wheels at the front for stability and is strongly made in natural wood and protected with melamine lacquer.

PRICE: £27.99.

AVAILABLE: Good toy shops; James Galt & Co Ltd, Brookfield Road, Cheadle, Cheshire SK8 2PN Tel: 061-428 1211 (Mail Order).

£50 AND ABOVE

Car Seat/Buggy

For infants, a soft recliner which lifts easily in and out of the car, is well balanced to carry, incredibly shockproof and will also double up as a buggy with room for the shopping basket underneath. For those slightly older, the Kiddy Seat comes in covered polystyrene and can be put in any car you like. The child is held in by the seatbelt.

PRICE: £129.99 MacLaren Superdreamer; £103 Kiddy Seat.

AVAILABLE: Mothercare, Adams, department stores; Kiddy Seat from VW dealers.

Cube High Chair

A solid wood high chair which ends up as a piece of nursery furniture with integral table and chair.

PRICE: £85.

AVAILABLE: Mothercare branches nationwide; Cherry Tree Road, Watford WD2 5SH Tel: 0932 240365 (Mail Order).

Name Picture

The child's name spelt out in 'heavenly' characters. Each picture is built up of an angel-alphabet, mounted and framed. Six weeks are needed for delivery, although Xanthe, Quentin and Zoë will be disappointed because they can't do Q, Xs or Zs. Alternatively, an 'initial' picture (with initial, name and date – framed in limed-pink or blue wood) is a smaller (cheaper) and equally charming option.

PRICE: £58.50 (name picture); £14.99 (initial picture).

AVAILABLE: Eximious (name picture), 10 West Halkin Street, London SW1R 8JL Tel: 071-235 7828 (Mail Order available); Letterbox (initial picture), P O Box 114, Truro, Cornwall TR1 1FZ Tel: 0872 580885 (Mail Order); also look in local classified sections and gift shops for local artists.

Nursery Box

Toy and nursery paraphernalia boxes and small 'what-not' boxes. Beautifully stencilled pine boxes which become permanent nursery furniture.

PRICE: £279.

AVAILABLE: Billie Bond Designs, 2 Warners Farm Cottage, Howe Street, Great Waltham, Essex CM3 1BL Tel: 0245 360164.

Nursery Design

A full make-up service for curtains, blinds, bedcovers and headboards for nurseries and children's rooms is offered by Turner Adams. Many of their designs are exclusive and they will make up to your own specifications.

PRICE: Quotes per job.

AVAILABLE: Turner Adams, 2A Askew Crescent, London W12 9DP Tel: 081-749 4161; Kingston Road, Bradford-on-Avon, Wiltshire BA15 1BD Tel: 0225 865 744 (Mail Order).

Nursery Furniture

Hand-painted furniture is the hallmark of Dragons of Walton Street. Limitless range made to order by craftsmen in Berkshire, including four-poster beds, toy boxes. Alternatively, wardrobes as castles, or houses, makes putting clothes away just a little bit more fun.

PRICE: From £55 to £200 upwards.

AVAILABLE: Dragons, 19-23 Walton Street, London SW3 Tel: 071-589 3795.

Playring

An award-winning variation on the playpen – the playring comprises a pair of soft foam-filled semi-circles covered in brightly covered PVC. It's covered in bells and rattles and other exciting things for children to investigate, and designed to offer babies and young children postural support as well as a cosy and safe environment in which to play.

PRICE: £117.50.

AVAILABLE: James Galt and Co Ltd, Brookfield Road, Cheadle, Cheshire SK8 2PN Tel: 061-428 8511 (Mail Order).

Reusable Nappies

Extremely easy to use, cheaper and not the 'environmental horror' that disposables are. All-in-one reusable nappies (Kooshies) are made in 100% cotton flannelette with a waterproof membrane between the layers to prevent leaking. They have a flap inside which can be adjusted for boys or girls to give extra absorbency where it's needed most. You change the whole thing every time.

PRICE: From £7.95 for a single small Kooshie; from £57.95 (ten small Kooshies).

AVAILABLE: The Green Catalogue, Freepost BS7348, Axbridge, Somerset BS26 2BR Tel: 0934 732469 (Mail Order).

The Bed-Side-Bed

The perfect compromise for parents who cannot bear physical separation from their baby but are not quite up to three in a bed. The Bed-Side-Bed fits against any adult bed and looks just like a traditional cot, except it only has three sides. Conversion to four-wall cot possible with separate kit.

PRICE: £250 (plus £16.20 delivery; cot conversion kit free).

AVAILABLE: The Bed-Side-Bed Company, 98 Woodlands Avenue, Wanstead, London E11 3QY Tel: 081-989 8683.

Travel Cot

An easily assembled fabric-sided cot that folds down compactly is invaluable for trips to friends and grandparents.

PRICE: £79 Travel Lite (complete with mattress and travel bag); £60 Fold Flat [both Cosattoo].

AVAILABLE: Children's specialists; department stores.

Tumbledrier

Need we say more?

PRICE: From £169 (vented); from £299 (condenser).

AVAILABLE: All good electrical appliance stores and department stores.

CHAPTER TWO

CHILDREN 2–5

KIDS used to go to school at five and thought it terribly grown up. Now creches and carers give way to nurseries when children are about two-and-a-half and over half of the under-fives have been there. Make no mistake – they love it. Combine school with the ability to zap the video and exert pressure on their parents to buy those yoghurts with feet, and you'll realize today's consumers start young.

UNDER £5

Acrylic Glasses and Decorated Mugs

Non-breakable acrylic: look for the ones which are made in two layers and have floating ducks and swimming frogs that move as the glass is tipped.

PRICE: From £4.

AVAILABLE: Gift shops, department stores.

BOOK CHOICE
Janet & Allen Ahlberg

A delight – from *The Baby Catalogue* as a first book, to *Burglar Bill*, *Each Peach Pear Plum*, *The Jolly Postman*, and any of *The Happy Family* series. Every one a winner.

PRICE: From £2.99.

AVAILABLE: Bookshops.

BOOK CHOICE
Learning to Read

Letterland is a fun way to learn the ABC with Annie Apple, Uppie Umbrella, etc. Pop-up books are very special for young readers who get a great thrill from pop-ups, lift and reveals and anything you can push and pull, or scratch 'n' sniff.

PRICE: From £2.99 [Heinemann young books].

AVAILABLE: Bookshops, toy shops, WH Smith.

Books on Tape

A saviour on long car journeys. Short stories for the very small, or compilations of nursery rhymes etc. At five the attention span is about 45 minutes.

PRICE: From £3.99.

AVAILABLE: Toy shops, bookshops and department stores.

Bows & Arrows/Cap Guns/Swords/Space Guns

It's been proven that fighting play has no bearing on long or short-term aggressiveness. Parents know small boys make guns from sticks or anything else available; possibly a more dangerous option. Noise is an added bonus – cap guns, space guns making variable noises, rifles which bang, anything that flashes.

PRICE: From £1.99.

AVAILABLE: Practically ALL toy shops (except The Early Learning Centre which has a policy against fighting toys), department stores, newsagents.

Cars

The sturdier the better because they will endure more than their fair share of bumps, crashes and flying leaps. The Burago range offers superb value for money on 1/43 scale and up into their large sizes where doors start opening and wheels turning, etc. (Not recommended for the under-threes).

PRICE: 99p (1/43 scale); from £4.99 (1/24 scale).

AVAILABLE: Branches of Beatties nationwide; newsagents, and good toy shops; Beatties, 10 The Broadway, Southgate, London N14 6PN Tel: 081-886 4258 (Mail Order).

Chubbie Crayons

Small hands can't grip thin pencils. Try special coloured pencils and crayons in chubbie sizes so budding Pollocks can actually come to grips with their tools.

PRICE: £1.75, eight chubbie pencils (short); £2.75, eight chubbie pencils (long).

AVAILABLE: All branches of The Early Learning Centre; South Marston, Swindon SN23 4TJ Tel: 0793 832832 (Mail Order); newsagents, toy shops.

Cooking Apron/Protective Overalls/Floormats

Cookery – whilst it can be frustrating for mothers – is a source of joy for youngsters, simply because it can be so messy. Look for elastic wrists and tough plastic.

PRICE: From £3.45 (aprons); £7.50 (overalls).

AVAILABLE: Department stores, toy shops; James Galt and Co Ltd, Brookfield Road, Cheadle, Cheshire SK8 2PN Tel: 061-428 1211 (Mail Order).

Face Paints/Glitter Face Paints/Face Paint Idea Books

Non-toxic and non-permanent (on faces or clothes). Specially formulated for fair or dark skins.

PRICE: £1.49.

AVAILABLE: WH Smith, toy shops; The Early Learning Centre branches nationwide; Mail Order Dept, South Marston, Swindon SN3 4TJ Tel: 0793 832832.

Farmyard/Jungle Animals

The natural catalyst for farmyard noises – likewise jungle animals. Horses and riding stables, farms and farm buildings are also very popular.

PRICE: From 35p each [Britains]; £4.55 selection of ten animals; from £3.99 for tractors; £22.75 Riding School Set (including horses, jumps and hay bales).

AVAILABLE: Most large toy shops and department stores; for nearest stockist contact: Britains Petite Ltd, Chelsea Street, New Basford, Nottingham NG7 7HR Tel: 0602 420777.

Fridge Magnets

A-Z to stick to the fridge and give early spelling lessons and hours of fun at low cost. Animals, planes, pretend chocolates, etc, also available.

PRICE: From £2.10.

AVAILABLE: Branches of John Lewis Partnership, kitchen shops, department stores.

Grow Chart

To measure the progress as David matures into Goliath. Fun pictures of giraffes, Pooh, etc.

PRICE: From £1.99.

AVAILABLE: Toy shops, branches of The Early Learning Centre, department stores.

Paints/Paint Pots/Paint Brushes

Finger paints for the very small – ominously messy but fun. Powder paints with non-spill pots for the slightly older – mix and use, then let them dry. To use again just add more water.

PRICE: Finger paint £2.50 (pack of three); ready-mixed paint £1.99 each; paint blocks £3.75 (six colours); powder paints £1.70 each; sponges £4.99; brushes from 43p; non-spill pots 49p each.

AVAILABLE: Branches of The Early Learning Centre, South Marston, Swindon SN3 4TJ Tel: 0793 832832 (Mail Order). (NB powder and ready-mixed paints not available mail order.) James Galt & Co Ltd, Brookfield Road, Cheadle, Cheshire SK8 2PN Tel: 061-428 1211.

Play-doh/Play-doh Kits

Various modelling materials are available; some harden and others don't. For small children, however, Play-doh is the best.

It's soft, malleable and extends to kits to make play-doh hair, shapes, hairy monsters, etc. Always store in an air-tight container.

PRICE: From £1.25 to £60 for big sets.

AVAILABLE: Toy shops, department stores, Woolworths, WH Smith.

Playmobil

The basic version of slot-together playing shapes with easy-to-handle pieces. Includes farm animals, people, sailors, etc. The range (as you can imagine) goes on and on.

PRICE: From £3.50 to £75 upwards.

AVAILABLE: Toy shops, department stores.

Soft Football

When aim is not accurate a foam football combines fun with intact windows.

PRICE: £3.95.

AVAILABLE: Most toy shops, DIY superstores.

Sponsor a Homeless Dog

For children who dream of owning a puppy but for whom domestic circumstances make it unfeasible – sponsoring a pet in a rescue home is a safe way to 'give' an animal. This involves paying a regular sum towards the animal's upkeep, and in return the child receives a photo, sometimes an adoption certificate and news of the animal concerned. Regular visits are encouraged.

PRICE: From £1 per week.

AVAILABLE: Contact: National Canine Defence League, Tel: 071-388 0137 or Cats Protection League, Tel: 071-272 6048.

Storage Boxes

It is incredible that children can create so much clobber. To tidy lego, jigsaws, play-doh and other items you'd otherwise trip over, try brightly coloured stackable plastic tubs and boxes. Crates with castors are even more useful (from Ikea) as they can roll into cupboards or under tables with a swift kick.

PRICE: From £2.50: e.g. £3.75 (crate) £2.30 (set of castors).

AVAILABLE: Habitat, DIY stores, The Early Learning Centre, branches of Ikea.

Trips Out – The Cinema

In an age of video, a trip to the cinema is still a real treat. Movies are usually more 'child-oriented' during the school holidays and half-term. Added bonus = popcorn.

PRICE: From £1.50 (child's ticket to matinee performance).

AVAILABLE: Local cinemas – seats can often be booked pre-performance by credit card.

BETWEEN £5-£10

Buckets and Spades

And rakes and scoops and moulds and sieves. In fact all they could possibly have imagined and more, for use by the seaside or in the sandpit.

PRICE: From £2: e.g. £6.99 three buckets and sieve set [Galt]; £14.35 (five-piece set of rubber sandtools including funnel & rake).

AVAILABLE: All toy shops, Woolworths; James Galt & Co Ltd, Brookfield Road, Cheadle, Cheshire SK8 2PN Tel: 061-428 1211 (Mail Order). Any seaside shop.

Fluppet Puppets

Cuddly, rural hand-puppets: choose from badger, fox, white rabbit, beaver and hedgehog.

PRICE: £9.99.

AVAILABLE: Larger toy shops.

Jigsaw Name

Children with very long names are often restricted for personalized presents because only 'up to seven letters' can be accommodated. A jigsaw name, made of free-standing interlocking wooden letters, can be as long or as short as necessary.

PRICE: 1-10 letters £11.99; 11-15 letters £14.99; 16-20 letters £17.99.

AVAILABLE: Craft fairs; Letterbox, PO Box 114, Truro, Cornwall TR1 1FZ Tel: 0872 580885 (Mail Order).

Jigsaws and Puzzles

Start on small pieces with handles for toddlers, and progress to 50-100 pieces for five-year-olds. Beautifully illustrated, giant jigsaw puzzles on nursery rhyme characters and the themes Teddy Bear's Picnic and the Toy Cupboard are available from Galt. Each include about eight pieces which double up as templates.

PRICE: From £4.75; £9.99 (Galt giant jigsaws).

AVAILABLE: Most toy shops; James Galt & Co Ltd, Brookfield Road, Cheadle, Cheshire SK8 2PN Tel: 061-428 1211 (Mail Order).

Macs and Wellies

Brightly coloured vinyl raincoats and boots make even rainy days fun. Yellow ducks or green dinosaurs are available (furry-lined and hooded) and wellies come in all colours of the rainbow.

PRICE: £7.95 from Mothercare.

AVAILABLE: Branches of Mothercare, Adams and other children's outfitters.

Overnight Case

A child-size case for sleeping over with friends. From bright sports bags to smart versions embroidered with initials to make them very grown-up.

PRICE: From £6 to £35.50.

AVAILABLE: Sports shops, branches of Salisburys, baggage departments; Eximious, 10 West Halkin Street, London SW1 Tel: 071-235 7828 (Mail Order available).

Personalized Birthday Party Goodies

Balloons, napkins, food boxes and going-home bags can all be personalized with the birthday boy/girl's name – 'Happy Birthday Thomas'.

PRICE: £9.50 (25 balloons); £4.50 (20 napkins); £3.50 (10 food boxes); £3.50 (10 white paper bags).

AVAILABLE: Frog Hollow Ltd, 21 High Street, Pewsey, Wiltshire SN9 5AF Tel: 0672 64222 (Mail Order – allow 21 days). Check *Yellow Pages* for party shops.

Personalized Books

Stories which feature the names and family details of the children who star in them.

PRICE: £6.99–£9.99.

AVAILABLE: My Book Ltd, Linkside Business Centre, First Floor, Summit Road, Potters Bar, Herts EN6 3JB Tel: 0707 661560 (Mail Order).

Personalized Pencils/Stationery

For first attempts at letter writing, personalized pens and stationery may initially just act as prompts for how to spell my name – later they are a very swish way to compose thank you notes, invitations and all manner of correspondence.

PRICE: £5.95 (24 pencils); £6.95 (24 crayons). Personalized stationery from £3.50; £6.95 boxed gift set of 15 correspondence cards, 20 sheets writing paper and 30 envelopes.

AVAILABLE: Pencils: The International Buyers Guide, Euroway Business Park, Swindon SN5 8SN Tel: 0793 513946 (Mail Order); Stationery: Modip Publications, P O Box 120, Chichester, West Sussex PO20 7AF Tel: 0243 513333 (Mail Order).

Pyjama Cases

As much a cuddly toy as pyjama holder, but useful encouragement to pick pyjamas or nighties off the floor!

PRICE: From £7.

AVAILABLE: Branches of Ikea, children's shops, department stores.

Russian Dolls

Beautiful varieties of traditional 'nesting dolls' (matrioshkas) which fit into each other. Nests start with three dolls and rise to 18.

PRICE: From £5.75 (3); £525 (18).

AVAILABLE: The Russian Shop, 99 The Strand, London WC2 Tel: 071-497 9104 (Mail Order available).

Silly Slippers

Lions, mice, monsters – more in evidence pre-Christmas than during the rest of the year when you'll have to hunt in shoe shops.

PRICE: £7.99 upwards.

AVAILABLE: Most large department stores, Sock Shop, Boots, M&S, BHS etc.

Singing Sponges

Small sponges that make a surprising racket and will ensure bathtime is even more hilarious. Either a pink pig who sings 'Old MacDonald' or a dinosaur who sings 'It's a Small World'.

PRICE: £5.50 the pair.

AVAILABLE: The Natural History Museum Collection, Freepost SU361, Dept 5315, Hendon Road, Sunderland SR9 9AD Tel: 091-514 2777 (Mail Order).

Umbrella/Parasol

An adult accessory in a child's size. A very grown-up version is by Swaine Adeney which has exactly the same malacca handle and vibrant colours as its father; less dear umbrellas in designs to appeal to children are widely available.

PRICE: £9.99 [Adams]; £38 [Swaine Adeney].

AVAILABLE: Branches of Adams, toy shops; Swaine Adeney, 185 Piccadilly, London W1 Tel: 071-734 4277 (Mail Order available).

Videos

Young children will watch Mickey Mouse, Thomas the Tank Engine or Mary Poppins again and again and again. Likewise Spot, The Snowman, etc, etc.

PRICE: From £4.99.

AVAILABLE: All good video outlets, WH Smith and large stationers.

BETWEEN £10–£20

Cash Register

Fisher Price's till helps two to four-year-olds learn about shapes, colours and sizes, with a drawer that pings and a bell that rings.

PRICE: £11.

AVAILABLE: All major toy shops, department stores.

Cooking Set

The Let's Cook set includes a pan with lid, frying pan, colander, measuring jug, mixing bowl, wooden spoon and spatula – extremely good quality and durable.

PRICE: £19.99 [Galt].

AVAILABLE: All good toy shops; James Galt & Co Ltd, Brookfield Road, Cheadle, Cheshire SK8 2PN Tel: 061-428 1211 (Mail Order).

Dolls – Black ones, White ones, Yellow ones

Galt produce a wonderful range of anatomically correct boy and girl dolls from the Western, Asian and Afro-Caribbean races. Also uncannily realistic new-born babies, accurate down to the finest detail (swabs over their umbilical cords).

PRICE: From £17.20; Just Born Babies from £21.50.

AVAILABLE: Good toy shops; James Galt & Co Ltd, Brookfield Road, Cheadle, Cheshire SK8 2PN Tel: 061-428 1211 (Mail Order).

Door Plaques

Personalized wooden door plaques which can be hung on bedroom or playroom doors or walls.

PRICE: £16.50 (teddy, clown or goose design).

AVAILABLE: Letterbox, P O Box 114, Truro, Cornwall TR1 1FZ Tel: 0872 580885 (Mail Order).

Dressing-up Kits

Costumes for Cowboys and Indians, Batman and Catwoman, Doctors and Nurses – all stimulate children's imaginations. A full medical team is available including costumes for a doctor, dentist, surgeon, nurse (male and female) and midwife.

PRICE: e.g. £12.50 (knight costume, including sword, shield, tabard and helmet); from £48.00 (full medical team).

AVAILABLE: Many toy shops; J & M Toys Ltd, 46 Finsbury Drive, Wrose, Bradford, West Yorkshire BD2 1QA Tel: 0274 599314 (Mail Order).

Easel

Young artists are not renowned for their light touch, so they demand extreme sturdiness from the easel they use. The Art Discovery Easel has huge feet to ensure it won't topple over, and a surface that can be used for painting/drawing or as a wipe-off board or chalkboard.

Price: £19.99.

Available: Branches of Beatties nationwide; 10 The Broadway, Southgate, London N14 6PN Tel: 081-886 4258 (Mail Order).

Flat-Footed Penguin

One of the most charming toys ever to have existed – a wooden penguin propelled by means of a stick; his wheels have rubber feet attached which slap onto the floor as he moves.

Price: £13.

Available: Some toy shops and craft fairs; Humble Bee Toys, The Oaklands, Stroat, Nr Chepstow, Gwent NP6 7LR Tel: 0594 529237 (Mail Order).

Floatie Swimsuit

Gone are the restrictions of armbands. The Pollyotter swimsuit has front and back pockets which take floats and is designed to give a natural swimming position in the water. As confidence improves, reduce the number of floats.

Price: From £12.49.

Available: Good sports shops; for nearest stockist contact: Pollyotter Ltd, 19 Wellington Square, Cheltenham, Gloucestershire GL50 4JS Tel: 0242 39230.

Gardening Set

Award-winning wheelbarrow with integral hosepipe and tank, plus a watering can, bucket, spade, trowel and rake which can be used for real or play gardening as well as for watering or pushing around friends.

Price: £19.99 [Chelful].

Available: Most good toy shops; for nearest stockist contact: Chelful Ltd, Pybus Street, Derby DE3 3BB Tel: 0332 292190.

Music Making: Percussion Instruments/Recorder/Mouth Organ

Rhythm is the basis for later music and the genuine articles are no more expensive than their 'toy' equivalents. As the quality is better they last longer, and the pitch is more tolerable.

PRICE: e.g. Bongo Drums £26.50; Tambourine £10.10 (20 cm); Tibetan Bells (finger cymbals) £14.60.

AVAILABLE: Music shops, department stores; James Galt & Co Ltd, Brookfield Road, Cheadle, Cheshire SK8 2PN Tel; 061-428 1211 (Mail Order).

Personalized Sweatshirts

The child's name spelt in colourful animal letters on a heavy-duty sweatshirt.

PRICE: From £10.99 (ages 3–11).

AVAILABLE: Initials International, 34 Bridge Street, Walton-on-Thames, Surrey KT12 1AJ Tel: 0932 841901.

Play House

Big enough to camp in, to set up tea in, and not to blow away in the wind. You could do worse than start with the very affordable version from Ikea.

PRICE: e.g. £11.90 [Ikea]; £36.95 [Chelful Junior Greenhouse].

AVAILABLE: Branches of Ikea, all good toy shops and department stores.

Pram/Buggy

Prams and pushchairs for children with a strong maternal or paternal instinct to show off their plastic progeny. Working brakes and framework – just like the real thing but smaller.

PRICE: From £11.99 (pushchairs), £15.50 (prams); £190 traditional double pram [Silver cross].

AVAILABLE: Good toy shops and department stores; for stockists contact: Silver Cross Ltd, Otley Road, Guiseley, Leeds LS20 Tel: 0943 870950.

Quilts and Pillows

Dream on hot air balloons, elephants and tigers or My Little Pony, Piglet and Pooh. The patchwork quilts by Turner Adams in pastel colours with matching bowed cushions are exquisite.

PRICE: Pillows from £3.99; duvet covers from £14.99 [BHS]; quilts from £32; cushions from £12 [Turner Adams].

AVAILABLE: Branches of BHS, department stores; Turner Adams, Kingston Road, Bradford-on-Avon, Wiltshire BA15 1BD Tel: 0225 865744 (Mail Order).

Roadway Floormats

Bustling roadways featuring schools, hospitals, garages, etc, with all road markings in accordance with the Highway Code. A countryscape may be more suited if someone has more farm animals than toy cars.

PRICE: Country £11.99; Town £21.95.

AVAILABLE: Branches of The Early Learning Centre, larger toy shops.

Towelling Bathrobe

A scaled-down version of the grown-up towelling bathrobe – complete with hood and embroidered name.

PRICE: £14.99 (ages: 2–4); £17.50 (ages: 4–5).

AVAILABLE: Letterbox, P O Box 114, Truro, Cornwall TR1 1FZ Tel: 0872 580885 (Mail Order).

Wall Clocks

Some are as pretty as pictures – a clown with a balloon; others educational, marking quarter to and quarter past the hour, etc; or fun, featuring Postman Pat, Thunderbirds and other characters.

PRICE: From £12.50.

AVAILABLE: Department stores, BHS, toy shops.

Wash Bag and Flannel Set

Pink for girls and blue for boys – a charming drawstring washbag with flannel in striped cotton, including name and motif in appliqué.

PRICE: £14.99.

AVAILABLE: Frog Hollow, 15 Victoria Grove, London W8 Tel: 071-581 5493; 21 High Street, Pewsey, Wiltshire SN9 5AE Tel: 0672 64222 (Mail Order).

Wooden Bricks

An essential part of childhood. Galt make either coloured cube bricks by the tub, or shaped pieces including pillars, arches and triangles.

PRICE: £5.99 (budget set of 50 assorted bricks); £10.60 (24 multicoloured cube bricks); £30.26 (60 hand-finished assorted bricks in fabric bag).

AVAILABLE: Most good toy shops; James Galt & Co Ltd, Brookfield Road, Cheadle, Cheshire SK8 2PN Tel: 061-428 1211 (Mail Order).

BETWEEN £20-£50

Bears

There's no substitute for a traditional Ted. Personally designed, hand-crafted bears in luxury mohair fabrics are suitable for children and adults and are the sort that DO last a lifetime. Soft bears and rabbits whose fur texture appears 'ready-loved' are available from the Manhattan Toy Company.

PRICE: From £30 for a small bear.

AVAILABLE: Only Natural – Mary Holden, 28 Whybourne Crest, Tunbridge Wells, Kent TN2 5BS Tel: 0892 527538 (commissions welcome). Manhattan Toy Company bears (from most toy shops).

Bike

Bikes for children this age need stabilizers – and they should be the sort that attach to the frame and not the axle. A 'step through' (rather than a cross-bar) frame is more manageable. If buying from toy shops check they match British Safety standards.

PRICE: £40–£60 upwards [Raleigh, Townsend].
AVAILABLE: Cycle shops, department stores.

Dolls – Baby Alive

A doll to feed and nappy change. Children love feeding her – though nasty clogs can occur if anything but the special 'food' is used. Nappies get authentically messy.
PRICE: £39.99 [Kenner].
AVAILABLE: Good toy shops and department stores.

Fort

The Playmobil version takes most knocks without collapsing. You can naturally invest as much as you like in Cowboys and Indians.
PRICE: £45.
AVAILABLE: Larger toy shops, department stores.

Garage

Fisher Price for indestructability! Lift for cars, ramp, turntable, etc, in cheerful colours known to survive anything!
PRICE: £25.50.
AVAILABLE: Toy shops, department stores.

Meccano Junior Set

Safety-conscious set. All the pieces are in plastic with smooth rounded edges. A change from plastic bricks and an excellent introduction to real-life mechanics for embryonic engineers.
PRICE: £24.99 (112 piece set – can make 42 different models).
AVAILABLE: Good toy shops.

Osh Kosh B'Gosh Clothes

Wearable, washable, fun, colourful, extremely durable, practical clothes for kids. Expensive but worth it. Dresses, T-shirts, etc, as well as the more familiar dungarees.

PRICE: T-shirts from £10.75; dungarees and dresses from £26.

AVAILABLE: Branches of John Lewis Partnership, specialist children's outfitters.

Paddling Pool/Sandpit

Ideally pay a bit more for reinforced sides to avoid constant spills. The Galt version is large enough for four children at a time and has a foldaway frame and drainage plug. Their turtle-shaped sandpit can also double up as a paddling pool.

PRICE: From £36.40.

AVAILABLE: Department stores, toy shops; James Galt & Co Ltd, Brookfield Road, Cheadle, Cheshire SK8 2PN Tel: 061-428 1211 (Mail Order).

Speak and Spell

Famous for starring role in ET's 'phoning home' scene and for 13 years of helping children to spell. Super Speak & Spell has 11 different games to catch children out, four levels of difficulty, upper and lower case letters as well as French accents.

PRICE: £49.99 [Super Speak & Spell].

AVAILABLE: Larger toy shops and department stores.

Train Set

Should be of the sturdy, non-delicate variety. Brio's train sets are made of solid beech and the track fits together like a jigsaw. One of the most indestructable for this age group.

PRICE: From £25.75 (figure of eight set including train and viaduct); £99.95 (Special Train Set – 7.8m of track including two trains and grand bridge).

AVAILABLE: Toy shops, department stores; branches of The Early Learning Centre, South Marston, Swindon SN3 4TJ Tel: 0793 832832 (Mail Order).

£50 AND ABOVE

Doll Bunk Bed and Linen

A complete miniature bunk bed which converts to two singles, has mattresses, sheets, duvets, etc.

PRICE: £88.

AVAILABLE: The World of Dolls, Willersley, Isle Abbotts, Taunton, Somerset TA3 6RW Tel: 0460 281407 (Mail Order).

Dolls' House/Dolls' House Furniture

To be cherished, loved and even handed down. It should be solid enough to be handled by several small people at once. For the best in dolls' houses, specialists are willing to build rather grand bespoke replicas – though exquisite, these are very delicate. Alternatively, there is the indestructible version from Playmobil which you can buy one floor at a time if the overall price seems too ghastly.

PRICE: From £40 upwards.

AVAILABLE: The Dolls' House Emporium, Park Hall, Denby, Derbyshire DE5 8ND Tel: 0773 513773 (for brochure); The Dolls' House, 29 The Market, Covent Garden, London WC3E 8RE Tel: 071-379 7243; The Singing Tree (wooden four-roomed Georgian House Kit £110) Tel: 071-736 4527.

Rocking Horse

A four-figure price is not unusual for a beautifully crafted hand-made article. If mounted on a rocker, care should be taken of small toes; if stand-mounted it should be extremely stable to cope with very vigorous rocking by older children.

PRICE: You could pay £565 (carved wooden rocking horse, stitched leather tack, real horsehair mane and tail – stand mounted) or tough fabric version from Habitat for £49.

AVAILABLE: Tridias, 124 Walcot Street, Bath BA1 5BG Tel: 0225 469455 (Mail Order) – carriage £20 extra. Also department stores; branches of Habitat.

Smocked Party Dress

This smocked party dress will turn a little girl into a princess. Alternatively a traditional smock top which can be worn by boys or girls (though it does make the boys look like yeomen).

PRICE: From £140 party dress; from £50 traditional smock.

AVAILABLE: Specially for You, Warnham Cottage, East Hoathly, Lewes, Sussex BN8 6DP Tel: 0825 840397 (Mail Order available).

Swings and Roundabouts

Look for stability, strength and a weatherproof finish, not just for the safety of children but also because as they grow older the equipment will get more and more (ab)use.

PRICE: £69.95 (climbing frame 1.6m square including ladder catwalk); £19.99 (swing frame – possible to choose seat to suit child – cosy swing seat for toddlers £17.99, plastic swing seat £8.99).

AVAILABLE: Larger DIY outlets, garden centres; The Early Learning Centre, South Marston, Swindon SN3 4NJ Tel: 0793 832832 (Mail Order).

CHAPTER THREE

CHILDREN 6–12

WHEN children go to school, they quickly learn to use a computer, love stuffed toys, crayons and cars. By nine they're sophisticated, self-confident and fashion conscious. They are developing their own sense of style – like Naf Naf and Benetton designer labels, subscribe to *Fast Forward* and know how to wrap parents round their little finger. Toys are becoming a thing of the past. On the verge of being a teenager they feel quite grown up. And why not when Mum and Dad are on the school Maths and Computers for Beginners' course?

UNDER £5

Annuals/Yearbooks

From *Blue Peter's* 101 things to do with an eggbox; to what Luke Perry from *Beverley Hill 90210* likes to have for breakfast.

PRICE: From £4.50.

AVAILABLE: WH Smith, Woolworths, toy shops.

Astronaut Icecream

The real stuff that's frozen to −40°C and then vacuum packed. Developed for astronauts during the first space mission, it's feather-light real food which recreates in the mouth.

PRICE: From £1.99.

AVAILABLE: Selected toy shops and food departments; call Buxton & King for stockists Tel: 071-637 5505.

Bath Accessories

Mainly for girls who love the 'Animals in Danger' Body Shop range of soaps, flannels and sponges, and may not be too old for stick-on shapes to decorate the bath with.

PRICE: 75p sponge, £1.15 flannel, 55p soap [Body Shop].

AVAILABLE: 'Animals in Danger' range from the Body Shop, Boots, all chemists.

BOOK CHOICE
Book of Knots

Fully illustrated step-by-step guide to tying the world's 25 most useful knots (includes the string!). Indispensible for scouts and guides, young fishermen and sailors. Other knot books for fishermen, sailors, etc, are available from bookshops and chandlers.

PRICE: £4.99.

AVAILABLE: Science Museum Brainwaves, Freepost SU361, Dept 5317, Hendon Road, Sunderland SR9 9AD Tel: 091-514 4666 (Mail Order).

BOOK CHOICE
Roald Dahl

Charlie and the Chocolate Factory, The Enormous Crocodile, Fantastic Mr Fox, The Giraffe, The Pelly and Me. Roald Dahl once said that if he went anywhere in the world a child would offer him a cup of tea – these are some of the reasons why.

PRICE: From £2.99.

AVAILABLE: All good bookshops.

Camera

With the advent of 'point and shoot' cameras, photography becomes child's play.

PRICE: From £4.99 (disposable).

AVAILABLE: Branches of Boots, Dixons.

Comics

Comics which are scarcely comprehensible to adults give children a great deal to enjoy. Watch out for part-works, designed to be collectables so you'll end up buying a whole set. *Beano* and *Dandy* are generally popular, whereas interest in heavily hyped 'comics of the TV series' tends to wane after a couple of issues.

PRICE: From 30p per copy.

AVAILABLE: Contact local newsagents.

Crazy Straws

Drinking straws in 'crazy' shapes – real value for money because children never get tired of using them. They are in fact the only people *capable* of using them, because being brought up on MacDonald's thick shakes they have strong enough lips to cope.

PRICE: From 69p.

AVAILABLE: Department stores, some supermarkets.

Dinosaur Club Membership

Newsletters, games, posters, pads, stickers, etc, for dino-crazy kids.

PRICE: £3.50 p.a.

AVAILABLE: The Dinosaur Club, Dorling Kindersley Ltd, 9 Henrietta Street, London WC2E 8PS Tel: 071-836 5411.

Fabric Paint

Paint for designs on T-shirts, caps or sneakers, which then survives machine-washing.

PRICE: £5.95 for six [Tomy]; £4.25 for three glitter (not washable).

AVAILABLE: Craft shops, toy shops, haberdashery departments.

Hair Decorations and Handbags

Hair clips, bows, scrunchies, bands all thrown together with a colour co-ordinated handbag – the more fancy and ridiculous the better. Part of the art of being grown-up when you're seven.

PRICE: From £1.50.

AVAILABLE: Chemists, department stores, hairdressers, some large toy shops, children's outfitters.

Handicraft Kits

First knitting, embroidery, tapestry, sewing sets, etc; available from John Adams Toys. Candle and paper-making kits amongst the 15 in the Get Set series by Waddingtons. These kits are brilliant – inspirational and absorbing – and can hardly be seen as toys. An inquisitive and industrious child can acquire skills which will last a lifetime.

PRICE: From £2.95 for First Knitting Set [John Adams Toys]; from £9.99 for Get Set kits [Waddington].

AVAILABLE: Most toy shops; for nearest stockists contact John Adams Toys, 32 Milton Park, Milton, Abingdon, Oxon OX14 4RT Tel: 0235 833066.

'In' Toys – Polly Pocket

Tiny Polly Pocket fits on rings and has her own accommodation – easy to lose or to swallow if anyone's too small.

PRICE: From £1.50–£24.99.

AVAILABLE: Toy shops.

'In' Toys – Sylvanians

Little woodland families plus the accoutrements of woodland life – such as dolls' house furniture (which is also good for any doll's house – represents great value in this area).

PRICE: £1.49–£79.99.

AVAILABLE: All toy shops.

'In' Toys – WWF Wrestlers/Gladiators

The figures are based on the weird and wonderful (and muscle-bound) figures from the American programmes. The wrestling figures are used in a WWF wrestling ring (of which 2.5 million were sold in 1991); the Gladiators in scaled-down versions of the Atlasphere, etc.

PRICE: £3.99 (figures) [Hasbro]; £20 (wrestling ring).
AVAILABLE: All large toy shops, department stores.

Make-Up

A range of children's make-up and cosmetics for dressing-up, in suitably lurid pink-and-white packaging.
PRICE: From £2.29 [Tinkerbell].
AVAILABLE: All toy shops.

Naturescope

A development of the jam jar, which includes everything needed for a pond-dipping expedition. A clear rectangular case, specimen pots, magnifying lenses, a mirror, measuring scale and tweezers. The accompanying booklet identifies likely 'finds'.
PRICE: £4.99 [Salter Science].
AVAILABLE: Good toy shops.

Non-Slip Socks

Snuggly socks with a non-slip design on the sole for those who hate shoes.
PRICE: From £4.95 [Totes].
AVAILABLE: Most department stores.

Origami Pad

The ancient Japanese art of paper folding – made easy! Coloured sheets of A4 paper printed with numbered lines to fold along and explanations of basic principles of origami.
PRICE: £3.50 [John Adams].
AVAILABLE: Toy shops; for nearest stockist call John Adams Trading Co Ltd, 32 Milton Park, Abingdon, Oxfordshire OX14 4RT Tel: 0235 833066 (Mail Order).

Pets

Unless you know the family well it is wise to stick to a goldfish, hamster or guinea pig rather than an unasked-for Shetland pony. Tanks and cages, mirrors and activity toys are also very welcome.

PRICE: e.g. guinea pig about £10; goldfish £3; fishbowls from £3.95; rabbit and guinea pig hutches from £26.

AVAILABLE: Pet shops, classified section of local paper.

Plot of Garden/Indoor Garden

Hand over a small vegetable patch or flowerbed and add bulbs and seeds or small annuals so the novice won't suffer crashing disappointment if their first harvest fails. It's quite feasible to start indoors with bulbs, strawberry plants or even potatoes in a paper sack – build up the earth as the greenery appears and have a full crop in a full sack.

PRICE: e.g. Winnie the Pooh's Garden for Butterflies kit contains ready-planted pots of butterfly-attracting flowers (buddleia, verbena, lavender and cornflower) £4.99 – or something similar.

AVAILABLE: WH Smith, all garden centres, some large supermarkets – or create your own.

Rubber Stamps and Stamp Pad

Decorative rubber stamps of hearts, roosters, Pooh – in fact anything you could possibly dream of. Ink pads come in all the colours of the rainbow and pigment inks (slightly more expensive) come in all the colours of the universe (including gold and silver).

PRICE: Stamps £1.70–£4.50; ink pads from £3.50; ink pigments from £5.64.

AVAILABLE: Most toy shops; The Blue Cat Toy Co, The Builders Yard, Silver Street, South Cerney, Gloucestershire GL7 5TS Tel: 0285 861867 (Mail Order).

Stencil Set

Help develop writing and creativity with simple stencil template – hours of silence are guaranteed. Farm, Out of Space, Prehistoric, and Safari Animals are some of the options available.

PRICE: £4.99 [Galt].

AVAILABLE: Stationers, toy shops, department stores.

Swimming Goggles

A variety of shapes and styles which make you realize why the expression 'goggle-eyed' is used as an insult. A lifesaver against chlorinated pools, however, especially for sensitive eyes.

PRICE: e.g. £3.50 [Speedo].

AVAILABLE: All sports shops.

Water Diviners

What look like a pair of old coat hangers, used for discovering fresh-water springs on picnics, rambles and in the back garden. Experienced users also find precious metals.

PRICE: £3.49.

AVAILABLE: Tridias branches nationwide; 124 Walcot Street, Bath BA1 5BG Tel: 0225 469455 (Mail Order).

Wildlife Fact-File

Fact cards with beautiful photographs which arrive every month and build up into files of all you ever wanted to know about things furry and fierce.

PRICE: £3.90 per month.

AVAILABLE: Wildlife Fact-File, Winchester House, 259-269 Old Marylebone Road, London NW1 5RW Tel: 071-706 3208.

—————————————————————————

BETWEEN £5–£10

—————————————————————————

Balloon Wizardry

With the right know-how it is possible to make a camel out of two long balloons – or so the instruction booklet would have you believe. Ideal for future party magicians or Butlins' Red Coats.

PRICE: £5.49 (50 balloons plus instructions and pump).

AVAILABLE: Large toy shops, department stores.

Children's Classics

The complete and unabridged versions in hardback often with the drawings adults remember from their childhood. Books first read in childhood can be enjoyed throughout adult life without ever losing the magic of that first reading. *Little Women, Treasure Island, Alice Through the Looking Glass, Wind in the Willows, The Lion, the Witch and the Wardrobe*, etc, etc, etc – but just one at a time.

PRICE: From £6 hardback [Everyman].

AVAILABLE: All good bookshops.

Calculator

Don't panic: most schools make them a maths requirement.

PRICE: From £5.99 [Texas Instruments].

AVAILABLE: Department stores, WH Smith, Dixons, etc.

Celestial Jigsaw

A scientifically accurate jigsaw of the Milky Way comprising 1000 pieces, which glows in the dark!

PRICE: £9.95.

AVAILABLE: The Natural History Museum Collection, Freepost SU361, Dept 5315, Hendon Road, Sunderland SR9 9AD Tel: 091-514 2777 (Mail Order).

Collectable Cowboys and Indians/Knights/Soldiers

Exquisite miniature warriors with which to do bloody battle. Available individually or in boxed sets of five, with numerous accessories including ramming rods, vats of oil, fiery dragons and camanche forts.

PRICE: From 99p per figure; from £5.99 for boxed set of six figures; castles/forts from £24.

AVAILABLE: Good toy shops; for nearest stockist contact: Britain's Petite Ltd, Chelsea Street, Basford, Nottingham NG7 7HR Tel: 0602 420777.

Crayola Case

A 72-crayon case is what we all hope for and have been disappointed with the meagre 12-crayon option. All the colours of the rainbow and the cosmos are represented and housed in a rigid plastic carrying case. Also 'Changeables' by Crayola when you write in one colour and can change it to another.

PRICE: £9.99 (72 crayons); £3.99 (changeable felt pens).

AVAILABLE: Toy shops and large stationers.

Crystal Radio Kit

All the kit needed to construct a crystal radio, including diode and earphone. The end result really works! Suitable for those aged eight upwards – with help (but helpers beware you don't take over!).

PRICE: £9.95 [John Adams Toys].

AVAILABLE: All good toy shops; for stockists contact: John Adams Trading Co Ltd, 32 Milton Park, Abingdon, Oxfordshire OX14 4RT Tel: 0235 833066.

Display Case

An attractive wooden box display case to hang on the wall. It has 24 compartments in which to place small ornaments, toys and other precious collections on display, when they might otherwise be lost or trampled.

PRICE: £5.75.

AVAILABLE: Branches of Ikea.

Football Club Membership/Football Kit

Miniature versions of club kit score instantly. Junior clubs are an adjunct to most popular teams. Manchester City's 'Junior Blues' for example offers a membership card and certificate, regular magazine, scarf, badge, pen and birthday card signed by the team.

PRICE: Kit starts from £5.99 (socks), £13.99 (shorts), £26.99 (shirt); Club membership, £2 p.a.

AVAILABLE: Kit from branches of Olympus Sport. Contact numbers should be in the phone book; or write to The Football Association, 16 Lancaster Gate, London W2 8LW Tel: 071-402 7151 (they publish a leaflet with the names and addresses of clubs in the League).

'In' Toys – My Little Pony

To anyone other than a little girl of six, these long-haired ponies are the most hideous things to have ever walked out of a toy shop. They have names, videos, merchandise galore, plus combs, stickers, etc, etc, etc.

PRICE: From £5.99.

AVAILABLE: Woolworths, toy shops, stationers.

Lunchboxes/Satchels/Knapsacks

Lunchboxes with matching flask, Dennis the Menace satchels, or sophisticated junior briefcases – all are popular.

PRICE: From £5.95.

AVAILABLE: BHS, WH Smith, department stores, hardware stores (lunchboxes only), luggage shops.

Modelling Clay

Prima, Fimo and Daz clays are what plasticine and play-doh users progress to. Prima and Fimo come in fade-proof colours and harden when baked in the oven; Daz dries when exposed to the air and needs painting.

PRICE: e.g. £5.49 (Daz terracotta block).

AVAILABLE: All good toy shops and craft shops.

Paint and Eat Cakes

Cakes covered in white icing for children to paint and eat. Come with edible paint.

PRICE: From £8.99.

AVAILABLE: Gourmet Greetings, 5 Magna Carta Lane, Wraysbury, Middlesex TW19 5AF Tel: 0784 482892/483980 (Mail Order).

Plaster of Paris Modelling Kit

Galt produce a modelling kit based on 'Threatened Animals' which features plastic moulds for giant pandas, tigers, polar bears, etc – the results are very impressive and can be painted. Has the added advantage of becoming a hobby.

PRICE: £9.99.

AVAILABLE: Most large toy shops; for nearest stockist call: James Galt and Co Ltd, Brookfield Road, Cheadle, Cheshire SK8 2PN Tel: 061-428 8511.

Scatch/Stick Ball

Two 'sticky' bats which slip over your hand and make catching easier. Many 'own labels' have been brought out in competition which are just as good and often half the price.

PRICE: £9.99 [Scatch]; £4.85 [Homebase's version – Sure Catch].

AVAILABLE: Larger toy shops; Homebase.

Sports Rackets/Bats

Cricket bats that have a smaller handle size, and small hockey sticks, etc, are available in junior sizes, which are shorter and lighter to use than standard equipment.

PRICE: From £5.99.

AVAILABLE: Most large sports shops.

Trapeze Bar

A sturdy tree and a sharp set of nerves are the only prerequisites to flying through the air with the greatest of ease.

PRICE: About £10.

AVAILABLE: Most toy shops; TP Activity Toys and Sports, Severn Road, Stourport, Worcestershire DY13 9EX Tel: 0299 827728 (contact for Mail Order and local stockists).

Volcano Kit

A mini-Vesuvius in kit form, that when constructed can be erupted again and again using baking powder and vinegar.

PRICE: £8.50.

AVAILABLE: Science Museum Brainwaves, Freepost SU361, Dept 5317, Hendon Road, Sunderland SR9 9AD Tel: 091-514 4666 (Mail Order).

Wristwatch/Stopwatch

Childhood is the only time anyone looks cool wearing a nodding Noddy watch. Alternatively, Treasure Trolls, Mr Men, Dennis the Menace, WWF Wrestlers, Snow White, *et al*, or a standard variety.

PRICE: From £9.95.

AVAILABLE: Jewellers, toy shops and department stores.

BETWEEN £10–£20

Adopt a Pony

Dreams of owning a pony is an important stage in practically every little girl's life. Through the 'Adopt a Pony' scheme they can choose a pony from the list provided, get a photo of him and his life history and more importantly can go and visit him, stroke him, feed him polos and groom him.

PRICE: £10 p.a.

AVAILABLE: Horses and Ponies Protection Association, 64 Station Road, Padiham, Lancs BB12 8EF Tel: 0282 779138.

BOOK CHOICE
Atlas

The Great Atlas of Discovery follows in the footsteps of Columbus and other great explorers as children discover the world. Gloriously illustrated.

PRICE: £18.75 [Dorling Kindersley].
AVAILABLE: Good bookshops.

Bow and Arrow

A high-powered bow fires safe foam arrows up to 35 feet.
PRICE: £17.99.
AVAILABLE: Woolworths (call 071-262 1222 for outlet details).

Cash Box

A locking cash box is much more grown up than a piggy bank. A removable coin tray leaves plenty of room to store wads of notes and other very precious belongings.
PRICE: £10.50.
AVAILABLE: W H Smith; all good stationery and office supply shops.

Foster an Orphan Elephant

Fostering means helping to feed and provide medical supplies for orphaned elephants of Kenya – and every six months you have a report of how he's getting on.
PRICE: From £14.95.
AVAILABLE: Care for the Wild, 1 Ashfolds, Horsham Road, Rusper, West Sussex RH12 4QX Tel: 0293 871596.

'In' Toys – Barbie/Sindy + Clothes + Club

Loathed by grown-ups, loved by little girls. In 1990 Barbie grossed more money worldwide than Madonna or Michael Jackson! Choice of 'standard', or top of the range Dream Ballet or Party Lights Sindy (with hair that lights up), or Rollerblade, Ultra-Hair or Sparkle Eyes Barbie. Once the collection of dolls and clothes has reached huge proportions it's wise to join the club – magazine and news on new clothes available.
PRICE: Sindy [Hasbro], Barbie [Mattel] from £5 to £25; Barbie Friends' Club £5.50 p.a.
AVAILABLE: *All* toy shops – although larger shops have larger variety; Barbie Friends' Club, PO Box 500, Leicester LE99 0AA.

'In' Toys – Game Boy Gear

Gear for the ubiquitous Game Gear and Game Boy includes travelling cases, magnifying lenses and a light booster for the Game Boy which enables play after lights-out.

PRICE: £12.99 Game Gear nylon case; £16.99 Game Boy carry-all (holds Game Boy, battery pack and eight games); £17.99 Game Boy magnifying glass plus light.

AVAILABLE: Toy shops and department stores.

Kites

The Kite Store supplies kites for beginners right through to high competition standard and takes kiting very seriously. An amazing catalogue including the Flexifoil Power Kites ('the fastest kites in the world') and a comprehensive selection of stunt kites. There's a less competitive approach at Malvern Kites, which has fun kites such as Olly Octopus as well as the stunt versions.

PRICE: £3–£500; (a good selection in the £10–£25 price bracket).

AVAILABLE: The Kite Store Ltd, 48 Neal Street, London WC2H 9PA Tel: 071-836 1666 (Mail Order); Malvern Kites, Unicorn Yard, Great Malvern, Worcs WR14 4PZ Tel: 0684 565504 (Mail Order); also larger toy shops.

Lego/Lego Club Membership

The Lego collection is probably only limited by your storage and display space, and can get complicated enough to test any adult. Enjoyed by girls as well as boys; whole towns and shopping precincts can be built.

PRICE: e.g. £14.99 Helicopter 6342; £69.99 Pirate Boat 6285; Club Membership £3.95 p.a.

AVAILABLE: All large toy shops.

Magic Tricks

Hocus Pocus is a collection of 100 tricks to impress the adults. For the real thing, and the chance of meeting Paul Daniels at the counter, venture to Davenport's Magic Shop.

PRICE: £17.

AVAILABLE: Alll good toy shops; Davenport's Magic Shop, 7 Charing Cross Underground Shopping Arcade, The Strand, London WC2N 4HZ Tel: 071-836 0408 (Mail Order available).

Microphone and Stand

If you would like to nurture a Mick Jagger in your family, microphone technique should start at an early age. The microphone and stand (which extends to 1.08m) comes with a speaker and cable (though batteries not included).

PRICE: £17.99.

AVAILABLE: Large toy shops; for nearest stockist contact: M Hohner Ltd, Bedwas House Industrial Estate, Bedwas, Newport, Gwent NP1 8XQ Tel: 0222 868889.

Model Making Kits

Plastic construction kits for making models that clip together to vaguely resemble a tank – or to-scale models of formula one racing cars.

PRICE: From £7.99 to £100. (A good selection for around £10.)

AVAILABLE: Toy shops, especially branches of Beatties; 10 The Broadway, Southgate, London N14 6PN Tel: 081-886 4258 (Mail Order).

Pencil Box for Left-Handers

Includes left-handed scissors and a fountain pen with a left-cut nib – two areas where left-handed children have most problems. Also includes a left-handed pencil sharpener as well as the usual rubber and pencils.

PRICE: £12.95.

AVAILABLE: Anything Left-Handed Ltd, 57 Brewer Street, London W1R 3FB Tel: 071-437 3910 (Mail Order available).

Personal Stereo

Boots' Bop Box has a sound depressor so they won't go deaf. Extremely useful when you go on long journeys and wish to listen to *Pick of the Week* instead of *The Enormous Crocodile* – again.

PRICE: £14.99.

AVAILABLE: Branches of Boots.

Personalized Book Ends

Hand-painted wooden book ends either in a Pink Goose design or a Soldier and Drum (choose as appropriate and include the relevant child's name).

PRICE: £14.95.

AVAILABLE: Frog Hollow, 15 Victoria Grove, London W8 Tel: 071-581 5493; 21 High Street, Pewsey, Wiltshire SN9 5AF Tel: 0672 64222 (Mail Order).

Personalized Hairbrush

Hand-painted Mason Pearson hairbrushes decorated for girls with their name surrounded by pink or blue flowers; boys may prefer a Kent wooden hairbrush with a boat decoration and their name.

PRICE: £18.99 [Mason Pearson]; £19.99 [Kent].

AVAILABLE: Letterbox, P O Box 114, Truro, Cornwall TR1 1FZ Tel: 0872 580885 (Mail Order).

Pony Club Membership

For children who actively ride and wish to take part in Pony Club Events/Days this is an essential ingredient.

PRICE: £19 p.a.

AVAILABLE: The Membership Secretary, The Pony Club, BEC, Stoneleigh, Kenilworth, Warwickshire CV8 2LR Tel: 0203 696697.

Scientific Toys

A miniature microscope, a sunpowered model or a 55 cm long periscope with unbreakable mirrors are educational for parents as well as children.

PRICE: Magnifier £11.05 [Tasco]; Periscope £14.51 [Galt]; Sunpower Kit £11.45 [John Adams].

AVAILABLE: Larger toy shops; department stores.

Sunglasses

It is not essential for children to wear sunglasses in the average British sunshine during normal play. The danger comes when children are exposed to strong sunlight for prolonged periods – in hot climates, near water or in areas of ozone depletion (e.g. Australia).

PRICE: From £10.

AVAILABLE: Mini Optics, 72A Gascony Avenue, London NW6 4NE Tel: 071-328 8455 (for Mail Order or stockists).

Videos in French

Animated stories which are a wonderful way to help children with French. Includes classics such as *Pierre et le loup* (*Peter and the Wolf*) and *Cendrillon* (*Cinderella*).

PRICE: e.g. *Le Noel de Mickey* £11.99.

AVAILABLE: The French Video Company, 26 Addison Place, London W11 4RJ Tel: 071-603 4690 (Mail Order).

Walkie Talkie

It can be terribly disappointing to receive a walkie talkie which doesn't have a long enough range – they don't work! The Asaki version operates on FM rather than AM, so it does!

PRICE: £19.99.

AVAILABLE: Branches of Beatties nationwide; 10 The Broadway, Southgate, London N14 6PN Tel: 081-886 4258 (Mail Order).

BETWEEN £20–£50

Children's Illustrated Encyclopedia

What better way to start school? Colourfully enjoyable by parents and offspring alike.

PRICE: £25 [Dorling Kindersley].

AVAILABLE: All good bookshops.

Goal Trainer

Young strikers would appreciate goal practice in the garden. This frame improves aim by means of netted 'holes' which bounce back the ball.

PRICE: £29.95 (Junior).

AVAILABLE: Selected toy shops; for Mail Order and stockists contact: TP Activity Toys & Sports, Severn Road, Stourport, Worcestershire, DY13 9EX Tel: 0299 827728.

'Junior' Board Games

Junior versions of word games save frustration.

PRICE: e.g. £19.99 Junior Pictionary [Parker]; £29.99 Junior Trivial Pursuit [Parker].

AVAILABLE: WH Smith, toy shops and department stores.

Moon Shoes

Shoes that are mini-trampolines and look rather like cornish pasties when strapped to the feet – whenever the wearer takes a step a bounce results, up to four feet in the air! Adults wish they were five stone lighter.

PRICE: £39.95.

AVAILABLE: Science Museum Brainwaves, Freepost SU361, Dept 5317, Hendon Road, Sunderland SR9 9AD Tel: 091-514 4666 (Mail Order).

Silver Tooth Holder

A receptacle which makes life for the tooth fairy a whole lot easier – instead of scrabbling under the pillow looking for lost teeth, she visits the small bell-shaped container on the bedside table and replaces lost teeth with coins.

PRICE: About £20.

AVAILABLE: Selected jewellers and antique shops.

Subbuteo

Table football that has its own international league.

PRICE: £29.99 for pitch set (£64.99 deluxe set); £2.99 for 3 extra balls.

AVAILABLE: Larger toy shops.

Tracy Island

This Thunderbirds-inspired plastic play set would have been the bestselling children's toy over Christmas 1992 if Matchbox had only made enough of them to meet demand. Parents camped overnight outside Toys 'R' Us and when *Blue Peter* showed how you could improvise (with little more than two eggboxes and some sticky-backed plastic) the postman nearly drowned under the avalanche of response.

PRICE: £29.99.

AVAILABLE: Good toy shops (if you can get them).

Train Set

The nerve centre of traditional toys for boys.

PRICE: From £25 (Lima basic set – includes locomotive, wagon and oval track). Hornby sets start at £50. Both, of course, can be added to in years to come.

AVAILABLE: Branches of Beatties nationwide; 10 The Broadway, Southgate, London N14 6PN Tel: 081-886 4258 (Mail Order).

Typing Tutor

The Type Right II is a grown-up introduction to touch typing for typewriters and computer keyboards. Comes with complete coursebook, and assesses typing speed and accuracy – typing games add excitement to the learning curve in this very necessary skill.

PRICE: About £30.

AVAILABLE: For stockists contact: VTech Electronics Ltd, 25 The Quadrant, Abingdon Science Park, Abingdon, Oxon OX14 3YS Tel: 0235 555545.

£50 AND ABOVE

Activity Holidays

PGL leave parents 'Home Alone' while their kids make new friends and discover the delights of archery, abseiling, canoeing and snorkelling amongst many, many other activities open to them. Some holidays are 'themed' including surfing, riding, biking, tennis, etc – with varying age ranges.

PRICE: Day camps start at £19; full week from £240.

AVAILABLE: PGL Adventure, 340 Penyard Lane, Ross-on-Wye, Herefordshire HR9 5NR Tel: 0989 763511.

Bikes/Bike Helmets/Safety Kit etc

Buy British, buy Raleigh. They have a broad range, are widely available and work.

PRICE: Bikes from about £90 to £160; safety helmets from £18.

AVAILABLE: Halfords, cycle retailers, department stores.

Farm Holiday

Town children on a farm holiday get their wellies dirty, fresh air in their lungs and stop being frightened of cows.

PRICE: About £15 per head (B&B); £150–£400 per week self-catering.

AVAILABLE: Farm Holiday Bureau, National Agricultural Centre, Stoneleigh Park, Warwickshire CV8 2LZ Tel: 0203 696909.

'In' Toys – Gameboys/Game Gear

Already legends in their own lunchtime – not only kids' street cred but their very existence is determined by whether they have the most up-to-date version of the Streetfighter game.

PRICE: Nintendo Entertainment System £130; Gameboy £70; Sega Megadrive Console £130; Game Gear £130.

AVAILABLE: All good toy shops, WH Smith, Woolworths, department stores, electronics shops.

Precomputers

Award-winners Precomputer 1000 and 2000 introduce BASIC programming, touch typing, word games, etc. Optional cartridges are available to extend the range.

PRICE: £69.99 Precomputer 1000 [VTech]; £90.00 Precomputer 2000.

AVAILABLE: Good toy shops and department stores; for nearest stockist contact: VTech Electronics Ltd, 25 The Quadrant, Abingdon Science Park, Abingdon, Oxon OX14 3YS Tel: 0235 555545.

CHAPTER FOUR

TEENS

IN today's society we see more single and divorced parents and an increasing number of working mums. The winner – through guilt perhaps – is in his or her teens! Toys have generally been left behind. Computer games are the main exception. This is a massive business loved by the users, but less so by teachers and parents as evidence of addiction and anti-social behaviour increases. It's nicer to think of our teenagers as the shampoo generation; squeaky clean with high self-esteem and an active social life.

UNDER £5

Baseball Cap

Standard headgear for groovy kids – whether they've been to NYC or not.

PRICE: From £4.95.

AVAILABLE: Sports shops, fashion outlets and department stores.

Bath Bombs

Drop a bath bomb, and the water fizzes until it's dissolved. The perfect way to soften the water and fragrance the skin and have a laugh in the bath – in either peach, blackberry, champagne or peppermint.

PRICE: £1.10.

AVAILABLE: Cosmetics To Go, Freepost, Poole, Dorset BH15 1BR Tel: 0800 373366 (Mail Order).

Body Shop Potions

A basket of goodies from The Body Shop is environmentally friendly, not tested on animals and smells wonderful. Products vary from a skin care range for teenagers, to a toe divider for painting toe nails.

PRICE: From under £1.

AVAILABLE: Body Shop branches nationwide.

Craft Tools

Now that model-making has become a serious business, the serious model makers, Tamiya, have a tool set specifically for the job. A design and craft knife, razor saw, screwdriver, scissors and Builder's 8 should meet the demands of any kit.

PRICE: From £1.20 to £12.99 plus.

AVAILABLE: Branches of Beatties nationwide; 10 The Broadway, Southgate, London N14 6PN Tel: 081-886 4258 (Mail Order).

Fan Club Membership

Enormous number of clubs for young pop group/pop star fanatics. Privileges usually include more paraphernalia than they will have wall space to cope with; newsletters and badges.

PRICE: Vary – should be in pocket money range, around £1 for six months' membership.

AVAILABLE: Through 'youth' magazines; e.g. *Smash Hits*, 52-55 Carnaby Street, London W1V 1PF.

Geo Stationery

Stationery which has a map printed on the reverse of the writing paper. The envelopes are sections of maps turned inside out – they are made from out-of-date, recycled Ordnance Survey maps!

PRICE: £1.30 (pad and 20 envelopes).

AVAILABLE: Friends of the Earth, Nancegollam, Helston, Cornwall TR13 0TE Tel: 0209 831999 (Mail Order); WH Smith.

Mood Rings

Extraordinary gems which change colour according to body temperature and therefore reveal inner emotions. There are seven mood changes varying from blackly tense to happy and passionately blue.

PRICE: £1.99–£3.25.

AVAILABLE: Sea Gems, Market Place, Marazion, Cornwall TR17 0AD Tel: 0736 710767 (Mail Order available).

Patterned Tights/Opaque Tights

Crazy patterns or darkly-opaque tights designed for very good legs under very short skirts.

PRICE: From £4.99.

AVAILABLE: The Sock Shop (branches nationwide).

Posters

'Artistic' shots of Madonna or Axl Rose; candid shots by Robert Doisneau or painterly strokes by Monet.

PRICE: From £4.99.

AVAILABLE: Athena branches nationwide.

Spray-in Highlights

Instant hair highlights in fun colours which can be sprayed on and then washed out.

PRICE: £3.99 [Jerome Russell].

AVAILABLE: Large chemists; John Bell & Croyden, 50 Wigmore Street, W1 Tel: 071-935 5555 (Mail Order available).

Ten Pin Bowling Trip

What has become a way of life for American teenagers is still largely undiscovered here. Ten pin bowling is a sociable group or family outing, which leaves the unathletic trailing. The uninitiated have to overcome the embarrassment of those shoes.

PRICE: From £3 per person per game.

AVAILABLE: Look in your local *Yellow Pages*.

BETWEEN £5–£10

Blank Video Tapes/Pop Videos

Blanks can be filled back to back with episodes of *Home and Away* without sacrificing mother's copy of *Now Voyager*. Also pop videos or Hollywood Classics – video libraries are becoming as important as book libraries to the young and swinging.

PRICE: From £3.29 for blank tapes; pop videos from £5.99 (boxed *Terminator 2* set: £29.99).

AVAILABLE: WH Smith, Boots, record shops, department stores.

BOOK CHOICE
Working Holiday Guides

Adventure Holidays produce guides to *Study Holidays*, *Working Holidays* and *A Year Between* to help guide teenagers with wanderlust.

PRICE: From £7.95 [Central Bureau and Vacation Work].

AVAILABLE: YHA Adventure Shops, 14 Southampton Street, London WC2 Tel: 071-836 8541.

Card Tricks Kit

Tricks and stunts to amaze family and friends. Deck of cards accompanied by a booklet written by a master performer.

PRICE: £5.95.

AVAILABLE: Large toy stores; Science Museum Brainwaves, Freepost SU361, Dept 5317, Hendon Road, Sunderland SR9 9AD Tel: 091-514 4666 (Mail Order).

Crib Sheet Hankie

Einstein's theory of relativity, Pythagoras' theorem, and all those formulae that seem to completely disappear from the memory in exams are cunningly written down on a cotton handkerchief.

PRICE: £6.95.

AVAILABLE: Magnificent Mouchoirs, 140 Battersea Park Road, London SW11 Tel: 071-720 5667 (Mail Order).

Little Black Book

It may be time to start that ubiquitous Little Black Book – the smaller the better so it stays safe from prying eyes. Smythsons produce TINY black books – variously titled 'Beaux', 'Belles', 'Blondes/Brunettes/Redheads'.

PRICE: £5.25.

AVAILABLE: Smythsons, 44 New Bond Street, London W1Y 0DE Tel: 071-629 8558 (Mail Order available).

Pin Board

Cork or fabric-covered boards on which to pin postcards, memos, photos, instead of ruining the wallpaper.

PRICE: From £5.49 to £8.75.

AVAILABLE: Texas, Homebase, etc, and WH Smith.

Professional Make-Up

At the experimental stage, find out what really works and what doesn't.

PRICE: From about £8.50.

AVAILABLE: Beauty salons, department stores, cosmetics counters.

———————— BETWEEN £10–£20 ————————

Bags and Baggage

Soft bags of all shapes and sizes for sleepovers, sports kit and weekends away.

PRICE: Depends on size/quality – from £12.95.

AVAILABLE: Luggage shops, sports shops and department stores.

Battery Recharger

Battery-operated toys seem to run down very quickly; likewise personal stereos, etc. Boots have worked out that using rechargeable batteries and chargers can save more than £70 a year.

PRICE: £7–£20.50 for a charger; £6.99 (pack of four rechargeable batteries).

AVAILABLE: Selected branches of Boots, electrical retailers, larger toy shops.

Beach Towel

The luxury of a towel which only the owner is allowed to make wet.

PRICE: From £12.99.

AVAILABLE: Branches of M&S, BHS, Ikea, department stores.

Bodies

Poppered leotards that are universally acceptable – but only if they are extremely slinky.

PRICE: From £14.99.

AVAILABLE: All clothes shops including M&S, BHS and C&A.

BOOK CHOICE
Guinness Book of Records

Fascinating facts and photos about ordinary people and incredible feats.

PRICE: £13.99.

AVAILABLE: All good bookshops; WH Smith.

Fountain Pen

Lamy have designed a fountain pen which not only looks smooth but writes extremely smoothly too. The stem is moulded specifically for a comfortable grip.

PRICE: £10.50.

AVAILABLE: WH Smith, stationers and department stores.

Glo T-Shirts

Following from Hypercolour T-shirts that change colour according to body temperature, Glo T-shirts have been treated so they glow in the dark. The dye absorbs natural or artificial light and then emits it for up to ten hours – good for drawing attention in the disco.

PRICE: From £12.99.

AVAILABLE: Virgin Megastores.

Greenpeace Subscription

Greenpeace campaigns to save the whales, save the rainforests and protect seals, dolphins, porpoises and sea turtles, etc. Become a member and keep informed.

PRICE: £14.50 p.a.

AVAILABLE: Greenpeace, Freepost, Canonbury Villas, London N1 2PN Tel: 071-354 5100.

Hairdryer

Save borrowing mother's.

PRICE: From £13.95.

AVAILABLE: Boots, large chemists, electrical appliance shops and department stores.

Lego Technic

Add a motor to your completed lego kit to make it work (motorized unit extra).

PRICE: e.g. £15.99 Digger 8828; £59.99 Combine Harvester 8862.

AVAILABLE: Larger toy shops, department stores.

Lockable Five-Year Diary

Secret assignations, emotions, hopes and fears stay that way – secret – firmly under lock and key.

PRICE: From £12.99.

AVAILABLE: WH Smith, good stationers.

MAGAZINE SUBSCRIPTION
Sky

Up-to-the-minute glossy with all the info on happening young things plus news and reviews.

PRICE: £19 p.a.

AVAILABLE: Worldwide Subscription Service Ltd, Unit 4, Gibbs Reed Farm, Ticehurst, East Sussex TN5 7HE Tel: 0580 200657.

MAGAZINE SUBSCRIPTION
Smash Hits

Rocking kids learn not only all there is to know about their pop idols, but also have all the words of their songs printed so they can sing along too.

PRICE: £24 p.a. (fortnightly).

AVAILABLE: *Smash Hits*, Subscription Services, Tower House, Sovereign Park, Market Harborough, Leics LE16 9EF Tel: 0858 468888.

Personal Alarm and Torch

If young girls are going to be walking alone after dark, even for a short distance, a personal security device provides peace of mind and genuine security. A 140 decibel alarm (for emergency use only) is combined with a torch that will neatly fit into handbags, satchels, pockets etc.

PRICE: £16.95.

AVAILABLE: Science Museum Brainwaves, Freepost SU361, Dept 5317, Hendon Road, Sunderland SR9 9AD Tel: 091-514 4666 (Mail Order).

Personal Organizer

Special 'School' or 'College' organizers come 'stuffed' with pages suited to the particular needs of its owner – including an 18-month diary, timetable, action (!) reminders, world map, and for a student, cash record sheets.

PRICE: e.g. £9.95 (Filofax School range); £15.25 (Filofax Student range).

AVAILABLE: Most branches of WH Smith, other stationers, department stores; Just Fax, 43 Broadwick Street, London W1V 1FT Tel: 071-734 5034 (Mail Order available).

Photo Reproduction on a T-shirt

Literally any design can be printed onto a T-shirt or sweatshirt, as long as the original is on a flat piece of paper – a photograph, slide, negative, postcard or print. Once printed, the shirts stay printed too, and can be ironed, tumble-dried and left in a pile in the corner of the bedroom without any cracking or fading.

PRICE: From £8.25 T-shirt; from £17.50 sweatshirt.

AVAILABLE: Yellow House Art Company, The Loft, Eskew Lane, Low Bentham, Nr Lancaster LA2 7DD Tel: 05242 62726 (Mail Order).

Pinhead

This bed of hundreds of pins allows you make 3-D images of your face (keeping your eyes shut) and any other shape you fancy.

PRICE: About £14.95.

AVAILABLE: Most large toy shops and department stores; Just Games, 71 Brewer Street, London W1R 3FB Tel: 071-734 6124 (Mail Order available).

Pinhole Photography Kit

Fascinating kit which contains everything you need to make a camera, take, develop and print snapshots. Recommended for 12 upwards, and many adults would be more than willing to help out.

PRICE: £14.95 [John Adams].

AVAILABLE: Good toy shops; for stockists contact: John Adams Trading Company Ltd, 32 Milton Park, Milton, Abingdon, Oxford IX14 4RT Tel: 0235 833066.

Softball Kit

A misnomer because the ball is hard and can do a lot of damage!
Popular American game (which is nearly as good as rounders)
and is played seasonally in the park.

PRICE: Softball £5–£8.50; Softball bat £14 (wooden), £25
upwards (aluminium).

AVAILABLE: Selected sports shops; Slick Willies, 41 Kensington
High Street, London W8 5ED Tel: 071-937 3824.

Stamp Starter Pack

Introduction to an absorbing hobby, which particularly appeals
to children with hoarding tendencies. This educational pastime
can become a lifetime obsession. Pack includes album, stamps,
hinges, magnifier, tweezers, etc.

PRICE: £10.49 [Stanley Gibbons].

AVAILABLE: Large toy shops; Tridias, 124 Walcot Street, Bath
BA1 5BG Tel: 0225 469455 (Mail Order).

Stunt Kites

None of this up and down rubbish – we want kites that loop the
loop and practically pull you off your feet.

PRICE: £6.95–£500.

AVAILABLE: The Kite Shop, 48 Neal Street, Covent Garden
London WC2H 9PA Tel: 071-836 1666 (Mail Order available).

Super Saturator

This fully automatic water pistol features a motorized pump that
spurts out up to 250 shots of water per minute.

PRICE: £19.95.

AVAILABLE: The Leading Edge shops; The Leading Edge (Retail)
Ltd, Euroway Business Park, Swindon SN5 8SN Tel: 0793
436648 (Mail Order).

———— BETWEEN £10–£20 ————

Swingball

An outdoor game which involves battering a tennis ball on a rope with the aim of getting it past your opponent. Needs to be very securely 'planted' in the lawn or mounted on a concrete base to avoid the whole contraption flying over the fence.

PRICE: £13.99.

AVAILABLE: Toy shops.

———

BETWEEN £20–£50

Articulate!

Anyone who has ever played this game (and woken up hoarse the next morning) will verify it is the best boardgame in the whole world. Players must be quick of wit and nimble of tongue in order to 'articulate' as many words as possible in 30 seconds.

PRICE: £26.95.

AVAILABLE: Menzies, John Lewis, WH Smith; Just Games, 71 Brewer Street, London W1R 3FB Tel: 071-734 6124 (Mail Order available).

Bean bags

Sloppy seats that can be tossed anywhere for horizontal reading, chatting and television watching.

PRICE: From £49.

AVAILABLE: Furniture and department stores.

Big Bell Alarm Clock/Small Alarm Clock

An old fashioned alarm clock (with a 12″ diameter face) and a pair of ringers to go with it. Even the most stubborn sleeper will not be able to ignore it, though volume can be controlled for more gentle awakenings. Can be freestanding or wall-mounted. Alternatively small, lightweights from £7–£8.

PRICE: £49.95 (Big Bell).

AVAILABLE: The Leading Edge stores; The Leading Edge (Retail) Ltd, Euroway Business Park, Swindon SN5 8SN Tel: 0793 436648 (Mail Order).

Celestial and Moon Globes

Globes which show the constellations of the sky or the surface of the moon (including craters, 'seas' and the first Apollo landing site). Perfect for people with their heads in the clouds.

PRICE: £43 (12″ Apollo celestial globe); £41 (12″ Moon globe).

AVAILABLE: Thanet Globe Emporium, Orange Street, Canterbury, Kent CT1 2JA Tel: 0227 450055 (Mail Order).

Cycle Lock/Cycle Helmet

The Citadel Lock defies large metal cutters, and includes £500 of free insurance with purchase, so you know it works. Personal security protected by lightweight dayglo helmets, which should have ANSI and Shell approved standards (American standards). (See also Mountain Bikes.)

PRICE: £22.99 cycle lock; £29.99 Britax cycle helmet.

AVAILABLE: Cycle shops and Homebase.

Early Driving Lessons

Driving experience for people before they reach 17 within Brands Hatch or Oulton to learn the basics of car control. Simulated 'urban layout'.

PRICE: £49 (2.5 hour session shared with two other pupils).

AVAILABLE: Redletter Days, 8–12 Woodhouse Road, North Finchley, London N12 0RG Tel: 081-343 9030.

Electric Razor/Aftershave

For when he starts to look like Grizzly Adams. A sensitive subject – perhaps offered with a first aftershave.

PRICE: From £23.99; (aftershave from £6).

AVAILABLE: Boots, all electrical appliance shops, department stores.

French Monopoly

Extremely good for students of the language, and it seems so much more romantic to be snapping up houses on the Avenue des Champs-Elysees.

PRICE: £23.95.

AVAILABLE: The Breton Shirt Company, 99 Watermoor Road, Cirencester, Glos GL7 1LD Tel: 0285 652351 (Mail Order).

Go-Karting Trip

Young Damon Hills who haven't yet got their licences will love the speed and realism of the track.

PRICE: £45 per hour, per person (£120 team entry).

AVAILABLE: The Kart Raceway, Deavinson's Leisure Ltd, Rye House Stadium, Rye Road, Hoddesdon, Herts EN11 0EH Tel: 0992 451170; Daytona Raceway (indoor), 54 Wood Lane, London W12 Tel: 081-749 2277.

Juggling Kit

A new craze which guarantees you will be centre of attention when proficiently executed. The 'thud' kit, so called because the extremely tactile balls thud when you drop them, consists of three hand-crafted balls in a presentation box (with instructional video).

PRICE: £21.95.

AVAILABLE: City Trading Ltd, 34 Upton Lane, Forest Gate, London E7 9LN Tel: 081-534 8855 (Mail Order).

MAGAZINE SUBSCRIPTION
Just Seventeen

Lots on pop, make-up, fashion and boys – though by 17 they've probably grown out of it.

PRICE: £50 p.a. (weekly).

AVAILABLE: Subscriptions Department, P O Box 500, Leicester LE99 0AA Tel: 0858 410510.

Mah Jong

This ancient Chinese games of tiles takes an hour to learn but a lifetime to master, so start early.

PRICE: From £24.95 to £59.95.

AVAILABLE: All good toy shops, department stores; Just Games, 71 Brewer Street, London W1R 3FB Tel: 071-734 6124 (Mail Order available).

Nintendo/Sega

They've probably got the kit – now they just need the games. A consultation is essential; what's one man's Mario is another man's poison.

PRICE: Games from £49.99.

AVAILABLE: Toy shops, electrical appliance stores, large stationers, department stores.

Radio-Controlled Cars

They go faster than could ever have been dreamt possible and can cope with practically any terrain. Some even have realistic engine sounds.

PRICE: From £34.99 to £70 [Taiyo].

AVAILABLE: Branches of Beatties nationwide; 10 The Broadway, Southgate, London N14 6PN Tel: 081-886 4258 (Mail Order).

Scuba Swatch Watches

'Diving' watches which incorporate the characteristic turning bezel which can be used to measure the amount of air left in diving tanks. Always useful.

PRICE: £27.50 [Swatch].

AVAILABLE: Selected jewellers, including Ratners, H Samuel.

Self-Assembly Rocket

Almost the real thing, to be launched anywhere there's open space away from airports! Rises to 1500 feet and then floats back down to earth on a parachute.

PRICE: £23.

AVAILABLE: Branches of Beatties nationwide; 10 The Broadway, Southgate, London N14 6PN Tel: 081-886 4258 (Mail Order).

Sheepskin Rug

Extremely cosy landing for toes as they emerge from bed; particularly in cold college bedsits!

PRICE: Around £29.

AVAILABLE: Branches of Ikea, leather shops and selected craft shops.

Ship in a Bottle Kit

A Victorian hobby which began around the time bottles started to be mass-produced – and now you can discover how it's done. Kit contains everything needed – including comprehensive instruction booklet.

PRICE: £24.95.

AVAILABLE: Past-Times, Witney, Oxford OX8 6BH Tel: 0993 779444 (Mail Order).

Starter Fishing Tackle Kit

There is a good second-hand market for rods through magazines (*Anglers' Mail/Angling Times*) and ask at local tackle shops or library for a list of fishing clubs.

PRICE: Starter tackle from £40; club fees £10–£25.

AVAILABLE: See *Anglers Times, Angling Times*.

Stud Box

Poppered, small round leather box for storing the (young) gentleman's essentials.

PRICE: From £39.95.

AVAILABLE: Smythsons, 44 New Bond Street, London W1Y 0DE Tel: 071-629 8558 (Mail Order available); department stores.

World Map Mural

See the world without leaving your chair. Meticulously detailed world map indicates times zones, ocean depths, nautical miles, land elevations and up-to-the-minute political boundaries (let's hope they're reprinting as we speak). When hanging measures 8'8" x 13' on eight heavily varnished pieces of paper.

PRICE: £49.95.

AVAILABLE: The Leading Edge Stores; The Leading Edge (Retail) Ltd, Euroway Business Park, Swindon SN5 8SN Tel: 0793 436648 (Mail Order).

£50 AND ABOVE

Bed in a Bag

Disappears into a colourful kit bag. Very convenient spare bed for when friends miss the last bus home.

PRICE: £55.

AVAILABLE: Branches of John Lewis Partnership.

Dinner Jacket

If boys 'have occasion' to wear dinner jackets they either have to borrow father's (which is two sizes too big) or wear one from Oxfam which comes with the gentle aroma of mothballs.

PRICE: From £169.

AVAILABLE: Gentleman's outfitters, department stores.

Interail Ticket

A rail ticket for unlimited train travel throughout Europe for a month, including discount on ferry crossing. Valid for those aged 16 to 26.

PRICE: From £249.

AVAILABLE: Enquire at local travel agent or BR Travel Office Tel: 071-834 2345.

Learn to Cook Holiday

An extremely useful option for someone who in a couple of years may have to fend for themselves in the bleak kitchen of student digs? Young Cooks of Britain runs cooking and activity holidays for children aged 11 to 16 – learn to roast a chicken in the morning and how to ride a horse in the afternoon.

PRICE: £265 per week (five days residential).

AVAILABLE: Young Cooks of Britain, Bridge Courtyard, Donnington, Chichester, West Sussex Tel: 0243 779239.

Microscope

For future doctors and microbiologists who have started dissecting already. Lens strength varies from what really merits a child's toy, to bona fide scientific instruments.

PRICE: From £60 to £600.

AVAILABLE: Broadhurst, Clarkson & Fuller Ltd, 63 Farrington Road, London EC1M 3JB Tel: 071-405 2156 (Mail Order available).

Motorcycle Driving Lessons

Strictly for Wild Ones – but make sure they have a professional and complete training before they're let out On the Road. On a Supercourse it is possible to gain a licence in just three days.

PRICE: £175 to full licence.

AVAILABLE: 40 CSM Centres nationwide: contact: CSM Supercourse, Freepost, Chelmsford, Essex CM1 3VU Tel: 0245 359478.

Mountain Bike

Tough bikes that are designed for mountain terrain but have become extremely popular 'on the street'.

PRICE: Basic models from £120 [Raleigh, Saracen, Marin].

AVAILABLE: Cycle stores, Halfords.

Portable TV

High on the list of teenage 'objects of desire' – now no reason to ever leave their rooms.

PRICE: e.g. £199 (Mitsubishi 14″ remote control colour TV).

AVAILABLE: Electrical stores nationwide.

Scalectrix

Electric racing track which must at least be as exciting as the real thing. Boys and girls would kill for a circuit.

PRICE: From £49 to £120.

AVAILABLE: Toy shops, department stores.

Sewing Machine

A professional machine that will reliably turn mini skirts into micro skirts and convert drainpipes into flares (or vice versa).

PRICE: £169.95 Singer Tempo 20; £249.95 Singer Tempo 50 – five built-in stitches.

AVAILABLE: Singer outlets nationwide. For nearest stockist contact: Singer UK Ltd, 91 Coleman Road, Leicester LE5 4LE Tel: 0533 769471.

Tennis Practice Net

A silent and much more efficient way of improving tennis strokes than the garage door. This garden-erected trainer bounces back balls and includes net height indicator.

PRICE: £85.

AVAILABLE: Selected sports shops; for mail order catalogue and stockists contact: TP Activity Toys & Sports, Severn Road, Stourport, Worcestershire, DY13 9EX Tel: 0299 827728.

CHAPTER FIVE

OLDIES & GOLDIES

O LD is quite clearly someone older than you. You are never old except in other people's eyes! The Yuppies are dead, welcome to the Woopies (Well Off Older People) – those who have the time and inclination to develop the hobbies and interests precluded earlier in life by the commitments of mortgages, children and work. Now is the time for self-fulfilment and choice – the French call it 'the age of living'.

UNDER £5

Aromatic Bubble Bath

Chunky glass bottles filled with scented potions which promise to soothe aches and pains, induce sleep, or perk you up depending on your frame of mind. Look beautiful in the bathroom; makes you feel good in the bath.

PRICE: From £3.99.

AVAILABLE: Selected branches of Marks & Spencer; independent chemists; The Conran Shop, 81 Fulham Road, London SW3 Tel: 071-589 7401.

Assorted Postcards

Packs of non-specific postcards on a favourite theme will save trips out for a (nearly) forgotten birthday or thank you. Choices include paintings from the National Gallery, cats, boats, dancers by Degas, etc.

PRICE: From £3.95 for 30 pictures.

AVAILABLE: Most bookshops, stationers and department stores.

BOOK CHOICE
We'll Eat Again

Written in association with the Imperial War Museum, this is a collection of recipes from the war years. Includes the famous Woolton pie and is illustrated with photos, cartoons and slogans of the time.

PRICE: £4.99.

AVAILABLE: Past-Times, Witney, Oxford OX8 6BH Tel: 0993 779444 (Mail Order).

Crossword Puzzle Book

The Times, Daily Telegraph, Daily Mail, et al – they all publish collections of their crosswords. If you know someone who's mad for them, buy a selection other than his daily – he's likely to have done them before.

PRICE: From £2.99.

AVAILABLE: W H Smith and other bookstores.

Freezer Meals

Cook, place in nice foil containers and deliver to the freezer. All your own work and much appreciated by those living alone.

PRICE: As you wish.

AVAILABLE: With love.

Flower Arranging Accessories

A plentiful supply of oasis (the green water-retaining block used in arrangements) would be a joy for anyone who has ever had to grapple with crumbling blocks; bud vases and pin blocks are other very welcome bases for beautiful arrangements.

PRICE: From 65p.

AVAILABLE: Garden centres, florists.

Glasses Repair Kit

If sellotape is a regular feature, a repair kit avoids the expense and inconvenience of a trip to the optician. Kit includes four screws, two hinge rings, mini tweezers and two nose pads.

PRICE: £3.50.

AVAILABLE: Science Museum Brainwaves, Freepost SU361, Dept 5317, Hendon Road, Sunderland SR9 9AD Tel: 091-514 4666 (Mail Order).

Mail Order Jams and Chutneys

Wendy Brandon's jams and chutneys are made traditionally and absolutely properly. Flavours are often unusual e.g. plum and crabapple with walnuts, and her Green Label range is made without added salt or sugar (sweetened with apple juice).

PRICE: From £2.35 (plus £5 p&p).

AVAILABLE: The Conran Shop, Michelin House, 81 Fulham Road, London SW3 6RD Tel: 071-589 7401; Wendy Brandon Hand Made Preserves, Felin Wen, Boncath, Dyfed, SA37 0JR Tel: 0239 841568 (Mail Order).

Pill Box

A compartmentalized pill box will ensure anyone on medication knows what they've actually taken or forgotten to take during the day. Available for either weekly or daily doses.

PRICE: From £1.20.

AVAILABLE: Boots, independent chemists.

Photo Frames

Always welcome – especially if already containing photos of the family (you can't go wrong with photos of the grandchildren). A photoframe handpainted with the child's name is a delightful variation.

PRICE: From £2 upwards. £16.99 (handpainted photo frame).

AVAILABLE: Letterbox (personalized frame) P O Box 114, Truro, Cornwall TR1 1FZ Tel: 0872 580885 (Mail Order).

Sing-a-Long Dancetime

An over-sixties opportunity to enjoy karaoke – includes all those songs that are so catchy you can't help singing along; to which anyone of a certain age seems to know the words e.g. 'Bye Bye Blackbird', 'We'll Meet Again', etc.

PRICE: £4.50 and 50p p&p.

AVAILABLE: Tony Savage, 21 Eaton Road, Margate, Kent CT9 1XB (Mail Order).

Spectacles Case

Designed by the Royal Academy for the half-glasses that perch on the end of the nose and can't be found anywhere.

PRICE: £4.95.

AVAILABLE: RA Enterprises Ltd, 8 Forge Court, Reading Road, Yateley, Camberley GU17 7RX Tel: 0252 861113 (Mail Order).

Walking Stick Grip

A small clip-on holder which allows walking sticks to hang from the table top from which the holder is hung.

PRICE: £4.35.

AVAILABLE: Homecraft, Sidings Road, Low Moor Estate, Kirkby-in-Ashfield, Notts NG17 7JZ Tel: 0623 754047 (Mail Order).

BETWEEN £5–£10

BOOK CHOICE
The Best of Rumpole

For all port-swilling, cigar-puffing fogeys who are watched over by 'She who must be obeyed'.

PRICE: £5.99 [Penguin – paperback]; £14.99 [Viking – hardback].

AVAILABLE: Bookshops.

Chinese Health Balls

Since the Ming Dynasty the Chinese have relaxed and meditated by rolling these chiming iron balls in their palms. They believe the smooth balls stimulate acupuncture points in their palms and fingers, a soothing experience if the old joints are getting a bit rusty.

PRICE: £5.25–£10.50.

AVAILABLE: Neal Street East, 5 Neal Street, London WC2H 9PU Tel: 071-240 0135; also department stores.

Clip-on Sunglasses

Shades which clip onto glasses are a cheaper alternative to having prescription sunglasses made.

PRICE: From £3.95 to £24.50.

AVAILABLE: Opticians, Boots, department stores.

Night Light

A light which plugs into any standard socket and automatically comes on at dusk and goes off at dawn. A very wise security precaution to deter burglars when in bed or away. Low running costs mean several can be used to light different rooms in the house.

PRICE: £7.99.

AVAILABLE: Pam's Shopping Service, Help the Aged, P O Box 28, London N18 3HG Tel: 081-803 6861 (Mail Order).

Nostalgic Cassettes + Musicals on Video

Recordings by artists such as Josef Locke, Gracie Fields and Jim Reeves available by mail. A choice of nine cassettes featuring all time greats plus 'Easter Parade', 'Brigadoon', 'Meet Me in St Louis' and other such classics on video so they can be enjoyed for the hundredth time.

PRICE: £6.99 (cassettes); £11.99 (MGM videos).

AVAILABLE: Memories By Mail, P O Box 1XX, Newcastle upon Tyne NE99 1XX Tel; 091-567 3466 (Mail Order); videos from video outlets and department stores.

Scented Drawliners

Antique drawers are particularly prone to mustiness but a sweet scents can easily be restored by lining them with gently fragranced drawliners which will also gradually pervade whatever is stored inside.

PRICE: £9.95.

AVAILABLE: Crabtree and Evelyn stores nationwide; 55 South Edwardes Square, London W8 Tel: 071-603 1611 (Mail Order available). Also Marks & Spencer, department stores.

Smoke Alarm

Most people don't realize it's the smoke and not the flames which are so lethal. Smoke alarms are easily fitted and will alert you when the toast is burning as well as when the sofa is in flames.

PRICE: From £8.50.

AVAILABLE: Electrical appliance shops, DIY stores and department stores.

World's Smallest Folding Umbrella

Tiny and light – this is the least cumbersome version available. Folding to only 8.5″ it's small enough to slip into any bag, yet opens to full size.

PRICE: £9.95.

AVAILABLE: Innovations Ltd, Euroway Business Park, Swindon SN5 8SN Tel: 0793 514666 (Mail Order).

BETWEEN £10–£20

All-in-One Hanging Basket

J Arthur Bower's hanging basket kit includes the basket, chain, bracket, liner and compost – all you need to buy are the plants to have an instant ornament.

PRICE: £13.79.

AVAILABLE: J Arthur Bowers, Firth Road, Lincoln LN6 7AH (Mail Order).

Bird Table

Placed in a suitable spot, perhaps outside the kitchen window where scraps can be thrown straight for the birds, a well-stocked table provides amusement and company all day long.

PRICE: From about £20 for a table.

AVAILABLE: Garden centres and pet shops.

BOOK CHOICE
Affordable Europe

Son of Fodor's *Gold Guides*, a publication which still focuses on quality and comfort but in the inexpensive league. B&Bs, hotels and excellent value family-run restaurants; how to get around and bargain shopping ... all at the very affordable price of ...

PRICE: £11.99 [Fodors].

AVAILABLE: Bookshops.

BOOK CHOICE
Miller's Antique Price Guide

Useful for researching future sales or discovering the little table in the bedroom that granny left is really worth a fortune. It contains 10,000 original illustrations including tips on furniture, silver, porcelain, toys, dolls, art nouveau and more.

PRICE: £19.99 [Miller's].

AVAILABLE: Bookshops.

BOOK CHOICE
The Gardener's Guide to Britain

Patrick Taylor's guide to the best gardens in Britain and Ireland, plus the best times to visit them. Includes precise directions on how to find them and opening times.

PRICE: £10.99 [Pavilion].

AVAILABLE: All good bookshops.

Card Shuffler

A battery-operated card shuffler is an enormous time-saver even for the most nimble of fingers. Shuffles one or two decks at the press of a lever.

PRICE: £12.45.

AVAILABLE: Chester-Care, Low Moor Estate, Kirkby-in-Ashfield, Notts NG17 7JZ Tel: 0623 757955 (Mail Order).

Cigar Cutter

If you haven't given up now you're sixty, you probably never will. An end snipper is essential for the biggest and best.

PRICE: From £15.50 for table cigar cutter.

AVAILABLE: Tobacconists, jewellers and department stores; The Cigar Club, 151 Harrow Road, Wembley, Middlesex HA9 6BR Tel: 081-902 2656 (Mail Order).

Cine Film transferred to Video

This is a wonderful way to sidestep the slide projector and make memories accessible at the flick of a button. Old cine films, 35 mm slides and photographs can all be converted to video tapes.

PRICE: From £17 (up to 100 ft of cine film – of any age, gauge and length); £30 (transfer of up to 75 photos onto video).

AVAILABLE: Memories on Video, 24 York Gardens, Winterbourne, Bristol BS17 1QT Tel: 0454 772857 (Mail Order).

Cool Box

Keep the refreshments refreshing with an insulated cool box which should accompany any day trip.

PRICE: From £13.

AVAILABLE: Department stores, Homebase, B&Q, Texas.

Folding Seat

Lightweight folding seat which converts from a walking stick in an instant – just the job when you need to take the weight off your feet.

PRICE: £19.99.

AVAILABLE: Agriframes Ltd, Charlwoods Road, East Grinstead, West Sussex RH19 2HG Tel: 0342 328644 (Mail Order).

Great War Double Album

First World War buffs will be fascinated by this compilation of music and drama recordings made at the time of the Great War, evoking life in the trenches and on the Home Front.

PRICE: £14.50 (including p&p); (cassette and CD also available: £6.50 & £11.00).

AVAILABLE: Major and Mrs Holt's Battlefield Tours Ltd, Golden Key Building, 15 Market Street, Sandwich, Kent CT13 9DA Tel: 0304 612248.

Lap Tray

Facilitates breakfast in bed or supper in front of the television. The Blue Willow pattern is copied from a nineteenth-century blue-and-white Staffordshire platter. A cushion filled with polystyrene beads is machine-washable and easily removable with velcro strips.

PRICE: £19.95.

AVAILABLE: Past-Times branches nationwide; Witney, Oxford OX8 6BH Tel: 0993 779444 (Mail Order).

Learn-to-Dance Videos

Master tricky dance manoeuvres in the comfort and privacy of your own home. Choose from either the beginners or master class collection where you learn more swivels and twists than in the early stages. Hosted by former world championship dancers. Each feature: the Foxtrot, Waltz, Quick Step, Tango, the Cha-Cha-Cha, Jive, Rumba and the Samba.

PRICE: £12.99 (Beginners' Collection – 45 mins); £14.95 (Master Class' Collection – 60 mins).

AVAILABLE: Instep Dance Promotions, Coppersnere, The Lane, Corston, Bath, BA2 9BA Tel: 0225 873603 (Mail Order).

MAGAZINE SUBSCRIPTION
This England

England as it used to be and still should be. Articles on towns, villages and churches; English heroes, royalty and past times. Great photographs, smashing nostalgia.

PRICE: £12.95 p.a. (quarterly).

AVAILABLE: This England, P O Box 52, Cheltenham, Glos GL50 1YQ Tel: 0242 577775.

Membership of The Archers' Fanclub

For serious *Archers* addicts, this club is run by the cast of the programme and includes a signed Christmas card all the way from Ambridge.

PRICE: £10.

AVAILABLE: P O Box 1951, Moseley, Birmingham B13 9DD.

Segmented Saucepan

A double or triple saucepan means that a whole meal or choice of veggies can be cooked using only one ring.

PRICE: £14.99 double pan; £17.99 triple pan.

AVAILABLE: Dale Street Mail Order, 53 Dale Street, Manchester M60 6ES Tel: 061-236 9911 (Mail Order).

Senior Railcard

The whole of the country becomes so much more accessible when you can watch it pass by through the window of a train – and there's a third off the standard rail fare.

PRICE: £16 p.a.

AVAILABLE: All BR Stations or Rail Appointed Travel Agents.

Tea Dance at the Waldorf

Tea accompanied by dancing and plenty of sandwiches – just the way it should be enjoyed! Or alternatively, a glass of sweet sherry accompanied by Freddy and the Dreamers at The Norbeck Castle in Blackpool.

PRICE: £19.50 (Saturdays and Sundays at the Waldorf); £11.50 (Summer Entertainment evening at The Norbeck Castle).

AVAILABLE: Waldorf Hotel, Aldwych, London WC2 Tel: 071-836 2400; The Norbeck Castle Hotel, Queens Promenade, Blackpool FY2 9AA Tel: 0252 52341.

Tippling Stick

An invigorating stroll can be combined with an equally invigorating tipple to guarantee a healthy glow. A brass knob cunningly unscrews to reveal a compass to point the way home and tiny bottle to be filled with a wee dram.

PRICE: £19.95.

AVAILABLE: National Maritime Museum & Old Royal Observatory, Greenwich Zero, Ferry Lane, Shepperton, Middlesex TW17 9LQ Tel: 0932 253333 (Mail Order).

Wheely Shopper

Bringing the shopping home on wheels can save a trip or two.

PRICE: From £12.50.

AVAILABLE: Luggage shops and department stores.

Window Thermometer

Sticks onto the window rather like a tax disc to a windscreen and tells you the temperature outside – from inside. Rational decisions can therefore be made about post-lunch walks and hat and glove wearing.

PRICE: £10.95.

AVAILABLE: Science Museum Brainwaves, Freepost SU361, Dept 5317, Hendon Road, Sunderland SR9 9AD Tel: 091-514 4666 (Mail Order).

BETWEEN £20–£50

Cordless Amplifying Headphones

When the walls of the television room throb with the level of the volume it may be time to invest in a pair of these. For insomniacs, those who like their music louder than everyone else and the hard of hearing. The infra-red transmitter means there are no cords and the sound quality is good up to 25 feet away.

PRICE: £49.95 [Infrasound].

AVAILABLE: The Leading Edge stores; The Leading Edge (Retail) Ltd, Euroway Business Park, Swindon SN5 8SN Tel: 0793 436648 (Mail Order).

Easy Kneeler Garden Stool

A stool which can be used just for admiring the vista, working in greenhouses, etc – and then flips over to convert into a kneeler with support arms to help you get up again.

PRICE: £32.80.

AVAILABLE: Pam's Shopping Service, Help the Aged, P O Box 28, London N18 3HG Tel: 081-803 6861 (Mail Order).

Foot Spa

The relaunched version features four speed settings to either relax or invigorate, contoured foot rests with 500 massage nodes to stimulate reflexology zones, and a built-in pumice bar.

PRICE: £39.50 [Clairol].

AVAILABLE: Electrical appliance stockists, department stores.

Garden Claw

A steel pole with a spiral 'claw' breaks and tumbles the soil with an effortless half turn of the handle. The job of weeding and soil aeration is made a whole lot easier.

PRICE: £29.95.

AVAILABLE: Garden Claw, 11/93 Admail, Plymouth PL1 2YD Tel: 0726 222132 (Mail Order).

Heated Underblankets

No excuse not to sleep as snug as a bug in a rug.

PRICE: From £24.75 (single) to £34.50 (kingsize).

AVAILABLE: Electrical appliance shops, department stores.

Jigroll

For jigsaw puzzle addicts, this could be a passport to a whole new way of life. No more up-all-night sessions because someone needs the dining-room table in the morning the jigsaw is 'rolled up' and can be 'unrolled' later.

PRICE: Four sizes from £20.95 to £38.95 (300–5000 pieces).

AVAILABLE: For mail order and list of stockists contact: Jigroll, Freepost, Barton, Cambridge CB3 7BR Tel: 0223 262592.

Lightweight Luggage

Old-fashioned luggage was designed in the day when porters cost less to hire than the price of a train ticket. Heavy and unwieldy suitcases can be replaced with tough, hardwearing but light-weight modern versions, with built-in wheels.

PRICE: From £41.

AVAILABLE: Luggage shops and department stores.

Magnifier with Light

Magnifying glass combined with a built-in light source. Ideal for enlarging print in books, on maps, etc, and also for mending and intricate needlework.

PRICE: £39.95.

AVAILABLE: Fred Aldous Ltd, PO Box 135, 37 Lever Street, Manchester M60 1UX Tel: 061-236 2477 (Mail Order).

MAGAZINE SUBSCRIPTION
Majesty

Keep up to date with the Queen Mum (isn't she marvellous), the Queen (doesn't she do a wonderful job), Diana (such a lovely girl) and the rest of the Royals.

PRICE: £20 p.a.

AVAILABLE: *Majesty* Subscription Dept, UMS, First Floor, Stephenson House, Brunel Centre, Bletchley, Milton Keynes MK2 2EN Tel: 0908 371981.

MAGAZINE SUBSCRIPTION
The Oldie

'Buy it before you snuff it' is the byline for Richard Ingrams' hilarious publication for the fogey of certain years.

PRICE: £35 p.a. (26 issues).

AVAILABLE: Oldie Subscriptions, 120-126 Lavender Avenue, Mitcham, Surrey CR4 3HP Tel: 081-685 9435.

Membership – Friends of Classics

A charitable association open to all who care about the study of the Classical world and have a consuming interest in 'the glory that was Greece and the grandeur that was Rome'. The annual subscription fee is set aside to develop and encourage all initiatives that will keep Classics in the public eye (offering financial support for educational schemes) – in return, Friends receive the biannual journal.

PRICE: £50 (Full Friend); £15 (Associate Friend).

AVAILABLE: Friends of Classics, c/o Jeannie Cohen, 51 Achilles Road, London NW6 1DZ Tel: 071-431 5088.

Napkin Hook

For the man who has everything except somewhere to tuck his napkin, a silver napkin hook which grips the napkin and hooks over buttons, collars etc.

PRICE: From £29.50.

AVAILABLE: S Thorn, Bellevue, Bude, Devon EX23 8JY Tel: 0288 353905 (Mail Order available).

Newspaper Clipper

A natty little tool for neatly clipping articles from newspapers, even small, tricky ones from the centre of the page.

PRICE: £35 (silver).
AVAILABLE: Tiffany, 25 Old Bond Street, London W1 Tel: 071-409 2790.

Punch Cartoon

An extensive range of original and contemporary cartoons, some of which have appeared in *Punch* and *Private Eye* are available from The Cartoon Gallery.
PRICE: £50–£100.
AVAILABLE: The Cartoon Gallery, 83 Lambs Conduit Street, London WC1 Tel: 071-242 5335.

Teasmade

The pleasure of waking up to something hot and steamy can be enjoyed at any age.
PRICE: From £22.50 (Philips Tea for Two).
AVAILABLE: Electrical appliance and department stores.

Weekend Breaks

Trips to historical, beautiful or just plain restful parts of the country. Many of the trips include rail fares.
PRICE: From £43 per person.
AVAILABLE: Book through any travel agent; Trust House Forte Leisure Break Reservations, 24-30 New Street, Aylesbury, Bucks HP20 3NW Tel: 0296 393388.

Wool Cardigan

Warm as well as comfortable to wear. The pockets should be large because they're going to filled with a constant supply of humbugs, plant ties and specs.
PRICE: From £25.
AVAILABLE: Branches of M&S, department stores.

£50 AND ABOVE

Ancestry Research

Does your family's wardrobe contain skeletons or treasure chests? Debrett can start research with just a name, date and place of birth and (in a couple of months) their experienced, international network of genealogists will present you with a bound narrative report, describing research and all references and documentation. Wherever appropriate a pedigree chart is included, so you can take a rational decision on stud fees.

PRICE: From £200 (including VAT) – short programme (based on time spent on research).

AVAILABLE: Debrett Ancestry Research, P O Box 7, Alresford, Hants SO24 9EN Tel: 0962 732676 (24-hour).

Automatic Garage Doors

Very Beverley Hills, but a real lifesaver in bad weather or if you've got a bad back. The door can be lifted from the comfort of your car, garage or house.

PRICE: £199 (Duralift 4500) (plus £10 delivery and £130 professional installation).

AVAILABLE: Autoport Systems Ltd, Hinton Road, Brackley, Northants NN13 5EU Tel: 0280 700421.

Battlefield Tour

Not just for those who can remember the war, but anyone who is interested in history. A Holt's tour aims to help you time-travel to the place, period and campaign of your choice whether it's the Second World War 'The Longest Day', Alamein or Gunfight at the OK Corral.

PRICE: e.g. Second World War 'The Longest Day' (Normandy) £314; Alamein (Egypt) about £999; Gunfight at the OK Corral (USA) £1956.

AVAILABLE: Major and Mrs Holt's Battlefield Tours Ltd, Golden Key Building, 15 Market Street, Sandwich, Kent CT13 9DA Tel: 0304 612248.

Car Telephone

A car phone could be a lifeline in a breakdown where phones could be long distances away. Line charges are expensive but airtime can be kept to a minimum if just used for emergencies.

PRICE: £299 (Sony Cellnet Lifeline).

AVAILABLE: Most electrical retailers. Call 0635 873322 for more details.

Circumnavigate the World

That crazy old trip of a lifetime – go all the way by air stopping off at New Zealand, LA or Hawaii and on the way back in Singapore or Bangkok.

PRICE: Saga round-the-world ticket from £960 per person depending on itinerary.

AVAILABLE: Saga Holidays Ltd, Freepost, Kent CT20 1BR Tel: 0800 414444.

Foreign Language Course

Berlitz conversation classes – any level so fluent speakers can enjoy conversation classes or complete beginners can maintain stony silence until they get a grasp on a language they've always wanted to learn. Teachers all speak in their mother tongue and classes are small with six to eight people – so you can't stay silent for too long! Linguaphone courses provide you with everything you need to teach yourself – in the privacy of your own home. You can learn a new language in as little as 12 weeks – they claim!

PRICE: £199 for ten-week conversation course at Berlitz; £160–£190 for Linguaphone course.

AVAILABLE: The Berlitz Schools of Languages Ltd, Wells House, 79 Wells Street, London W1A 3BZ Tel: 071-580 6482; Linguaphone Language Centre, 124-126 Brompton Rd, London SW3. Free information line: 0800 282417.

Gardening Holidays

For those whose interest is practical or merely recreational, Saga holidays are tailormade for people over sixty. Accommodation is specially selected and transport provided to all venues – which on the gardening holidays may include gardening and flower shows, an enormous range of gardens (large and small) and historic houses.

PRICE: e.g. From £109 for a weekend break (half board); week breaks from about £230.

AVAILABLE: Saga Holidays Ltd, Freepost, Kent CT20 1BR Tel: 0800 414444.

Microwave

It's surprising how those who succumb find they can't live without one. New models are available incorporating a conventional convection oven, a grill, rotisserie, etc, which integrate the speed of a microwave with the browning and crisping of conventional heat. Ideal for quickly heating ready-cooked or plated meals, small amounts of milk, hot drinks, etc.

PRICE: From £89.99 to £899.90 (Bosch Combination – microwave, grill and fan oven).

AVAILABLE: Electrical shops, department stores.

Motifed Slippers

A hard-soled velvet slipper, personalized by initials is what all slippers hope to be when they grow up – extremely personal and extremely luxurious. And so is the same velvet slipper with a hand-embroidered motif of coronet, grouse, etc.

PRICE: £200 (initialled slipper); £89.95 (slipper with motif).

AVAILABLE: Bowhill & Elliott, 65 London Street, Norwich NR2 1HW Tel: 0603 620116 (Mail Order).

Reclining Chair

'The comfort of your own armchair' taken to its extreme. Reclining chairs not only offer a most comfortable, relaxing and snooze-inducing position, the back position and leg support are also good for backache and heaviness in the legs.

PRICE: From £420 (including VAT and delivery).

AVAILABLE: Everstyl, 91 South End, Croydon CR0 1BG Tel: 081-760 5178.

Remote Control TV

Switch channels without leaving your armchair – if the TV has teletext it is also possible to get the news headlines, the latest cricket score, recipes and travel news ... all at the touch of a button.

PRICE: From about £180 (portable TV with remote control); £629 for a Panasonic 28″ Nicam Stereo TV with teletext and remote control.

AVAILABLE: Electrical and audio/visual shops.

Tunstall Lifeline

Immediate and speedy assistance for the elderly and disabled especially those living alone. The system provides a small alarm button which you carry at all times; and a specially adapted telephone with a sensitive microphone and powerful loudspeaker. A team of experienced carers is on duty 24 hours a day, seven days a week.

PRICE: £295 purchase price, plus annual monitoring fee of £90; Rental and installation £75, plus annual monitoring fee of £52.

AVAILABLE: Tunstall Lifeline Ltd, Whitley Lodge, Whitley Bridge, Yorkshire DN14 0HR Tel: 0977 662480.

TV/Phone Stamps

Savings stamps which take the sting out of TV licence renewals and phone bills. If you live long-distance, you may be receiving more frequent checking-up calls!

PRICE: Up to you – an entire licence fee for colour TV would be £85.

AVAILABLE: All post offices.

Umbrella Shooting Stick

Suitable for all outdoor sporting occasions, whatever the weather. The lightweight stick incorporates a standard or extra large multicoloured umbrella as well as the pigskin sling seat.

PRICE: £69.95 (standard size seat); £73.50 (large seat) [Gamebird].

AVAILABLE: William Powell & Son Ltd, 35 Carrs Lane, Birmingham B4 7SX Tel: 021-643 0689 (Mail Order).

Video Camera

Camcorders became generally available in the 1980s, and now one in ten households owns one and take every opportunity to film – not only weddings and christenings, but house decoration and barbecues. They combine a video camera and video cassette in one unit, and although they look complex are frighteningly easy to operate with focusing and exposure dealt with automatically, so anyone can become an instant Coppola or star on *You've Been Framed*.

PRICE: From £440.

AVAILABLE: All good audio-visual stockists.

Wooden Model Ship Kit

Artesamia kits can take weeks, months or the whole of the winter to complete and when finished are exquisite. Accurate to the most minute detail, they are precise scale models of each ship – including the rigging. Easy-to-find bits in boxes, with a full-size plan and photos of each ship.

PRICE: e.g. HMS Endeavour £129.99.

AVAILABLE: Branches of Beatties nationwide; 10 The Broadway, Southgate, London N14 6PN Tel: 081-886 4258 (Mail Order); Hamleys, Harrods.

CHAPTER SIX

COUNTRY & OUTDOORS

Does it surprise you to know that more is spent on hunting, shooting and fishing every year than on books? Or that 10% of Britain is still woodland, efficiently removing carbon dioxide and slowing down global warming? So pack your wellies and walk! Get back to nature and appreciate this green and pleasant land.

UNDER £5

Dry Fly Floatant

For buoyant fishing flies, this spray is ozone friendly. The quick-drying formula does not discolour flies or leave an oily ring on the water's surface.

PRICE: £2.99 (50g).

AVAILABLE: House of Hardy, Willowburn, Alnwick, Northumberland NE66 2PG Tel: 0665 602771 (Mail Order).

Earplugs/Stereo Earmuffs

Do they shoot? Do they need an ear trumpet? Earplugs are an effective way of cutting down the damaging noise which can lead to tinnitus. A pair of stereo earmuffs will provide total protection from the boom of the gun but a built-in amplifier means the flush of birds can be heard at a surprising distance. Slimline, so action is not impeded when the gun is brought up.

PRICE: From 95p (Muffles Wax Earplugs); Ear-Fit Sponge Plugs (four) £1.25; Stereo Ear Muffs £120.

AVAILABLE: Boots, chemists, country sports shops; stereo earmuffs from The Orvis Co Inc, The Mill, Nether Wallop, Stockbridge, Hampshire SO20 8ES Tel: 0264 781212 (Mail Order).

Handwarmers/Footwarmers

Disposable sachets which keep hands as warm as toast. Shake the sachets to activate the charcoal and just pop them in gloves or pockets. Toe heaters work on the same principle; attach them to the bottom of the sock with self-adhesive strips before putting on boots.

PRICE: £1.50 Glove heaters (two sachets); £5.50 (six-pack at Lillywhites); £6.00 toewarmers (pack of five pairs).

AVAILABLE: Most outdoor sports shops, YHA Adventure Shops (handwarmers only).

Maps/Special Touring Maps/Walking Maps

Ordnance Survey maps cover every inch of the country and mark all the footpaths. Touring and walking maps suggest special routes which assure the most delightful scenery and encompass the most interesting historic monuments.

PRICE: £4.25.

AVAILABLE: Good bookshops, newsagents.

Riding Accessories

A host of small items to get lost at frequent intervals!

PRICE: From 70p. jodphur clips: £2.95; hairnets: 70p, hoof oil: £3.95 (half litre); hoof pick: 95p, leadropes: £3.95, plaiting kit (including needles, thread, sponge, comb, plait braids, scissors etc): £9.50; saddlesoap: £2.75 per bar; stock pin: from £3.99 (goldplated).

AVAILABLE: All good riding accessory shops; W & H Gidden, 15D Clifford Street, London W1X 1RF Tel: 071-734 2788 (Mail Order available).

Zingers

Extremely useful little devices which clip onto waistcoats and contain about 13″ of retractable cord. Fishermen may have two or three about their person with scissors/forceps, etc, attached which may be needed immediately to hand.

PRICE: £1.60 [Masterline]; £11.99 [Hardy].

AVAILABLE: Most fishing tackle stockists; John Norris, 21 Victoria Road, Penrith, Cumbria CA11 8HP Tel: 0768 64211 (Mail Order).

BETWEEN £5–£10

Almost Unwearoutable Socks

If socks can be legendary, these are! Made from durable 75% wool yarn to be really tough AND comfortable. You can also have them personalized with names or messages.

PRICE: From £8.50.

AVAILABLE: Nicholl Knitwear, Piper Close, Corbridge, Northumberland Tel: 0434 632283 (Mail Order).

BOOK CHOICE
Birds of Britain and Europe

Over 2000 birds illustrated in full colour. It's pocket-size and makes any outing more enjoyable.

PRICE: £9.99 [Collins].

AVAILABLE: All good bookshops.

BOOK CHOICE
Knot Reference Book

A reference book for fishermen, climbers, sailors and campers who have forgotten everything they learned at boy scouts. *The Alternative Knot Book* by Dr Harry Asher gives you 75 knots including some new ones.

PRICE: £7.99 [Nautical Books].

AVAILABLE: All good bookshops; also chandlers.

Wainwright's Walking Books

Classic UK walking guides that help with the navigation and negotiation of country terrain. Tackle the Pennine Way, Southern Fells, etc, with confidence.

PRICE: From £8.99 [Michael Joseph].

AVAILABLE: All good bookshops.

Cartridge Extractor

Specialist tool for removing spent broken cartridges from gun barrels – without damage to instrument or fingernails.

PRICE: £5.95 (three claw and lever variety).

AVAILABLE: William Powell, 35 Carrs Lane, Birmingham B4 7SX Tel: 021-643 0689 (Mail Order).

Compass

Walkers know it's fun to explore but easy to get lost.

PRICE: From £10.50 [Recta].

AVAILABLE: All good outdoor activities shops.

Fish Filleting Knife

Essential for preparing the morning's catch for the evening's dinner. A Laser 7″ stainless steel knife will never need sharpening.

PRICE: £11.

AVAILABLE: Good kitchen shops, The John Lewis Partnership and other department stores.

Fly Boxes

A Wheatley fly box is known and prized by fly fishermen in almost every country in the world. Available for wet flies (containing eartha foam – a material that does not absorb water and therefore allows flies to dry quickly without danger of hooks rusting) or for dry flies (with clips or lidded compartments).

PRICE: From £6.75.

AVAILABLE: Good country sports shops; John Norris of Penrith, 21 Victoria Road, Penrith, Cumbria CA11 8HP Tel: 0768 64211 (Mail Order).

Protective Car Set Covers/Waterproof Pet Sheets

Wipe-clean plastic seat covers which will slip over the back seat of the car and prevent it being covered in mud and hairs after muddy walks. With an added waterproof pad even animals with amphibious tendencies won't leave a mark.

PRICE: From £7.50 (small pet sheet); from £9 (waterproof pads).

AVAILABLE: Over the Top Textiles, Bernard Stuart Ltd, Barley Hill House, Chadlington, Oxfordshire OX7 3NU Tel: 060876 625.

Sportsman's Diary

Reminders about Glorious Goodwood and the Glorious Twelfth for those who may be keen to know.

PRICE: £8.95.

AVAILABLE: Smythsons, 44 New Bond Street, London W1Y 0DE Tel: 071-629 8558 (Mail Order available).

Thermal Underwear

Smart people's essentials – now in styles no-one's embarrassed to be seen in.

PRICE: From £6.99.

AVAILABLE: M&S and sports shops; Damart, Bowling Green Mills, Bingley X, West Yorkshire BD97 1AD Tel: 0274 510000 (Mail Order).

Umbrella

Active sportsmen get wet, fishermen need shelter, as does anyone attending the races or maybe taking the dogs for a walk. Buy the very large variety.

PRICE: From £9.95.

AVAILABLE: All large sporting shops (try the golfing dept), department stores.

Warm Wellie Liners/Thermal Silk Glove Liners

Husky Sox can be worn in wellingtons, waders or boots by children or adults. They are warm, and although impervious to moths, midlew and perspiration rot, you can pop them in the wash. Thermal silk is lightweight, non-bulky and comfortable to wear as it draws moisture away from the body – also extremely warm!

PRICE: £5 (wellie liners); £5.95 (glove liners).

AVAILABLE: Most country outfitters; for nearest stockist contact: Husky of Tosktock Ltd, Bury Street, Stowmarket, Suffolk IP14 1HE Tel: 0449 674471; Patra Selections Ltd, 1-5 Nant Road, London NW2 2AL Tel: 081-209 1112 (Mail Order).

Weatherproof Map Case

A clear plastic wallet which protects your map from the elements.

PRICE: From £2.99; £5.99 [Hi-gear].

AVAILABLE: Lillywhites, all good outdoor sports and camping stores.

YHA Membership

YHA hostels aren't what they used to be. You don't have to be young, the sheets aren't all nylon and you don't have to sweep the whole house before breakfast. Very reasonably priced accommodation available to YHA members in some of the country's most beautiful spots.

PRICE: Senior (18 and over) £9 p.a.; Junior (15–17) £3 p.a.

AVAILABLE: YHA Membership Department, National Office, 8 St Stephens Hill, St Albans, Herts AL1 2DY Tel: 0727 855215.

BETWEEN £10–£20

Barbout Tool

The fishing accessory that you hope you will never need! The first emergency device for removing fish hooks from people – resembling a small crane it first pushes and then withdraws the barb. The manufacturer suggests that the technique should first be practised on a broccoli stalk!

PRICE: £19.95.

AVAILABLE: Farlows of Pall Mall, 5 Pall Mall, London SW1 5YNP Tel: 071-839 2423 (Mail Order available).

BOOK CHOICE
Game Cookery Book

Mrs Beeton's *Game Cookery Book* is packed with well-tested and traditionally wonderful ways with game. Includes tips on preparation and presentation as well as the cooking of game.

PRICE: £16.95 [Ward Lock].

AVAILABLE: All good bookshops and selected kitchen shops.

BOOK CHOICE
Good Bed and Breakfast Guide

Rather than a hotel guide, a bed and breakfast guide gives access to inns, farmhouses and guest houses which may be off the beaten track and have a more local flavour.

PRICE: £12.99 [Hodder & Stoughton].

AVAILABLE: All good bookshops.

Butterfly Net/Collecting Kit

Entomology is a pastime that may not have occurred to country lovers. Nets are usually collapsible to make travelling easier.

PRICE: From £12.95 (14″ diameter); £44.95 (professional kite net); £39.50 (cork-lined storebox – 17″ x 12″).

AVAILABLE: Worldwide Butterflies Ltd, Sherborne, Dorset DT9 4QN Tel: 0935 74608 (Mail Order available).

Cracker Thrower

A hand-held thrower tosses Ritz crackers up to 60 yards so sharp shooters can get their eye in. Will throw singles or doubles.

PRICE: £16.

AVAILABLE: Orvis Co Inc Ltd, The Mill, Nether Wallop, Stockbridge, Hampshire SO20 8ES Tel: 0264 781212 (Mail Order).

Decoys/Decoy Call

Invaluable for attracting the live versions into your line of fire.

PRICE: £12.95 ('championship' duck calls); £12.95 (widgeon, teal, fox).

AVAILABLE: Ralph Grant & Son Ltd, Green Lane Road, Leicester LE5 4PD Tel: 0533 767551.

Fish Balances

For those who dispute (quite rightly) the myth that size isn't important. Spring balances with a large hook come in five sizes (including large salmon) and with metric and imperial markings.

PRICE: £12.95.

AVAILABLE: Fishing accessory shops; House of Hardy, Willowburn, Alnwick, Northumberland NE66 2PG Tel: 0665 602771 (Mail Order).

Fishing Mitts

Made from warm non-absorbent polypropylene. When they get wet just wring them out or shake them dry. Elastic cuffs keep wrists protected from wind and rain.

PRICE: £11.

AVAILABLE: The Orvis Co Inc, The Mill, Nether Wallop, Stockbridge, Hampshire SO20 8ES Tel: 0264 781212 (Mail Order).

Hand Tally Counter

So busy shooting you forget to count? This records 1–9999 hits on a shooting day.

PRICE: £10.95.

AVAILABLE: Ralph Grant & Son Ltd, Green Lane Road, Leicester LE5 4PD Tel: 0533 767551 (Mail Order).

Hunting Accessories

The real McCoy. A hunting horn, available with or without a leather holster; hunting whip with a stag horn top and silver collar, lash and thong; wire cutters in a leather holster (Hunt followers – see Riding Accessories).

PRICE: Horn £14.95 (£66 with leather holster); wire cutters and holster £54.

AVAILABLE: W & H Gidden, 15D Clifford Street, London W1X 1RF Tel: 071-734 2788 (Mail Order available).

Maglite Torch

So much in demand that stockists have been known to sell out completely. An incredibly powerful beam, extremely durable and completely watertight.

PRICE: £9.99–£31.50.

AVAILABLE: All good outdoor sports shops, hardware and department stores.

Map Measurer

In principal like a pedometer – run over the intended route on your map and it will tell you whether or not to take the car.

PRICE: £10.75.

AVAILABLE: Outdoor sports shops.

Swiss Army Knife

The most indispensable penknife; from a single blade to a version with which you could probably break out of jail. Fish scalers and corkscrew options might be very appropriate. Also, highly recommended for fishermen is the Leatherman tool. Weighing only 5 oz it folds up to measure 4″ but contains all the pliers, cutters and bottle openers an outdoor sportsman could ever need. Comes with a leather wallet and a 25-year guarantee.

PRICE: From £4.50 (for Victorinox single blade); £22.50 (Huntsman – 9 functions); £47.95 (Champion – 28 functions); £20.75 (Leatherman tool).

AVAILABLE: All good outdoor sports shops, YHA Adventure shops; John Norris of Penrith, 21 Victoria Road, Penrith, Cumbria CA11 8HP Tel: 0768 64211 (Mail Order).

Walking Stick

For breaking through undergrowth and reaching up for high blackberries.

PRICE: About £19.50 (for a horn head and seasoned hazel shank – a seriously smooth stick that will last a lifetime).

AVAILABLE: Local saddler, country shops and country fairs, or department stores.

Welly Boot Bag

Dirty-boot carrier (or Portable Wellington Wardrobe) for the town/country goer. Made of washable nylon with a non-rusting zip. The whole folds down to its small stiffening base.

PRICE: £19.

AVAILABLE: Good country shops; The Orvis Co Inc, The Mill, Nether Wallop, Stockbridge, Hampshire SP20 8ES Tel: 0264 781221 (Mail Order).

Wetland and Wildfowl Trust Membership

Free admission to a variety of Trust Centres and events, together with a quarterly magazine. The profits from membership help conserve the world's wildfowl.

PRICE: £15 p.a. Family membership (two adults, and two children under 16) £24.

AVAILABLE: The Membership Office, The Wildfowl & Wetlands Trust, Slimbridge, Gloucester GL2 7BT Tel: 0453 890333.

BETWEEN £20–£50

Alcoholic Survival Kits

The packaged version consists of a bottle of whisky, cognac and gin – you could always consider compiling your own.
PRICE: £39.50.
AVAILABLE: Berry Bros & Rudd, 3 St James Street, London SW1A 1EG Tel: 071-396 9600 (Mail Order available).

BASC Membership

The British Association for Shooting and Conservation is the largest shooting organization in the sport of country shooting. It also aims to conserve and manage the wildlife and habitats of the UK. Benefits include automatic third-party legal liability insurance, a quarterly magazine and free advice on legal and professional matters.
PRICE: £21 p.a. (full membership).
AVAILABLE: The BASC, Marford Hill, Rossett, Wrexham, Clywd LL12 0HL Tel: 0244 570881.

Boot-Scraper

A bristly boot-scraper which brushes mud off boots before trailing it into the house. Henry the Hedgehog could be mistaken for the real thing – if it was a very dark night.
PRICE: £32.50 (pine); £34.50 (hardwood).
AVAILABLE: The Original Henry Hedgehog Company, 5 Shipham Lane, Winscombe, Avon BS2 1JU Tel: 0934 853153 (Mail Order).

Cartridge Bag/Belt/Pouch

Barbour make well-designed and extremely hard-wearing cartridge bags and belts. The bag is made from laminated textured canvas with a single buckle for ease of access; the thick leather belt is comfortable as well as practical and can take up to 25 12-bore cartridges. Cartridge pouches can be worn ON the belt, each holding 25 cartridges.
PRICE: £36.95 (bag); £23.95 (belt); £25 (pouch).

AVAILABLE: Barbour stockists (call 091-455 4444); John Norris, 21 Victoria Road, Penrith, Cumbria CA11 8HP Tel: 0768 64211 (Mail Order); Farlows of Pall Mall, 5 Pall Mall, London SW1 Tel: 071-839 2423 (Mail Order available).

Cool Fish Bag

Insulated to keep fish cool and fresh. Comes complete with freezer blocks and in three sizes: 21" (trout), 24" (sea trout) and 36" (salmon).

PRICE: From £39.

AVAILABLE: Fishing tackle stockists; Farlows of Pall Mall, 5 Pall Mall, London SW1 Tel: 071-839 2423 (Mail Order available).

Day Membership of Hunt

Can be arranged for a keen hunter who may be staying for a few days.

PRICE: By arrangement with the Master; about £45 (£30 for a weekday).

AVAILABLE: Contact local hunt masters.

Dog Drying Coat

A reversible thermal-lined towelling coat designed for gun dogs to keep them warm and dry after a day's shooting.

PRICE: £26.95 (spaniel); £29.95 (labrador).

AVAILABLE: Comfy Pet Products, 2-4 Parsonage Street, Bradninch, Nr Exeter, Devon EX5 4NW Tel: 0392 881285 (Mail Order available).

Fishing Glasses

Special lenses sharpen vision and eliminate surface glare and reflections. The photocromic glass continuously adjusts so they are very comfortable to wear.

PRICE: £33.95 (Polaroid sunglasses with side panels for eye protection).

AVAILABLE: Selected opticians; Farlows of Pall Mall, 5 Pall Mall, London SW1 Tel: 071-839 2423 (Mail Order available).

Fishing Net

'Favourite' trout fisher's net from Hardy. Superb for river and stillwater use – bow-shaped net with telescopic handle which is easily extendable with one hand.

PRICE: £44.95 (knotted·or knotless net).

AVAILABLE: House of Hardy, Willowburn, Alnwick, Northumberland NE66 2PG Tel: 0665 602771 (Mail Order).

Fly Pattern Index

Tying your own flies? An illustrated guide to 235 patterns of trout, salmon and saltwater flies. Printed on varnished card and bound in a ring binder to be easily removed for use at the tying bench.

PRICE: £20.50.

AVAILABLE: The Orvis Co Inc, The Mill, Nether Wallop, Stockbridge, Hampshire SO20 8ES Tel: 0264 781212 (Mail Order).

Game Book

To go with the bag and the gun – the record of the shoot.

PRICE: £36 (long grain leather); £190 (fully leather-bound – 14″ x 9.5″).

AVAILABLE: Smythsons, 44 New Bond Street, London W1Y 0DE Tel: 071-629 8558 (Mail Order available).

Game Shooting Video

Holland & Holland's *Game Shooting* is essential viewing for anyone wishing to learn or improve the basic principles of game shooting; stance, handling and mounting the gun each applied to rough shooting, grouse and high pheasant. A video is also available on pigeon shooting.

PRICE: £24.95.

AVAILABLE: Holland & Holland, PO Box 44, Leatherhead, Surrey KT22 7AE Tel: 0372 457358 (Mail Order).

Gun Sleeve

Available for broken or unbroken gun carriages. Before buying check you know the barrel lenth of the gun. Available in canvas or fleece-lined leather.

PRICE: From £37.65 (canvas); from £133.25 (leather).

AVAILABLE: Farlows of Pall Mall, 5 Pall Mall, London SW1 Tel: 071-839 2423 (Mail Order available).

Hats

Fashion dictates wide brimmed, rabbit fur, felt Australian bushman-style hats (without the corks). Real sporting personalities may prefer the more traditional tweed flat caps – a broad rim will displace a hat when a prone shot is attempted.

PRICE: £65 (heavy felt hats with names like 'White Fang'); £30 approx (Barbour's waxed version).

AVAILABLE: RM Williams Ltd, 179-181 Regent Street, London W1R 7FB Tel: 071-434 0061; J Barbour & Sons Ltd, Simonside, South Shields, Tyne & Wear NE34 9PD Tel: 091-455 4444.

Heated Boot Rack

Drys, airs or simply warms damp boots, shoes or waders; this electrically heated rack can be left on for long periods or just used when required. Very low running cost.

PRICE: £46.50.

AVAILABLE: Farlows of Pall Mall, 5 Pall Mall, London SW1 Tel: 071-839 2423 (Mail Order available).

Heritage Home Search

If the old pile has appeared for sale in either *Country Life*, *Homes and Gardens* or *The Field*, Heritage Home Search will unearth the relevant issue.

PRICE: £20–£25.

AVAILABLE: Heritage Home Search, Haye Farm House, Sheboick, Torpoint, Cornwall, PL11 3EW Tel: 0503 30793.

Hip Flask

Together with nip cups, this must be the all time favourite for freezing days up to your ears in muck.

PRICE: From about £24.50.

AVAILABLE: Country sports shops, gift shops and department stores.

Lightweight Shooting Sticks

Weighing only 2 lb, this version of the classic shooting stick packs into a small shoulder bag and adjusts to the height of the sitter. The Elite Packaway has interchangeable feet for hard or soft ground.

PRICE: £29.50.

AVAILABLE: Guy Brian Leisure Ltd, 39 Falkland Road, Evesham, Worcs, WR11 6XS Tel: 0386 765320 (Mail Order).

MAGAZINE SUBSCRIPTION
The Field

Perhaps the definitive field sports and country pursuits magazine. News about all that's best in the British countryside and coverage of sports, art and literature; social, cultural and national events.

PRICE: £35 p.a. (monthly).

AVAILABLE: The Field, Quadrant Subscription Services, Freepost SL140, Haywards Heath, West Sussex TH16 3DH Tel: 0444 445316 (*The Scottish Field* is also available).

MAGAZINE SUBSCRIPTION
Trout and Salmon

Packed to the gills with features and advice for fishermen. Britain's oldest and most established game-fishing magazine (UK only).

PRICE: £27 p.a. (monthly).

AVAILABLE: Trout and Salmon Subscriptions, PO Box 500, Leicester LE99 0AA Tel: 0858 410510.

Map Centred on Your Home

Ordnance Survey create unique maps centred around specific towns or villages. The finished maps measure 24″ x 24″ and cover approx 18 miles around the selected point.

PRICE: £33.90 (laminated version); £53.90 (laminated, mounted, edged).

AVAILABLE: Map Marketing Ltd, Freepost, London SW6 3BR Tel: 071-736 0297 (Mail Order).

Membership of The Country Gentlemen's Association

Purveyors of professional services, special offers and social events to country folk. Amongst the impressive list of benefits and associations offered are: a good monthly magazine, a wine club, discounts off new cars, access to a London club, and regular antique roadshows and horseracing days out for members.

PRICE: £30 annual membership (husband and wife); from £200 life membership.

AVAILABLE: Country Gentlemen's Association, London Road, Baldock, Herts SG7 6ND Tel: 0462 490206.

National Trust Membership

Free entry to all National Trust houses, parkland and gardens, as well as the *National Trust Handbook*, newsletters and a magazine three times a year.

PRICE: £24 p.a. (adult); £11 p.a. (junior – under 25).

AVAILABLE: National Trust Membership Dept, PO Box 39, Bromley, Kent BR1 1NH Tel: 081-464 1111.

Riding Boot Trees

Equitrees are specifically designed for riding boots, to preserve their shape and stiffness.

PRICE: £24.99.

AVAILABLE: Lillywhites, good outdoor sports shops and saddlers.

Shooting Gloves

Soft, pliable leather with only the back of the hand lined for warmth. Trigger finger hinges back with velcro strips if needed. Available for right or left-handed shots.

PRICE: £32.

AVAILABLE: The Orvis Co Inc, The Mill, Nether Wallop, Stockbridge, Hampshire SO20 7ES Tel: 0264 781212 (Mail Order).

Smuggler Fishing Rods

Hardys make the most successful range of travel rods in the world. Rods divide into six, seven or eight pieces, none of which measure more than 40 cm. They are so well balanced that apparently many fishermen find they have a better action than most two-piece rods. Cheaper ranges of sectioned rods are also available from Shakespeare and recently from Daiwa: from 7'6" to 9'6".

PRICE: Hardys, from £226 (7ft rod – six pieces); Shakespeare/Daiwa, from £40 to £70.

AVAILABLE: House of Hardy, Willowburn, Alnwick, Northumberland NE66 2PG Tel: 0665 602771 (Mail Order); John Norris of Penrith, 21 Victoria Road, Penrith, Cumbria, CA11 8HP Tel: 0768 64211 (Mail Order).

Tent

Consider first sleeping capacity, seasonal use, ease of erecting, weight and packed size. For lightweight travelling the YHA recommends the Canalight (two-man traditional tent shape); or the Protech D (three-man – dome-shaped).

PRICE: From £26.95.

AVAILABLE: YHA Adventure Shops (Contact 07884 458625 for nearest branch).

Unbreakable Flasks

Heavy-duty flasks which expect to be kicked, dropped and still be usable. A double wall of stainless steel will keep drinks hot or cool for up to 12 hours.

PRICE: From £21.95.

AVAILABLE: Survival Aids Ltd, Morland, Penrith, Cumbria CA10 3AT Tel: 0800 262752 (Mail Order).

Waterproof-Backed Picnic Rugs

Bottoms need not be as soggy as the sandwiches. Made from 100% worsted wool, with 100% waterproof backing. All the tartans are from Scotland and can be embroidered with initials.

PRICE: £37 (60" x 54").

AVAILABLE: Department stores; Hobby Horse, Seaview Farm, Otterham Station, Nr Camelford, Cornwall PL32 9SW Tel: 08406 588 (Mail Order).

Waterproof Lighter

Windproof, refillable lighter with a lid which locks into place for a complete seal. The owner will never be caught wet and cold without a way to light a life-saving fire or cigarette.

PRICE: £29.

AVAILABLE: Good outdoor sports shops; The Orvis Co Inc, The Mill, Nether Wallop, Stockbridge, Hampshire SO20 7ES Tel: 0264 781212 (Mail Order).

£50 AND ABOVE

Beckington Boot Jack

For prising off riding boots and wellies that have welded themselves to the foot after a hard day in the field. The Beckington Boot Jack is hand-crafted and bound with leather to protect the boots.

PRICE: £89.99.

AVAILABLE: The Beckington Boot Jack Co, Sunbury House, Gloucester Road, Bath BA1 8BH Tel: 0373 830082 (Mail Order).

Binoculars

Self-focusing, waterproof, lightweight? Technology means that you can select the best possible model for any function, but prices vary enormously.

PRICE: From about £70.

AVAILABLE: Most large department stores, technical and optical equipment suppliers; Self-focusing from Normack Sport Ltd, Pottery Road, Bovey Tracey, Newton Abbot, Devon TQ13 9DS Tel: 0626 832889.

Country Clothing

A few of the better-known names are listed here – but check out country shops and even major branches of M&S for a more affordable version. Decent clothing in this changeable climate is commonsense, not snobbism!

PRICE: Plus-twos £140; shooting stockings £49 and £59; garters £7.50.

AVAILABLE: e.g. Gieves & Hawkes, No 1 Saville Row, London W1X 2JR Tel: 071-434 2001; Holland & Holland, 31 Bruton Street, London W1X 7DD Tel: 071-499 4411; for stockists call Husky Tel: 0449 674471; Rohan Tel: 0908 216655; John Partridge Tel: 0889 584438.

Fisherman's Flotation Jacket

The 'Sospender's Shorty' is a flotation device that is specifically designed for use with chest waders. In its uninflated state it's a short fishing waistcoat with pockets, D-rings etc; the only giveaways are the blow tube and orange rup pull.

PRICE: £129.95 [Leeda]; £79.00 (Sospender's inflatable braces).

AVAILABLE: Leeda stockists; John Norris of Penrith, 21 Victoria Road, Penrith, Cumbria CA11 8HP Tel: 0768 64211 (Mail Order).

Fishing and Shooting Trousers

Regular cotton chinos with added waxproof cotton patches which cover the legs from mid-thigh to ankle and the whole of the seat of the trousers – you can sit or kneel in puddles without becoming uncomfortable for the rest of the day.

PRICE: £56.

AVAILABLE: The Orvis Co Inc, The Mill, Nether Wallop, Stockbridge, Hampshire SO20 8ES Tel: 0264 781212 (Mail Order).

Goretex Garments

Goretex is a fabric which doesn't allow rain and drizzle to pass inwards, but does allow body moisture to evaporate into the atmosphere. Brilliant for outdoor pursuits – breathable, waterproof, lightweight and durable.

PRICE: e.g. Musto 'Highland' Goretex jacket £245; (expect to pay around £200 for a jacket; from about £30 for gloves).

AVAILABLE: Most sportswear stockists; Farlows of Pall Mall, London SW1 Tel: 071-839 2423 (Mail Order).

MAGAZINE SUBSCRIPTION
Country Life

Superbly produced magazine for cultured and country people. Regular articles on the performing arts, gardens and gardening, famous houses; together with saleroom news, bits on bridge, book reviews, etc.

PRICE: £108 p.a. (weekly).

AVAILABLE: Country Life Subscriptions, Freepost 1061, Haywards Heath, West Sussex RH16 3ZA Tel: 0444 445522.

MAGAZINE SUBSCRIPTION
Horse and Hound

All you ever wanted to know about horses and horse events.

PRICE: £63 p.a. (weekly).

AVAILABLE: IPC Magazines Ltd, King's Reach Tower, Stamford Street, London SE1 9LS Tel: 071-444 4412.

MAGAZINE SUBSCRIPTION
The Shooting Times

'The shooting man's bible' with coverage of shooting news, features and weekly details of events.

PRICE: £65 p.a. (weekly).

AVAILABLE: Quadrant Subscription Services, Oakfield House, Haywards Heath, West Sussex RH16 3DH Tel: 0444 445533.

Part Owner of a Racehorse

The Formula Racehorse Scheme is a monthly payment plan, covering your share in the purchase price, training, farrier, vet and jockey fees and includes automatic entry to the Members' Enclosure every time your horse races and a share of the winnings. The scheme also reimburses your share of the value of the horse when sold. As they say, your investment can go down as well as up!

PRICE: From £150 per month.

AVAILABLE: The Owners Room, Pendley Farm Racing Stables, Station Road, Tring, Herts HP23 5QY Tel: 0442 826393 (Mail Order).

Picnic Hamper

In sizes to cater for parties of hungry sportsmen or an intimate diner à deux; available empty or with crockery sets.

PRICE: £79–£350.

AVAILABLE: Most department stores.

Rambling Holiday

Glorious routes in Britain and around the world with tours graded from A (very tough) to E (very easy) – taking into account hours walked, gradients, terrain involved, etc. Usually numbers between 12 and 24 people, many of whom are travelling alone.

PRICE: From £190.

AVAILABLE: Ramblers Holidays, Box 43, Welwyn Garden, Herts A18 6PQ Tel: 0707 331133.

Rucksacks

The main criterion of choice is size: will the pack be used for days/weekends/backpacking expeditions? (A big sack can be left empty; too small a sack is difficult to enlarge.) Is the backlength correct? Rucksacks are subject to heavy knocks, so choose one made from robust material and look carefully at seams and load-bearing stitching – often weak areas.

PRICE: From £16.95 for a day trekking sack; Recommended: Karrimor Jaguar GR65 (with lifetime guarantee) backpacking size £99.95.

AVAILABLE: All good outdoor shops; Survival Aids Ltd, Morland, Penrith, Cumbria CA10 3AT Tel: 0800 262752 (Mail Order).

Sleeping Bag/Sleeping Mats

Like duvets, choose from the cheap to the very expensive. The bestselling Softie range is a combination of parachute silk and 'down-soft' thermal fibre. RAB sleeping bags are the choice of Himalayan expeditions and the British Antarctic Survey – filled with goosedown. For added protection against cold hard ground, sleeping mats and inflatable camping mattresses.

PRICE: Softies from: £54.95; RAB range, Ladakh 1000 £199.95 (bags); Sleeping mats from £3.99 and Camping Mattresses £54.95 (Therm-a-Rest).

AVAILABLE: YHA Adventure Shops and outdoor sports shops.

The Ultimate Green Wellie

Le Chameau are what all wellies hope to be when they grow up. Leather-lined for year-round comfort and durability – absorb excess moisture and provide comfortable insulation. Zippered side makes on/off operations easier and draw strap at the top keeps out rain and draughts.

PRICE: £169 (standard calf); £187 (wide calf).

AVAILABLE: Contact: Gunmark Ltd, Carlo Beretta House, 11 Brunel Way, Fareham, Hampshire PO15 5TX Tel: 0489 579999 for stockists.

120

Waders

Top quality waders need to be reliably waterproof and afford a secure grip. Welly Waders conceal beneath their tops an ingeniously compressed set of leggings that extend into thigh-waders. Cleated and studded soles.

PRICE: Chest-waders £87.95 (to size 11), £97.95 (from size 12); £54.95 (Welly Waders).

AVAILABLE: Good outdoor sports shops; Farlows of Pall Mall, 5 Pall Mall, London SW1 Tel: 071-839 2423 (Mail Order); Welly Waders, Edington Development Co, Edington, Westbury, Wilts BA13 4NP Tel: 0373 825469.

Walking Boots

The Brasher 'Hillmaster' and 'Fellmasters', developed by Reebok are classic lightweight boots, ideally suited for men and women walkers, built on running shoe last that's sprung to give a natural walking action.

PRICE: £79.95.

AVAILABLE: Most outdoor shops; YHA Adventure Shops nationwide.

Waxed Jacket

Windproof, water- and thorn-resistant, Barbours have become the uniform of the country. Enormous pockets, and moleskin lined handwarmers. Either the Beaufort or the slightly longer Border.

PRICE: £130 (Beaufort); £140 (Border); £85 (Spey Wading Jacket – designed to be worn with waders).

AVAILABLE: Most outdoor and country sports shops; for stockists call: J Barbour & Sons Ltd, Simonside, South Shields, Tyne & Wear, NE34 9PD Tel: 091-455 4444.

Weather Vane

A more traditional way of predicting the weather is with a hand-made cast-iron weather vane. Myriad designs and sizes available from small to huge horses, angels, eagles and sailboats.

PRICE: £175 [National Trust]; £44.65 (small horse); £228.50 (large horse) [Flora & Fauna].

AVAILABLE: National Trust shops nationwide; Postal Shopping Service, P O Box 101, Western Way, Melksham, Wiltshire SN12 8EA Tel: 0225 705676 (Mail Order); Flora & Fauna Ltd, Orchard House, Patmore End, Ugley, Bishop's Stortford, Hertfordshire CM22 6JA.

CHAPTER SEVEN

CRAFTS & HOBBIES

How long is a piece of string? Accessible evening classes see girls mending cars, men decorating cakes and grannies learning to disco dance! This is an ever-expanding and often profitable area, as new collectors of phonecards will agree Live by the philosophy. 'Try it – you might find you like it' and you could find some ideas for yourself in this chapter!

UNDER £5

BOOK CHOICE
Bonsai Trees

Anne Swinton's pocket size guide to miniature trees – selecting, care, maintenance, display and how to avoid pests and disease.
PRICE: £3.99 [Collins – part of the garden guide series].
AVAILABLE: Bookshops.

Dried Flowers

Beautiful bunches of dried roses or cornflowers or anything else that looks pretty are available from some flowershops. They form the basis of any long-lasting arrangement.
PRICE: From £1.20 (a bunch of 20 roses is about £5).
AVAILABLE: Most flowershops. Contact: Norpar Dried Flowers, Navestock Hall, Navestock, Essex RM4 1HA Tel: 0277 374968 (they will send orders by mail – although they don't have a catalogue).

Friendly Plastic

This plastic is a soft malleable material which can be cut and is then easily shaped when placed in hot water or in the oven. Modellers and jewellery makers may welcome the opportunity to diversify into a new medium.

PRICE: 89p per sheet (24 colours available); £2.65 Friendly Plastic Starter Book.

AVAILABLE: Fred Aldous, 37 Lever Street, Manchester 1, M60 1UX Tel: 061-236 2477 (Mail Order available).

Garment Labels

Someone who designs and makes their own clothes can become 'a label'. Perhaps you could consider the words 'A .... Design' to distinguish this designer label from a nametape.

PRICE: £4.50 (Irish satin ribbon 15 & 23 mm).

AVAILABLE: Jacqueline Crouch, 10 Hatch Way, Kirtlington, Oxon OX5 3JS Tel: 0869 50408 (Mail Order).

Goggles

You don't have to be a foundry worker to warrant a pair of these! Goggles are sensible protection against any dust or chemical fumes where chipping, grinding or mixing is going on. Wide choice – all of which can be worn over specs.

PRICE: From £4.78 (like school lab goggles).

AVAILABLE: Alec Tiranti Ltd, 27 Warren Street, London W1P 5DG Tel: 071-636 8565; 70 High Street, Theale, Reading RG7 5AR Tel: 0734 302775 (Mail Order).

Image Maker

Magic solution which transfers pictures onto fabric, so you can make your own T-shirts, tea towels, duvets .... The picture should be in the form of a photostat, and both black-and-white and colour images can be transferred.

PRICE: £2.09.

AVAILABLE: All good craft shops.

Metal Rule

Essential for cutting accurately and smoothly – plastic rulers become planed and scratched very easily and are soon made quite useless.

PRICE: From £2.28 (6"); from £4.20 (12").

AVAILABLE: All good craft shops and graphic supply stores.

Modelling Clay

Probably the heaviest present around! Prepared clay (in either grey or terracotta) is the route to all models and pottery. Needs to be fired, unlike 'Newclay' which is self-hardening and ideal for smaller models and decorative pottery. Both are ready to use and can be damped down with water.

PRICE: From £2.44 (5 kg bag); prepared clay from £2.99 (3 kg superfine modelling clay); £3.86 (Newclay 5 kg bag); £4.49 (Daz – self-hardening real clay 980g).

AVAILABLE: Most good craft shops.

Permanent Marker Pen

Needs to be really permanent, because anything else can soil the rest of your work. Designs for tapestry/embroidery are particularly at risk because hot hands permanently handling the material can lead to ink transfer.

PRICE: About £1.25.

AVAILABLE: All good craft shops; selected stationers.

Ribbons

VV Rouleaux have a stock of over 7000 ribbons and any sort of catalogue would be along the lines of a blockbuster. If you have a particular idea for trimming a hat, or edging a cushion, just give them a call and they'll be happy to send a sample. Many of their braids, tassels, ropes and fringes as well as ribbons are unusual as well as exquisite.

PRICE: 15p – £45 per metre.

AVAILABLE: VV Rouleaux, 201 New Kings Road, London SW6 4SR Tel: 071-371 5929.

Rubber Moulds

For candles, plaster or resin – easily removeable and reusable. Available in a full gamut of designs from kittens in buckets to Buddahs to owl with mouse, and Nativity scenes.

PRICE: From £1.15 for 75 mm mould to £14.38 for 250 mm mould.

AVAILABLE: Craft shops, department stores, larger toy shops; Fred Aldous Ltd, 37 Lever Street, Manchester 1, M60 1UX Tel: 061-236 2477 (Mail Order available).

Scalpel

Essential for all types of fine work where a Stanley knife is too cumbersome. Surgical precision is possible and a variety of shapes of blade can be fitted to a choice of five handles.

PRICE: Scalpel handles £2.91 [Swann Morton]; blades 55p (pack of six).

AVAILABLE: Most craft shops.

Scissors

Scissors specifically for embroidery, tapestry, lacemaking, etc., with miniature super-sharp blades which cut right to the points. Also 'Lift 'n' Snip' scissors which have a small hook at the end which you insert under the errant stitch or stitches and then 'lift and snip'.

PRICE: e.g. 3.5″ Embroidery scissors £3.05; Tapestry scissors £3.50; Lift 'n' snip £3.85.

AVAILABLE: Simply Scissors Ltd, 48 Midholm, London NW11 6LN Tel: 081-458 4814 (Mail Order).

Silk Paints

Sophisticated version of fluffy T-shirt paints, Deka silk paints can in fact be used on most fabrics, not only silk. An outliner will contain the painted shape.

PRICE: £2.25 (45 ml); £3.95 (45 ml) outliner – clear, black, gold, silver.

AVAILABLE: Most craft shops.

Spray Mount

The professionals' clear, non-staining spray adhesive which goes on in a mist. Indispensable in the early stages of design because it allows for repositioning. Photomount offers a more secure bond, but is not adjustable.

PRICE: £3.40.

AVAILABLE: Most craft and graphic supply shops.

Tapestry Frames/Embroidery Rings

Very useful for preventing the end result of weeks of work looking like a used tea towel. Saves the need to stretch the work into shape after the job has been done.

PRICE: From 75p for a 5″ wooden embroidery ring; rotating tapestry frames from £3.15 (9″); floor-standing frames from £27 (27″).

AVAILABLE: All good craft shops, haberdashers and department stores.

Transpaseal

As anyone who grew up with *Blue Peter* knows, this sticky-backed plastic is a vital component in making anything out of cardboard or paper!

PRICE: From £1.93 for one metre roll (gloss), £2.30 (matt).

AVAILABLE: Most craft shops.

Tweezers and Pliers

Long-nosed and fine-pointed for all kinds of precision work where accurate picking and placing is required, e.g. repairing watches, jewellery and lace-making.

PRICE: eg. Straight tweezers from £2.80; Long reach tweezers £4.85; Jewellery pliers £5.95.

AVAILABLE: Simply Scissors Ltd, 48 Midholm, London NW11 6LN Tel: 081-458 4814 (Mail Order).

BETWEEN £5–£10

Air Spray Lens Cleaner

Photographers will find this air nozzle a more effective way of clearing dust from lenses on cameras than blowing or smearing with a cloth.

PRICE: £8.40 nozzle [Leeds]; £3.99 12 oz air refills.

AVAILABLE: Leeds Photovisual Ltd; branches in London, Birmingham, Leeds, Manchester and Newport. London branch: 20/26 Brunswick Centre, Bernard Street, London WC1N 1AE Tel: 071-833 1661.

BOOK CHOICE
Guide to Starting in Crafts

A guide to all you need to know about how to start in crafts and exhibit at craft fairs. Advice on selling work, pricing and packaging, legal aspects, trade sales – in fact a reference book for anyone who sees themselves as a handicraft magnate.

PRICE: £5.95.

AVAILABLE: *The Craftsman Magazine*, 5 Lower Mead, Iver Heath, Bucks SL0 0DX Tel: 0753 817860 (Mail Order).

Calligraphy Starter Set

Four pens with different width nibs and a 'how to do it' book.

PRICE: £6.99 [Berol].

AVAILABLE: Most craft shops, toy shops and branches of Homebase.

Collectors – Albums

Stamps are only the start of it – collections of postcards, coins, banknotes, cigarette cards and phone cards can be displayed within their own specially tailored album.

PRICE: Stamp albums from £8.95; first-day-cover albums from £5.95; postcard albums from £6.25; coin albums from £8.25; banknote albums from £8.25; cigarette card albums from £7.75.

AVAILABLE: Filac Sales, Llamendos, 75 York Road, Birkdale, Southport PR8 2DU Tel; 0704 60232 (Mail Order).

Collectors – Currency Year Set

Coin collectors' interests tend towards the antique, but a modern proof year set (uncirculated parenty) in a presentation pack brings a collection right up to date.

PRICE: £8.95.

AVAILABLE: Spink & Sons Modern Collection, P O Box 564, London SW20 8XS Tel: 081-540 9660 (Mail Order).

Cutting Mat

Seem terribly expensive – but absolutely indispensable. 'Self-healing' so you don't get caught in grooves when using time after time.

PRICE: From £8.45 (A4) to £41 (A1).

AVAILABLE: All good craft shops and graphic design shops.

Design Source Books

Decorative motifs including alphabets, monograms, borders, silhouettes and illustrations that can all be copied ad infinitum because they're out of copyright. Useful for any sort of design, from a decoupage picture-frame to a party invitation; it does help if you've got access to a photocopier!

PRICE: From £5 to £10.

AVAILABLE: The Dover Bookshop, 18 Earlham Street, London EC2H 9LN Tel: 071-836 2111 (Mail Order).

Double-Sided Tape

As useful in craftwork as the ubiquitous sticky-backed plastic (so beloved of the *Blue Peter* team). Incredibly strong – and has been known to fix hems as well as its multifarious more crafty uses.

PRICE: £5.95 (33m).

AVAILABLE: WH Smith; all good stationers and graphic supply shops.

Folding Magni-specs

Folding-frame magni-specs prevent serious eyestrain when concentrating on close-up work. Folds small enough to fit into a pocket or purse.

PRICE: £7.99.

AVAILABLE: Anthony Green & Co Ltd, Sutton Fields, Hull HU8 0XD Tel: 0482 822158 (Mail Order).

Kits

Devotees of a particular craft may enjoy the chance to broaden their talents either laterally or into a completely different metier. Dryad kits are deservedly well respected and contain all the instructions and materials necessary to get started on anything from glass engraving to weaving, marbling, lacemaking, stoolcraft, screen printing, and many, many more.

PRICE: From about £7.75 (Fabric Painting Starter Kit) to £21.98 (Decorative Clock Kit).

AVAILABLE: Good craft shops; contact Reeves for nearest stockist Tel: 081-863 7177.

Left-Handed Scissors

The natural effect of using right-handed scissors in the left hand tends to force the blades apart so that no cutting takes place. Also, for fine work, it's difficult to see the cutting line because there is a blade in the way. A pair of multi-purpose scissors for a left-hander will make practical work a whole lot easier.

PRICE: e.g. £5.95 (general purpose 8″ scissors); £26.95 (tailor's shears); £7.65 (embroidery scissors).

AVAILABLE: Anything Left-Handed Ltd, 57 Brewer Street, London W1R 3FB Tel: 071-437 3910 (Mail Order).

Respirators

If involved with any kind of chemicals or solvents, craftspeople may suffer from 'unexplained' headaches, feelings of nausea and light-headedness. Protection against dusts and vapours can miraculously remedy these symptoms. Although disposable, masks can be used more than once and last up to eight hours.

PRICE: Dust and mist respirator from £1.61 each (pack of five £6.67).

AVAILABLE: Alec Tiranti Ltd, 27 Warren Street, London W1P 5DG Tel: 071-636 8565; 70 High Street, Theale, Reading RG7 5AR Tel: 0734 302775 (Mail Order).

Vogue Patterns

Hot from the catwalk, patterns for clothes which are very much 'in vogue'.

PRICE: £5.45 and £10.95.

AVAILABLE: Branches of John Lewis Partnership, other department stores.

BETWEEN £10–£20

Batik Wax

A fabric-printing process in which hot wax is drizzled onto the fabric, cracked when hardened, colourwashed, and then the wax is ironed off. Now that the seventies have been resurrected – everything that we thought was tasteless is trendy again. Design T-shirts, wraparound skirts, or even kaftans if you want to go all the way.

PRICE: £4.69 (250g Batik Wax); Tjanting tool £8.99 (small, medium, large); £12.49 Dylon Ultra Batik dye; £87.49 electric wax melting pot.

AVAILABLE: All good craft shops; Fred Aldous, 37 Lever Street, Manchester 1, M60 1UX Tel: 061-236 2477 (Mail Order available).

Chess Guide

Three books by Kotov straight from the horse's mouth, on how to Train, Play and even Think like a Grandmaster; if someone needs a little help in their development.

PRICE: £12.99 each [Batsford].

AVAILABLE: Bookshops.

Formulas for Painters

R Massey's 200 formulas for making paints, glazes, varnishes, grounds, fixatives, sizes and adhesives.

PRICE: £12.95 [Fidden Press].

AVAILABLE: Art bookshops; L Cornelissen & Son, 105 Great Russell Street, London WC1B 3RY Tel: 071-636 1045 (Mail Order).

Miller's Collectables Price Guide

On the same lines as Miller's famous *Antique Price Guide*, this particular publication provides all the information collectors need, from beermats to teddybears.

PRICE: £14.99.

AVAILABLE: Bookshops; Vera Trinder Ltd, 38 Bedford Street, Strand, London WC2E 9EU Tel: 071-836 2365 (Mail Order available).

Bottle Cutter

A tool very much in the interests of economy and ecology. With a little practice you can saw the tops off old bottles and transform them into vases, spice jars, ashtrays. The award-winning blue 'Original Water' bottles would make wonderful drinking goblets.

PRICE: £12.99.

AVAILABLE: The Chelsea Herbalist, Regency House, 2 Bedford Row, Worthing, West Sussex BN11 3DR Tel: 0903 210225 (Mail Order).

Collectors – Watermark Detector

A handy device which will instantly identify watermarks on stamps. There is a fractional difference in relief on the paper's surface where a watermark appears – this can be revealed by putting the stamp over a sealed sachet of ink, covering with the small piece of glass and applying thumb pressure. The ink will disperse to define the relief and reveal the watermark.

PRICE: £13.95 Morley Bright Inst-A-Tector.

AVAILABLE: Vera Trinder Ltd, 38 Bedford Street, Strand, London WC2E 9EU Tel: 071-836 2365 (Mail Order available).

Cotton Reel Holder

An ingenious device which stores up to 24 cotton reels on a rack so they don't roll about, get tangled or lost.

PRICE: £14.99 (hand-crafted natural timber).

AVAILABLE: Elmley Heritage, Stone House, Elmley Lovett, Nr Droitwich, Worcs WR9 0PS Tel: 029 923447 (Mail Order available).

Darkroom Safelight

A ten-watt lamp which is the 'safe' darkness for the darkroom.

PRICE: About £15 (coloured bulb £3.40).

AVAILABLE: Leeds Photovisual Ltd; branches in London, Birmingham, Leeds, Manchester and Newport. London branch: 20/26 Brunswick Centre, Bernard Street, London WC1N 1AE Tel: 071-833 1661.

Developing Trays

Accessories for the darkroom. As the prints get larger so must the developing trays.

PRICE: £3.65 (10″ × 12″), £11.70 (20″ × 24″).

AVAILABLE: Leeds Photovisual Ltd; branches in London, Birmingham, Leeds, Manchester and Newport. London branch: 20/26 Brunswick Centre, Bernard Street, London WC1N 1AE Tel: 071-833 1661.

Gold Leaf

A book of 22-carat gold leaf (25 leaves over 3″ square) together with an easy-to-use gilding medium for application.

PRICE: £20 (book of double gold leaf); £14 (normal gold); £4.50 (60 ml of Goldsize glue – drying times from 1 to 24 hours).

AVAILABLE: L Cornelissen & Son, 105 Great Russell Street, London WC1B 3RY Tel: 071-636 1045 (Mail Order available).

Inkwells

Ceramic inkwells fitted into a polished mahogany inkwell holder – a dream for calligraphers and essential for someone whom you think would enjoy the hobby.

PRICE: £15.95.

AVAILABLE: L Cornelissen & Son, 105 Great Russell Street, London WC1B 3RY Tel: 071-636 1045 (Mail Order available).

MC Escher Jigsaws

Maurits Cornelis Escher, whose optical illusions are boggling enough *per se*, are monstrous when transformed into a jigsaw. His famous 'Relativity' and 'Ascending and Descending' are both available.

PRICE: £14.95 (1000 pieces).

AVAILABLE: Just Games, 71 Brewer Street, London W1R 3FB Tel: 071-734 6124 (Mail Order available).

Model Cars

Tamiya have a reputation for producing the most precise to scale models on the market and are accurate down to the shock absorbers. Their 1/20 car or motorcycle kits can be completed in a week – but the *pièces de résistance* are the radio-controlled car kits. When complete, you are probably more than amply qualified as a car mechanic! They turn, they reverse, they go like the clappers (up to 30 mph – considering this on a 1 to 10 scale, that's about 300 mph).

PRICE: £10.50 (1/20 scale models); £165 (1/10 radio-controlled models).

AVAILABLE: Branches of Beatties nationwide; 10 The Broadway, Southgate, London N14 6PN Tel: 081-886 4258 (Mail Order).

Monogrammed Playing Cards

Handsome decks indeed – choice of either navy/red and green/red double decks, personalized with a gold-blocked monogram of up to four initials.

PRICE: £16.50 (double-pack box).

AVAILABLE: Eximious, 10 West Halkin Street, London SW1R 8JL Tel: 071-235 7828 (Mail Order available).

Trestle Table

No work surface is ever big enough and however big the space is it is always possible to fill it. At Ikea you can buy table tops and legs separately to build the table you need.

PRICE: £15, £19 and £35.

AVAILABLE: Ikea branches.

—————— BETWEEN £20–£50 ——————

Air Brush

A studio-quality set of air brush and compressed air canister should meet the demands of any modelmaker who needs finer detail spray work, an artist who may wish to try a new medium, or a car mechanic who fancies something more inspirational than metallic blue for his Ford Transit.

PRICE: £39.99.

AVAILABLE: Branches of Beatties nationwide; 10 The Broadway, Southgate, London N14 6PN Tel: 081-886 4258 (Mail Order).

Artists' Smocks/Boiler Suits/Overalls

For artists and artisans of all persuasions.

PRICE: Calico smocks £22.25; black-and-white T-shirt £15.50.

AVAILABLE: All good artists' supply shops; Green & Stone, 259 Kings Road, London SW3 Tel: 071-352 0837 (Mail Order available).

Backgammon Set

Traditional backgammon sets in an attaché case style which makes them easier to transport. It's surprising how many of these you see at the airport embarking for a fortnight in Greece.

PRICE: £24.95 (11" size); £34.95 (15" size).

AVAILABLE: Most toy shops and department stores.

Card Shoe

The professional's card dealer. Enthusiasts will appreciate the panache this adds to any green baize card table.

PRICE: About £30.

AVAILABLE: Large department stores.

Collectors – 'One Country' Stamp Albums

Large stamp collections may have particular strengths or may be so cosmopolitan that some national barriers need establishing. A 'Unified Germany' album could be a politically correct move to make.

PRICE: e.g. GB Volume 1 (1840-1970) £22.50; GB Volume 2 (1970-90) £26.50; Australia (1913-1990) £30 [Stanley Gibbons]; Unified Germany £38.75 [Davo].

AVAILABLE: Filac Sales, Llamendos, 75 York Road, Birkdale, Southport PR8 2DU Tel: 0704 60232 (Mail Order for Stanley Gibbons); Vera Trinder Ltd, 38 Bedford Street, Strand, London WC2E 9EU Tel: 071-836 2365 (Mail Order available).

Dressmaker's Dummy

Adjustable dummies that will compensate for seasonal variations in hip measurements.

PRICE: £95 Superfit deluxe.

AVAILABLE: Branches of John Lewis nationwide.

Glue Gun

Interminably useful for large as well as small jobs, the Low Melt glue gun has a low glue temperature so can be used for writing on balloons as well as sticking upholstery. The glue sticks can be fed continuously through the back of the gun without unplugging it for a larger job.

PRICE: £23.99 (including ten glue sticks).

AVAILABLE: New Waves Marketing, 1 Cross Keys Court, High Street, Brackley, Northants NN13 5BD Tel: 0280 701362 (Mail Order).

MAGAZINE SUBSCRIPTION
Crafts

A glossy, produced by the Crafts Council, which concentrates on applied and decorative arts, ceramics, weaving, etc, and tends to be more artsy than crafty. Includes comprehensive guide to national craft shows and events as well as features and book/exhibition reviews.

PRICE: £25 p.a. (six editions).

AVAILABLE: The Crafts Council, 44a Pentonville Road, London N1 9BY Tel: 071278 7700.

MAGAZINE SUBSCRIPTION
Popular Crafts

Projects, news, features and ideas for crafty people every month.

PRICE: £21 p.a.

AVAILABLE: Subscriptions Dept, Argus Publications, Queensway House, 2 Queensway, Redhill, Surrey RH1 1QS Tel: 0737 768611.

MAGAZINE SUBSCRIPTION
Stamp Magazine

Keeps you posted on auction news, exhibitions, fairs, new books and features; subjects that would tickle the fancy of any philatelist.

PRICE: £29.70 p.a. (12 issues).

AVAILABLE: *Stamp Magazine*, Subscription Department, Link House Magazines, Freepost 8403, Bletchley, Milton Keynes MK2 2YA Tel: 0908 371981.

MAGAZINE SUBSCRIPTION
The Antique Collector

A glossy featuring saleroom previews and reviews, exhibition and book reviews, news on fairs, articles.

PRICE: £30 p.a. (12 issues).

AVAILABLE: *The Antique Collector*, Subscription Services, Freepost Licence No CY838, Pennymount Road, Haywards Heath, West Sussex RH16 3ZA Tel: 0622 721555.

Mini Chest of Drawers

It's the drawers which appeal – because they can be filled with all manner of paraphernalia; be it string, wire, beads, nails, ribbon – and kept in one place.

PRICE: £24.

AVAILABLE: Branches of Ikea.

Pen Rolls

Every fluffy pencilcase hopes one day to turn into a beautiful calfskin pen roll. Lined with pigskin and supplied with a 6″ steel rule and two pencils, this is a way of gathering writing and marking accoutrements with panache.

PRICE: £34.95.

AVAILABLE: Papyrus, 25 Broad Street, Bath Tel: 0225 463418; 48 Fulham Road, London SW3 Tel: 584 8022 (Mail Order available).

Polaroid Camera

Superb for any artist, designer or craftsman. Records any vista, posture or colour change *en plein air* so that the result can be reproduced in the studio.

PRICE: From £25.

AVAILABLE: All good camera shops and department stores.

Sewing Box

Beautiful Shaker-style hinged sewing box in cherrywood.

PRICE: £44.95.

AVAILABLE: The Shaker Shop, 25 Harcourt Street, London W1 Tel: 071-724 7672 (Mail Order available). Also department stores for different versions.

Soldering Iron

A tool which will open up new avenues for Fix-Its everywhere. Used to heat up solders (alloys of metal) to fuse models of all kinds, but also larger constructions in the form of engines, car bodies, etc, etc.

PRICE: e.g. £35.77 Portasol Professional (portable gas operated tool kit); £46.96 Tiranti Basic Soldering Kit (includes safety stand).

AVAILABLE: Alec Tiranti Ltd, 27 Warren Street, London W1P 5DG Tel: 071-636 8565; 70 High Street, Theale, Reading RG7 5AR Tel: 0734 302775 (Mail Order).

Staple Gun

Much handier than hammer and nails. Uses two pronged staples and makes easy work of upholstery.

PRICE: £26.99 (Rexel Staple Gun).

AVAILABLE: DIY stores.

Tapestry Kits

Meek bookmarks and extravagant firescreens as well as more cushion designs that you have sofa space to fill. Some kits are exquisite and very conveniently contain all the wool you need to complete the design.

PRICE: £10.50–£45.

AVAILABLE: Glorafilia, Old Mill House, The Ridgeway, Mill Hill Village, London NW7 4EB Tel: 081-906 0212 (Mail Order); Ehrman Kits Ltd, 14/16 Lancer Square, London W8 4EP Tel: 071-937 8123 (Mail Order available).

£50 AND ABOVE

Bridge Accessories

Wildly extravagant accessories for enthusiasts including a velvet cloth (or a spectacular hand-embroidered version), silver bridge pens, or a matching bridge scorer and pencils. Also a leather travelling bridge set.

PRICE: cloth £79.95; pens £86 (hallmarked silver); scorer and pencils £21; travelling set £40.

AVAILABLE: Barclay and Bodie, 7-9 Blenheim Terrace, London NW8 0EH Tel: 071-372 5705 (Mail Order available).

Bridge Computer

Ideal when you can't raise another three players and you're desperate for a rubber, this lap-top bridge computer plays with five different bidding systems including ACOL, Precision Club and American Standard, so should be suitable for all solitary players.

PRICE: £230 (Pro Bridge 510).

AVAILABLE: Good games shops, department stores; Just Games, 71 Brewer Street, London W1R 3FB Tel: 071-734 6124 (Mail Order available).

DIY Slippers

A tapestry kit which when complete can be sent back to the manufacturers and transformed into a pair of slippers. Follow a suggested pattern or make up your own.

PRICE: £40 for tapestry kit; £70 to make up slippers.

AVAILABLE: Bowhill & Elliott, 65 London Street, Norwich NR2 1HW Tel: 0603 620116 (Mail Order available).

Drawing Board

Basis for any pastime that involves an element of design – if the prototype doesn't work then you've got to get right back there. A1 is a good size because it can cope with large-scale designs but will still fit onto a desk. Boards made by Blundell Harling will fold down so they can be used flat or stored easily.

PRICE: Blundell Harling True Line Sherbourne Unit £142 plus VAT (A1); £114 plus VAT (A2).

AVAILABLE: All good graphic supply stores.

Games Compendium

A mock leather (seven-in-one) game set including all the classics – chess, backgammon, draughts, cards, dice, dominoes, cribbage and bridge; so you can keep some of the people happy some of the time.

PRICE: £75.

AVAILABLE: Branches of John Lewis Partnership nationwide.

Heavy-Duty Sewing Machine

It seems that some machines these days stop only a little short of going down to the shops to select the material. The Singer Professional can sew patterns in two colours, write in three scripts and has over 300 stitches available on the key pad. This is the top of the range, but versatile machines are available from the Concerto range with the least expensive offering ten built-in stitches.

Price: £1339.95 (Singer XL Professional); £399.95 (Singer Concerto 1).

Available: Singer outlets nationwide. For nearest stockist contact: Singer UK Ltd, 91 Coleman Road, Leicester LE5 4LE Tel: 0533 769471.

Kaffe Fassett Jumper Kit

All you need to knit one of the gorgeous KF designed jumpers, except the time the job will take.

Price: From £50 to £89.

Available: Harrods, branches of John Lewis Partnership, other department stores.

Metal Detector

The editor of *The Searcher* (a metal-detecting magazine) receives six new subscriptions a day – and they can't all be coin collectors. You have to give the landowner half the value of anything you find – so confine yourselves to the back garden or look for ancient field names such as 'Moneyfield' – named for a reason.

Price: £79.90–£559.

Available: C-Scope Intermat Ltd, Kingsworth Technology Park, Wotton Road, Ashford, Kent TN23 2LN Tel: 0800 525365.

Modelling Stand

The firm foundation on which to build busts and statuettes. Adjustable height and tabletop which can be locked at any angle. Ideal for beginners or modellers who may wish to move up from their modelling boards.

Price: e.g. £210.87 Student Stand (popular general purpose stand).

Available: Alec Tiranti Ltd, 27 Warren Street, London W1P 5DG Tel: 071-636 8565; 70 High Street, Theale, Reading RG7 5AR Tel: 0734 302775 (Mail Order).

Palmcorder

So-called because some camcorders have become so small they fit into the palm of the hand. Directors who have already changed their names to Speilberg and kitted themselves out with state-of-the-art equipment will appreciate a camera small and light enough to take even on the shortest trips.

PRICE: e.g. Canon E60 £550 (6.5" x 5.5", weighing 1.5 lbs).

AVAILABLE: All good electrical equipment stockists and large department stores.

Parallel Motion

A professional tool used by designers, architects, etc – which ensures edges are straight, corners meet, angles are right when undertaking any kind of precision design. A welcome asset on any drawing board.

PRICE: e.g. £75.11 Mayline parallel motion (fits onto A1 drawing board); £68.44 (A2 size).

AVAILABLE: All good graphic supply shops.

Spotlight

Very important when poring over close work. Halogen lamps give constant (very hot and bright) light.

PRICE: e.g. £62.60 (clamps to desk).

AVAILABLE: All good graphic supplies stores e.g. London Graphic Centre, 107-115 Long Acre, Covent Garden London WC2 Tel: 071-739 7766.

Staunton Chessmen

Any other style of men is a corruption of the original 1840 design where a king looks like a king and you couldn't possibly confuse a bishop with a pawn.

PRICE: e.g. £129.95 (double weighted ebony and boxwood chessmen).

AVAILABLE: Most toy shops and department stores; Just Games, 71 Brewer Street, London W1R 3FB Tel: 071-734 6124 (Mail Order available).

CHAPTER EIGHT

FASHION & ACCESSORIES

Fashion is ephemeral and, despite the efforts of the trade, you rarely see anyone kitted out in the street as they are in the pages of *Vogue*. There's been a jewellery revolution, with even the younger Royals openly wearing glitz, and the *Next Directory* has played its part in helping us accept mail order. Fashion today is as much fun as comfort, and, though quality counts, variety is often the spice of life. It's worth a present or two on the wild side, just to bring a smile to everyone's face.

UNDER £5

Berets

Worn at a jaunty angle, you can instantly create a bohemian image.

PRICE: £4.95 [Kangol].

AVAILABLE: Branches of John Lewis Partnership.

Buttons/Button Covers

Replacing old buttons or covering them with 'button clips' is a simple way of transforming a plain outfit. Haberdashery departments are rich source, where even unusual designs are remarkably cheap. Button clips snap over existing buttons and can of course be swapped whenever it takes your fancy. If an exact match is needed, Taylors will dye buttons, belts and buckles or cover them in matching material.

PRICE: buttons (unusual design) from about 50p each; button cover sets (5) from £14.99; Taylor's service from 25p per button.

AVAILABLE: Department stores; Taylors Buttons, 1 Silver Place, off Lexington Place, London W1 Tel: 071-437 1016 (Mail Order).

Choker

They've always been glamorous; now they've become trendy. Acceptable in diamanté, velvet, bone beads, pearls, or as just a length of black ribbon or a leather thong tied in a bow (probably the cheapest versions you will find).

PRICE: From 21p! (a metre of black satin ribbon); Fashion chokers from £2.99.

AVAILABLE: High street fashion stores; VV Rouleaux, 201 New Kings Road, London SW6 4SR Tel: 071-371 5929.

Collar Stiffeners

Collar stiffeners, like socks, never seem to hunt in pairs. Silver collar stiffeners for the man who has everything – a handy pack of ten for a man who often doesn't have anything at all.

PRICE: e.g. £25 silver collar stiffeners (Hackett); £4.50 a pair of bone stiffeners.

AVAILABLE: Hackett, 137/138 Sloane Street, London SW1X 9AY Tel: 071-730 3331; most gentlemen's outfitters.

Cufflinks

Like bubblebath and soap, cufflinks are the sort of present that used to make you yawn, but are now prized above most others. Enormous variety available from silk knots to golden nuggets (but check he or she wears double cuffs first!).

PRICE: e.g. Silk knots £3.99 (Tie Rack); Pig's head and tail £58, Salmon and wellie £58, $ and £ £55 [Links].

AVAILABLE: Branches of Tie Rack; Links, 27 Broadgate Circle, London EC2M 2QS Tel: 071-628 9668 (Mail Order available).

Hatboxes

There's something very decadent about an enormous box which houses nothing but a little assembly of feathers and straw. Various sizes available.

PRICE: From £4.50 to £20 upwards.

AVAILABLE: Branches of Ikea.

Hat Pins

Not the sole preserve of soft-skinned old ladies with cornish pastie hats, jaunty hat pins will sharpen up all manner of headgear.

PRICE: 75p–£13 [Penny Pins].

AVAILABLE: Harrods, Fenwick, Selfridges and selected department stores.

Shoe Bags

Protects shoes (and the rest of your packing) when travelling, and prevent scuffing if your shoes are just kicking around in the bottom of the wardrobe.

PRICE: e.g. £2.35 (John Lewis); £14.95 (The Monogrammed Linen Shop – one for each shoe – monogramming extra).

AVAILABLE: John Lewis stores nationwide; The Monogrammed Linen Shop, 168 Walton Street, London SW3 Tel: 071-589 4033.

Sleeve Holders

Whether an accountant or a wolf in accountant's clothing, silver armbands will keep sleeves hitched and out of the figure books.

PRICE: £4.99.

AVAILABLE: Branches of Tie Rack nationwide.

Temporary Tattoos

Tattoos that look just like the real thing, but come off in the bath.

PRICE: From 99p.

AVAILABLE: Way In at Harrods; Boots branches nationwide.

Tie Rack

An eponymous purchase from the shop. They do a very reasonably priced version which holds ten ties.

PRICE: £4.95.

AVAILABLE: Branches of Tie Rack nationwide.

BETWEEN £5–£10

Clothes Shaver

If you think the 'electronic pil remover' sounds like something from the Victor Kiam stable, you'd be right. These devices remove the pils and bobbles that appear on jumpers by gently shaving them off and restoring the jumper to new.

PRICE: £9.95 (Remington fuzz-away clother-shaver – cordless).

AVAILABLE: Large department stores.

Opaque Tights

Modern-day classic – matt black adorns all the chicest legs. Available very reasonably from M&S although the 'must-have' variety are made by Wolford and can be identified by their seam.

PRICE: e.g. from £2.50 [M&S]; from £5.50, £19.99 (luxury opaque) [Wolford].

AVAILABLE: Wolford: available in department stores nationwide. Tel: 071-935 9202 for information.

Shoe Clips

Plain shoes can be transformed into glittering dancing slippers by popping on a shoe clip. Diamanté and feather versions are available for the ball, and more sober bows and buttons for daywear.

PRICE: £6–£25.

AVAILABLE: Most department stores.

Snazzy Socks

If you must buy socks, try and make them cashmere and packaged in a very smart box. Alternatively, boys and girls love Burlingtons.

PRICE: £50 a pair (cashmere socks from Ralph Lauren); from £5.99 [Burlington].

AVAILABLE: Ralph Lauren, 143 Bond Street, London W1; Harvey Nichols, London SW1 Enquiries Tel: 071-491 4967; Burlington socks from department stores and Sock Shop branches nationwide.

BETWEEN £10–£20

Body

Has become a fashion classic in just a couple of years and a basic on which wardrobes are built. A leotard with poppers, a high lycra content will ensure a close fit. 'Shirt-bodies' are also available – these are shirts with knickers attached which sound unconvincing but are in fact practical, comfortable, and slimming (no shirt tails to tuck in).

PRICE: From £12.99.

AVAILABLE: Most fashion stores; M&S make very good ones.

BOOK CHOICE
Designer Clothes Discount Guide

Where and when to find sales of designer samples, cancelled and returned orders from all the top names, including Armani, Byblos, Valentino, Arabella Pollen, Galliano and many more.

PRICE: £12.95.

AVAILABLE: *The Designer Clothes Discount Guide*, Carnell Ltd, Alresford, Nr Colchester, Essex CO7 8AP (Mail Order).

Breton Shirt

The traditional French fisherman's working shirt that is so reminiscent of onion sellers and Jean Seberg in *Un Bout de Souffle*. The manufacturers claim they're so comfortable they're addictive.

PRICE: £16.50.

AVAILABLE: The Breton Shirt Company, 99 Watermoor Road, Cirencester, Glos GL7 1LD Tel: 0285 652997 (Mail Order).

Clogs

Extremely comfortable and satisfying to wear – and you always announce your entry down stone corridors. The Natural Shoe Store stock a brand called Flexolette that has an rubber insert which gives some flexibility.

PRICE: From £19.95; (£39 – flexible clogs from The Natural Shoe Company).

AVAILABLE: Most fashion shoe stores; The Natural Shoe Store, 21 Neal St, London WC2H 9PU Tel: 071-836 5254 (Mail Order available).

Design-A-Tie

There will never be another complaint if the recipient is allowed to design his own tie – or the present-giver designs it for him. The kit includes a pure cotton handmade tie plus a set of pens for permanent colouring.

PRICE: £12.95.

AVAILABLE: RA Enterprises Ltd, 8 Forge Court, Reading Road, Yateley, Camberley GU17 7RX Tel: 0252 861113 (Mail Order).

Faux Pearls

Chunky chokers, necklaces, bracelets and earrings – they're terribly Chanel and terribly chic. Pearls suit just about everyone and a good heavy cluster will 'lift' any outfit.

PRICE: e.g. waist-length rope from £15 [Next], from £15 [Butler & Wilson], from £195 [Chanel].

AVAILABLE: Many high street shops and department stores.

Hats – The Hat Shop

Immense selection of own label hats for men and women – all sorts of styles and a good price range (from about £6 to £150). You can have a hat made up from material you provide.

PRICE: From £2.99 (cotton caps) to £255.

AVAILABLE: The Hat Shop, 58 Neal Street, London WC2 Tel: 971-836 6718; 99 Gees Court, St Christophers Place, London W1; 30 Wilton Street, Glasgow Tel: 041-553 2469.

Jewels – Glitzy and Glam

Butler & Wilson are costume jewellers to the Princess of Wales. They started 22 years ago, have gone from strength to strength and their glitzy collections are seen in the best shops all over the world.

PRICE: From £11 (pearl/diamanté earrings) to £500 (solid silver collar).

AVAILABLE: Butler & Wilson, 20 South Molton Street, London W1 Tel: 071-409 2955; 189 Fulham Road, London SW3 Tel: 071-352 3045; 33 Princes Square, Glasgow Tel: 041-204 0980 (Mail Order available).

Large Sizes – High and Mighty

Large and tall men can be kitted with collars that won't choke them, trousers that will reach their ankles, and shoes where they can move their toes.

PRICE: e.g. shirts (48″–60″ chests) £17; shoes (sizes 11-15) £30.

AVAILABLE: Branches of High and Mighty; 33 Knightsbridge, London SW1X 7RB Tel: 071-589 7454 (Mail Order available).

Leggings

An offshoot from the dance/fitness craze – the leggings that women wore for workouts were just so comfortable that instead of confining them to the gym, they started to go shopping in them. Available in a myriad of colours and printed designs in designer and high street collections.

PRICE: e.g. Pineapple £18.95; M&S £16.99; Joseph £79 (cotton).

AVAILABLE: From all high street fashion shops.

Keds

Keds are a sneaker-type shoe which are worlds away from Soft-Steps – the classic 'comfortable shoe' for women – these have street-cred. Available in canvas or leather, they have to be worn to be believed.

PRICE: £19.95–£39.95.

AVAILABLE: Branches of Russell and Bromley, and Carvela nationwide.

MAGAZINE SUBSCRIPTION
Elle

Like *Vogue*, *Elle* has French, German, American, etc, versions all of which are available on subscription – so it is possible to keep a finger on the pulse all over the world (even if you only look at the pictures).

PRICE: £18 p.a.; French *Elle* £100 p.a. (monthly).

AVAILABLE: *Elle* UK, Freepost, Wadhurst, East Sussex BN5 7HE Tel: 0580 200657.

MAGAZINE SUBSCRIPTION
GQ

The male fashion and style magazine that is rather like a cross between *Elle* and *Vogue* and terribly readable. Girls love it as much as boys.

PRICE: £16.50 (monthly).

AVAILABLE: Quadrant Subscriptions, Oakfield House, 35 Perrymount Road, Haywards Heath, West Sussex RH16 3BM Tel: 0444 445510.

Mail Order – Next

Big-league catalogue which is an extension from the chain of Next high street shops. Very good value for leisure as well as business wear and a bright and chirpy kids' section.

PRICE: e.g. Linen shirt £10–£20 (Catalogue £3).

AVAILABLE: Tel: 0345 100500.

Silk Hankies

Not for blowing your nose on – brightly coloured silk squares for the top pockets of pin-striped suits – girls love to use them as a belt for jeans or a hair tie.

PRICE: From £18 (about 10″ × 10″).

AVAILABLE: Hackett, 137/138 Sloane Street, London SW1X 9AY Tel: 071-730 3331; most gentlemen's outfitters.

Undies – Silk

It would be inconceivable for anyone to deny the feel of silk against skin is one of the most sensual experiences known to man and woman. Silk boxers for men and silky bits of fluff for women – horribly impractical, but who cares?

PRICE: e.g. silk boxers from £12.99 [M&S]; silk knickers from £39.95 to £100 [Janet Reger] or £18 [Next/M&S].

AVAILABLE: Janet Reger, 2 Beauchamp Place, London SW3 Tel: 071-584 9800 (Mail Order available); branches of Next and M&S nationwide.

Vests

Simple, snug-fitting vests and singlets form a second skin over perfectly formed male and female chests. They should be worn tight.

PRICE: e.g. £9.99 (two-pack M&S American Style – very Marlon Brando in *Streetcar*); £12–£40 [John Smedley].

AVAILABLE: M&S branches nationwide; John Smedley's Second Skin range available at Harvey Nichols or Tel: 0234 347526 (Mail Order).

Wonderbra

Gossard's bestselling design that has remained unchanged since 1968 and is constructed to give even the smallest chest a cleavage – 'say goodbye to your toes'! It should be worn fearlessly and is the one design that women buy for themselves in black, which outsells the white two to one. The more recently launched Balconette recreates spilling French rococo necklines.

PRICE: £14.99 (Wonderbra); £16.55 (Balconette).

AVAILABLE: All good lingerie shops and department stores.

BETWEEN £20–£50

Bags – Chapelier

All the cachet of a classic bag without spending the cash. In their native France, Chapelier bags are used on a huge scale and are carried by students as well as grandmothers – in Britain they have been adopted mainly by younger style-conscious women. These bucket-shaped bags are made in practical, hardwearing nylon, canvas and PVC and come in all sizes from tiny to huge.

PRICE: Around £30; (£9 for a purse).

AVAILABLE: Harrods, Harvey Nichols; Graham & Green, 7 Elgin Crescent, London W11; Cruise, 39 Renfield Street, Glasgow. For nearest stockist call Tel: 071-589 5755.

Braces

Some men prefer trousers hanging from their shoulders rather than their waists – and some just like to make doubly sure. Albert Thurston makes felt braces with buttons, in traditional or Gordon Gekko-style crazy designs.

PRICE: £28 (felt braces); £49 (silk).

AVAILABLE: Boden, 2 Pembroke Buildings, Cumberland Park, Scrubs Lane, London NW10 6RG Tel: 081-964 2662 (Mail Order); Hackett, 137/138 Sloane Street, London SW1X 9AY Tel: 071-730 3331; most gentlemen's outfitters.

Button-Through Dress

Designed nowadays to be worn undone over a T-shirt or singlet and tight-fitting shorts and teamed with espadrilles or heavy boots – or even wear it as a dress!

PRICE: From around £25.

AVAILABLE: All high street stores including Miss Selfridge and French Connection as well as designer versions from Ralph Lauren and Chlöe.

Colour Consultation

Consultants which help you discover your own particular colouring and offer guidelines on colour and style so women (and men) can hopefully avoid any future wardrobe howlers.

PRICE: e.g. £50 per colour consultation [Colour Me Beautiful]; £55 colour analysis and make-up consultation [First Impressions].

AVAILABLE: Colour Me Beautiful, 66 Abbey Business Centre, Ingate Place, London SW8 3NS Tel: 072-627 5211; First Impressions, Downing Park, Swaffham Bulbeck, Cambridgeshire CB5 0NW Tel: 0223 813121 (Consultations Worldwide).

Cummerbund

A bright waistband to be worn with single-breasted dinner jackets. Can coordinate or clash with bow tie.

PRICE: From £35 for plain black silk cummerbund; patterned start from £49.

AVAILABLE: Hackett, 137/138 Sloane Street, London SW1X 9AY Tel: 071-730 3331; selected gentlemen's outfitters.

Jogging Suit

A hooded sweatshirt is Switzerland in the war of shellsuits v designer logos – neutral. In grey, this is the universally acceptable face of leisurewear.

PRICE: Around £23 (top), £22.50 (track pants); £45 (Racing Green's zip-up hooded top).

AVAILABLE: Sportshops; Racing Green, P O Box 100, Morley, Leeds, LS27 0BX Tel: 0345 331177 (Mail Order).

Large Sizes – 1647 Ltd

Gets its name because 47% of women are over size 16. Created by Dawn French and Helen Teague, they aim to provide quality clothes up to size 47. The shop spans two floors and has a catalogue (£1).

PRICE: e.g. Jersey tops £36; linen trousers £45; cotton jersey button-through dress £74.

AVAILABLE: 1647 Ltd, 69 Gloucester Avenue, London NW1 8LD Tel: 071-722 1647 (Mail Order available).

Large Sizes – Long Tall Sally

A collection of clothes specially proportioned for taller women. Sleeves that actually reach wrists (sleeve length is 26″) and trousers that reach ankles (most are left unhemmed), but most importantly bathing suits that are long enough in the body to be comfortable to wear.

PRICE: eg. £23.95 striped swimsuit (sizes 12-20).

AVAILABLE: Long Tall Sally branches nationwide; Mail Order Dept: 3 Quarry Park Close, Moulton Park, Northampton, Northants NN13 1QB Tel: 0604 494349.

Leather Gloves

The Queen, the RSC and Batman (for his movies) are all customers of Dents gloves. Their range is huge and includes knitted as well as leather gloves – they will also make up gloves from material you provide. The warmest and most luxurious gloves are cashmere-lined.

PRICE: Standard leather gloves from £20 to £200 for a special creation.

AVAILABLE: Dents: available countrywide, for nearest stockist call: Tel: 0985 212291.

MAGAZINE SUBSCRIPTION
Marie Claire

Deservedly won many awards and is right-on with fashion news (including a 101 ideas section) as well as health, beauty and the lives of women in other countries.

PRICE: £22.50 p.a. (monthly).

AVAILABLE: Quadrant Subscriptions, Oakfield House, 35 Perrymount Road, Haywards Heath, West Sussex RH16 3BM Tel: 0444 445511.

MAGAZINE SUBSCRIPTION
Vogue

The queen of the glossies. Timeless.

PRICE: £21 p.a. (monthly).

AVAILABLE: Quadrant Subscriptions, Oakfield House, 35 Perrymount Road, Haywards Heath, West Sussex RH16 3BM Tel: 0444 445511.

Mail Order – Boden

The friendliest catalogue you could ever hope to encounter, with garments modelled by family and friends. Specializes in good quality men's clothing and accessories (plus a small selection of women's wear).

PRICE: e.g. £55 (Corduroys – 37" unfinished length; you specify length); Ties from £24.

AVAILABLE: Boden, 2 Pembroke Buildings, Cumberland Park, Scrubs Lane, London NW10 6RG Tel: 081-964 2662 (Mail Order).

Monogrammed Clothes Covers

Terribly smart covers, suitable for travelling or storing clothes. Lightweight but very strong, they come in three sizes including 'hard-to-find' ladies' 65" length. May be monogrammed with up to three initials.

PRICE: From £29.50 (Suit cover 40"); £36 (Evening dress cover 65").

AVAILABLE: Eximious, 10 West Halkin Street, London SW1R 8JL Tel: 071-235 7828 (Mail Order available).

Navvy Belts

Traditionally worn by labourers at the turn of the century, these heavy leather belts have a brass buckle, shaped to hang tools from. Their function nowadays is to hold up the roughest pair of Levis.

PRICE: £35 (available in medium or large).

AVAILABLE: The Wealth of Nations, Unit 28, The Trading Centre, Bagleys Lane, London SW6 2BW Tel: 071-371 5333 (Mail Order).

Panama Hat

A genuine Panama hat, made from straw handpicked in the Andean foothills of Ecuador, which is possible to roll up and fit into a pocket! Just in case the afternoon turns sunny.

PRICE: £59.95 (high crown); £49.95 (low crown – non roll up).

AVAILABLE: The Genuine Panama Hat Company, 140 Battersea Park Road, London SW11 4NB Tel: 071-720 3300 (Mail Order). Also gentlemen's outfitters.

Shirts – Denim

Hardwearing casual shirt for boys and girls of all ages, in red green or cream to coordinate with jeans.

PRICE: e.g. £50 [Levis]; £35 [Racing Green].

AVAILABLE: Levis stockists nationwide; Racing Green, PO Box 100, Morley, Leeds LS27 0BX Tel: 071-371 5333 (Mail Order).

Shirts – Stripey Work Shirt

'Most people knew Winston Churchill as a great statesman, we knew him as size 46' say Turnbull & Asser, who also make shirts for the Prince of Wales. The epitome of Jermyn Street tailoring – an amazing variety of stripes are available from their ready-to-wear selection or have them custom-made (minimum order is six). Alternatively, try Pinks (identifiable because of the pink cotton insert between the shirt tails), or James Meade; both offer the Jermyn Street style without the second mortgage.

PRICE: Turnbull & Asser from £51 (£60 striped); Pinks from £32.

AVAILABLE: Turnbull & Asser, 71 Jermyn Street, London W1 Tel: 071-930 0502; Thomas Pink, 2 Donovan Court, Drayton Gardens London SW10 Tel: 071-373 5795 (Mail Order available).

Shirts – Women's Shirts

Shirts, and not blouses, are the subject of Ted Baker's new range – Wild Women. The simple tailoring, that is the mark of a man's shirt, is available in 50 styles ranging from white to loud prints, cut for women.

PRICE: From £35.99.

AVAILABLE: Wild Women, 19 The Market, Covent Garden, London WC2; Way-In at Harrods, London SW1; 23 Princes Square, Buchanan Street, Glasgow.

Steam Iron

This is how shops keep clothes crumple-free – light enough to use on clothes while they're still on the hanger and gentle enough for delicate silks that may otherwise end up looking and feeling like a crisp.

PRICE: £29.75 (Rowenta Steam Brush).

AVAILABLE: Branches of John Lewis Partnership.

Sunglasses

One in six people in Britain now buys a pair of sunglasses each year. Poor quality glasses made from dark plastic are no good whatsoever, offering no protection from dangerous UV rays and in fact fooling eyes in bright sunlight. Reputable glasses should conform to BS2723 (1987) Section B61 and then guarantee protection from dangerous rays.

PRICE: e.g. Rayban Wayfarer £45.

AVAILABLE: Opticians, chemists, large department stores.

Travel – Hand-Turned Travel Slipper

Hand-turning was introduced to Britain in the sixteenth century by Huguenots from the European courts. The shoe is quite literally sewn and stitched inside out, then 'turned' to reveal the supple leather exterior. Extremely soft, comfortable and luxurious.

PRICE: £39.95.

AVAILABLE: Bowhill & Elliott, 65 London Street, Norwich NR2 1HW Tel: 0603 620116 (Mail Order).

Twinset

This combination of short-sleeved jumper and cardigan is as chic and feminine today as it has always been – and equally coveted by groovers and great aunts.

PRICE: e.g. £195 (cashmere); £25 (cardigan) £19 (jumper) [wool – M&S].

AVAILABLE: The Cashmere Store, 207 High Street, Edinburgh EH1 1PE Tel: 031-226 4861 (Mail Order); branches of M&S nationwide.

Undies – Thermal

The 'Juliet Dunn' range of thermal undies for Damart are beautifully lacey and also gloriously snuggly.

PRICE: e.g. Body £39.99; Catsuit £39.99.

AVAILABLE: Damart, Bingley X, West Yorkshire BD97 1AD Tel: 0274 510000 (Mail Order).

Valet Stand

What appears to be a coathanger with legs, stands in the corner of a room and has clothes draped over it – in much the same way as a valet would. For men or women, with a very useful tray for keys and change. Award-winning his 'n' hers valet stands (in manly and womanly shapes) are available from Ikea.

PRICE: £25 (pine, walnut); £29 (Ikea).

AVAILABLE: The Chelsea Trading Co Ltd, 3 Astwood Mews, London SW7 4DE Tel: 071-373 8188 (Mail Order); Ikea.

Vouchers

We all have our 'top shops' where we just know we'll find that crazy little number that doesn't appear anywhere else – and what's more it fits. Most ladies' and gentlemen's outfitters have vouchers which are redeemable at any of their stores.

PRICE: Up to you, but bear in mind you can't buy much other than 'basics' for under £20!

AVAILABLE: e.g. Jigsaw, The Gap, Blazer, French Connection, Hobbs.

Wigs and Hairpieces

Fake it and flaunt it. Wigs are now commonplace on the catwalks and hairpieces are integral in the creation of many intricate and outrageous 'do's.

PRICE: From £35 for a hairpiece. Custom-made and real hair wigs £60–£130.

AVAILABLE: The Trend Hair Supplies Group Ltd, Norfolk House, 116 Western Road, Brighton BN1 2AB Tel: 0273 774977 (Mail Order).

—————————————————————————————

£50 AND ABOVE

—————————————————————————————

Aran Sweater

The genuine handknitted luxurious article.

PRICE: Around £75 (cardigans a little more expensive); Hats from £9.

AVAILABLE: The Irish Shop, 14 King Street, London WC2 Tel: 071-379 3625 (Mail Order available).

Bags – Classics

Classic handbags made by Vuitton, Prada, Gucci and Mulberry have remained and will remain worthy objects of desire. Packed with panache, they are so much less obvious than gold logos and chains which now don't quite fit in with the pervading mood of underdressing.

PRICE: Capacious bags from £260 upwards.

AVAILABLE: Harrods; specialist luggage shops, and smart department stores.

Black Leather Jacket

Due to increased demand and better tanning it is possible to acquire good quality leather jackets, that WILL wear in, even at the cheaper end of the market. The classic style is aka Marlon Brando (in *The Wild One*) – as if we doubted it for a minute – fitted and waist-length. For the dedicated, and only if you've got serious amounts to spend, check out what Cher and Billy Idol see in the Chrome Hearts range.

PRICE: From about £85; Chrome Hearts £4220!

AVAILABLE: Kensington Market, Kensington High Street, London W8; also try high street stores e.g. Miss Selfridge, Jigsaw; Chrome Hearts available at Browns, 23 South Molton Street, London W1.

Cashmere Cardie

Feel the quality!

PRICE: £150–£900.

AVAILABLE: N Peal, 37 Burlington Arcade, London W1; 54 Brompton Road, London SW3, 192 Piccadilly, London W1 Tel: 071-493 5378; The Scotch House, 2 Brompton Road, London SW1 Tel: 071-581 2151 (Mail Order available).

Custom-Made Shoes

It is possible to have shoes made to fit like a glove and for more than a century John Lobb has been doing just that. The best boots money can buy which, although it'll probably cost you one of your legs to buy them, will last a lifetime. (Director Eric Lobb wears a pair he has had for 20 years.)

PRICE: £1075 (calf leather brogues – take about six months to a year to deliver).

AVAILABLE: John Lobb Ltd, 9 St James's Street, London SW1A 1EF Tel: 071-930 3664.

Flying Jacket

In the First World War the introduction of single-wing unheated aircraft like the Spitfire and Hurricane led to the introduction of a Flyer's Kit by the RAF. The original jacket featured a leather-backed stand-up collar, triple-stitched seams, belt, underarm vents and heavy duty brass zips. Should be worn with a pair of Aviator sunglasses.

PRICE: £235.

AVAILABLE: Top Gear Clothing Ltd, 19 Willis Way, Fleets Industrial Estate, Poole, Dorset BH15 3SS Tel: 0202 667766 (Mail Order).

Handmade Shoes

Emma Hope's art-inspired shoes are gorgeous, terribly extravagant and not really for everyday use. Lots of embroidery and extraordinary heel shapes.

PRICE: Around £200.

AVAILABLE: Emma Hope, 33 Amwell Street, London EC1 Tel: 071-833 2367.

Hats – Trilby

Whether Dick Tracy or Arthur Dailey, a trilby is a style statement in any circle.

PRICE: e.g. £85 (men); £145 ladies (available in scarlet and pale pink).

AVAILABLE: Herbie Johnson, 30 New Bond Street, London W1 Tel: 071-408 1174.

Headscarf Print Shirt

Extremely versatile wardrobe staple – can be worn loose and open over a tight top, or buttoned up and untucked over tight leggings (or casual trousers or skirts). Richly decorated, they exude luxury. Prices range from the very expensive to the very reasonable.

PRICE: e.g. English Eccentrics £280; Timney Fowler £75–£215.

AVAILABLE: English Eccentrics, 9–10 Charlotte Road, London EC2A 3DH Tel: 071-729 6233; Timney Fowler, 388 Kings Road, London SW3 Tel: 071-352 2263.

Jewels – Designer

You could no worse than take a trip to Jess James (Jess Canty and James Knight) who offer a tempting display of contemporary jewellery by hot and happening designers. All precious metals and stones.

PRICE: From £9 (brass tie tack) to £9000.

AVAILABLE: Jess James, 3 Newburgh Street, London W1 Tel: 071-437 0199.

Jodhpurs

Like the waxed jacket, another example of country wear easily transposing from the field to the street! Real riding jodhpurs, e.g. Harry Hall, are the best, but very good jodhpur-style trousers are available from most high street stores.

PRICE: £62 [Harry Hall]; £35 [Jigsaw]; £95 [Swaine Adeney, breeches].

AVAILABLE: High Street fashion stores; Swaine Adeney, 185 Piccadilly, London W1 Tel: 071-734 4277 (Mail Order available).

Hermes Scarf

World-famous, world-coveted printed silk scarves. New designs are launched twice a year and each scarf contains at least 30 colours (sometimes as many as 40) whereas other manufacturers sometimes can reach 20.

PRICE: £135.

AVAILABLE: Hermes, 155 New Bond Street, London W1 Tel: 071-499 8856.

Made-to-Measure Bra

Jane Kenton, corsetiere to the Queen, claims that 85% of women are wearing an ill-fitting bra. So do the Dolly Parton in your life a favour and get one custom-made.

PRICE: Around £150; (basque/corset around £575).

AVAILABLE: Rigby & Peller, 2 Hans Road, London SW3 1RX Tel; 071-589 9293.

Mail Order – Kingshill

A small and very chic collection of clothes with the working woman in mind. Features only British designers (including Caroline Charles and Paul Costelloe) plus a few bags and a few tasteful accessories. Catalogues have come a long way since Freemans.

PRICE: e.g. Linen shirts about £80; (Catalogue £3).

AVAILABLE: The Kingshill Collection Ltd, Freepost, Great Missenden, Buckinghamshire HP16 0DZ Tel: 0494 890555.

Nightshirt

An airy option if they find pyjamas too constrictive.

PRICE: eg. £89 (Hackett cotton poplin).

AVAILABLE: Department stores; Hackett, 137/138 Sloane Street, London SW1X 9AY Tel: 071-730 3331.

'Rip Offs' Jacket

Standard linen or wool jackets from which you literally rip off the collars, cuffs and buttons (they are velcro-backed), replace them and transform your outfit from a workaday into a dance-all-nite creation.

PRICE: From £75; collar and cuff sets £20.

AVAILABLE: Ripoffs, 28 Kelmscott Road, London SW11 6QY Tel: 071-978 4181.

Rupert Trousers

Yellow checked 'Rupert the Bear' trousers appear in Johnnie Boden's mail order catalogue. They have been a runaway success and although not designed to be worn every day, he guarantees when you do wear them you will feel happier (or send them back!).

PRICE: £75 (100% worsted wool).

AVAILABLE: Boden, 2 Pembroke Buildings, Cumberland Park, Scrubs Lane, London NW10 6RG Tel: 081-964 2662 (Mail Order).

Shoes – Heavy Boots

Heavy duty walking boots have serious street cred and may never hear the sound of snapping twigs underfoot. Extremely comfortable, extremely hardwearing, extremely trendy.

PRICE: From £110 [Timberland boots]; £75.95 [Caterpillar boots]; £69.99 [Panama Jacks].

AVAILABLE: Selected sportshops and 'fashion' footwear stockists and department stores.

Shoes – Small Size

Ladies' small and large size shoes are available unsurprisingly at the Small and Tall Shoe shop. Small sizes from 13 to 2.5 and large sizes from 8.5 to 11.5.

PRICE: £50–£80 (Italian leather).

AVAILABLE: Small and Tall Shoe Shop, 71 York Street, London W1 Tel: 071-723 5321.

Shoes – Snaffled Shoes

Whether they're loafers, platforms or clogs, a shoe now seems naked without a snaffle. Gucci has a lot to answer for! They are still the 'brandleader' but many imitations are practically identical and cost a third of the price.

PRICE: e.g. Gucci loafers £191 (£200 high heeled); Hobbs snaffled loafers £54.99.

AVAILABLE: Branches of Hobbs; Gucci, 32-33 Bond Street, London W1; 17-18 Sloane Street, London SW1. Enquiries: 071-235 6707.

Waistcoat

Available tailored for men or women. Leather is coveted by youngsters, but also branch into tapestry or leopard fake fur. An authentic round-necked Sikósak (Hungarian) version or an Irish linen waistcoat are available from Wealth of Nations.

PRICE: e.g. £85–£130 [Tom Gilbey]; made to measure £195; £55 Sikósak (wool-cashmere); £55 Irish linen.

AVAILABLE: The Tom Gilbey Waistcoat Gallery, 2 New Burlington Place, Savile Row, London W1 Tel: 071-734 4877. Wealth of Nations, Unit 28, The Talina Centre, Bagley's Lane, London SW6 2BW Tel: 071-371 5333 (Mail Order).

Woollen Capes

Crosses between *The French Lieutenant's Woman* and *Little Riding Hood* have become familiar sights on our streets. Woollen capes are extremely versatile and can be worn over jeans *au casuel* or over sparkly dresses for evening wear, and always look very elegant.

PRICE: From £85 (pure wool) to £425 (cashmere); acrylic and wool-mix versions available from department stores from £15.

AVAILABLE: The Scotch House, 2 Brompton Road, London SW1 Tel: 071-581 2151 (Mail Order available); department stores.

CHAPTER NINE

FOODIES & COOKS

How tastes have changed! We eat less beef, milk and potatoes; more poultry, cheese and fruit. We spend £1 million a day on Indian food and have more Indian restuarants in London than Bombay or Delhi. We eat out more, but drink less. As a nation we're moving from breakfast, lunch and dinner to 'grazing'. So, long live the foodies and cooks! Those amongst us who take time to cook delectable delicacies and encourage the art of conversation round a table with family and friends.

UNDER £5

BOOK CHOICE
A Feast of Vegetables

An A-Z of vegetables and different ways of cooking them by John Tovey, the owner of the famous The Miller Howe Hotel in Cumbria.

PRICE: £4.99 [Century].

AVAILABLE: Most good bookshops.

Delicatessen Choice – Flavoured coffees/teas

American flavoured coffees include amaretto, vanilla, Irish cream and toasted nut fudge varieties. Jamaica Blue Mountain coffee is said to be the rarest, most expensive and best coffee in the world. If you fancy something that sounds a little more refreshing a scented tisane might be more your cuppa.

PRICE: Coffee: around £3.80 for 8 oz; Teas: 130 different teas, fruit and herbal teas – from £1 for 4 oz.

AVAILABLE: Delicatessens; Algerian Coffee Stores, 52 Old Compton Street, London W1V 6BP Tel: 071-437 2480 (Mail

Order); Whittards of Chelsea, 73 Northcote Road, London SW11 and branches nationwide Tel: 071-924 1888 (Mail Order available).

Delicatessen Choice – Flavoured Oils and Vinegars

Oils ground from nuts or infused with truffle or chilli, and vinegars gently scented with herbs and flowers or the delicious balsamic vinegar from Modena (which is almost good enough to drink from the bottle) are wonderful when used in salads, stir-fries, or sauces, and offer a whole gamut of new flavour sensations.

PRICE: From 95p.

AVAILABLE: All good delicatessens; Culpepper Ltd, Hadstock Road, Linton, Cambridge CB1 6NJ Tel: 0223 894054 (Mail Order available).

Jelly Moulds

From plastic versions for children to copper kitchen adornments – all add equal fun to the finished article.

PRICE: 69p for small plastic rabbit; £7.99 for small copper fish.

AVAILABLE: Kitchen shops.

Mail Order – Spices

A mail order service that brings Chinese, Indian, Japanese, Thai, Indonesian, Malaysian and West Indian spices to your doorstep – catering for the changing British tastebuds by providing ingredients that are not readily available in local shops and supermarkets.

PRICE: From 60p (plus p&p).

AVAILABLE: Exotic Speciality Food Ltd, 8 Sycamore Centre, Fell Road, Sheffield S9 2AL Tel: 0742 611318; Virani Food Products Ltd, 10-14 Stewarts Road, Finedon Road Industrial Estate, Wellingborough, Northamptonshire NN8 4RJ Tel: 0933 226015.

Mouli Herb Chopper

Hand-held rotary chopper with rotating inner cutter for shredding parsley, mint, tarragon, etc, in seconds.

PRICE: £4.50.

AVAILABLE: Good kitchen shops.

Salad Spinner

For flat-dwellers who can't swing the lettuce in the garden.

PRICE: £3.95.

AVAILABLE: Branches of John Lewis Partnership, hardware and other department stores.

Steaming Baskets

Steamed veg are healthy, crunchy and delicious. An expandable stainless steel basket will adjust to fit on a variety of pots and pans; Chinese-style bamboo steamers can be stacked one on top of the other.

PRICE: £2.95 (expandable basket – fits pans from 5.5″ to 9″); £5.25 each (bamboo steamers).

AVAILABLE: Branches of John Lewis Partnership, kitchen shops, ironmongers.

Tomato/Soft Fruit Knife

A thin curved knife with a serrated edge that actually cuts through tomatoes, skinned oranges and other squashable items in thin slices, cleanly.

PRICE: £3.55 [Laser].

AVAILABLE: Kitchen shops and hardware stores.

BETWEEN £5–£10

BOOK CHOICE
Pocket Wine Book

Hugh Johnson's authoritative annually updated guide to put in the pocket and take out to restaurants.

PRICE: £6.99 [Mitchell Beazeley].

AVAILABLE: Most good bookshops.

BOOK CHOICE

The Organic Directory

Directory about where to find all organic products, from meat and dairy products to restaurants and composts for growing your own.

PRICE: £7.95.

AVAILABLE: *The Organic Directory*, Freepost, Wham Marketing, BM2600, Birmingham B18 4BR Tel: 021-449 6691 (Mail Order).

Booze – Madeira/Malmsey – Alternatives to Port

Lighter in taste and alcohol than port, Madeira has a slightly 'burnt' flavour and is absolutely delicious. Surprisingly unpopular in this country, which means that the prices are absurdly cheap in comparison with other fortified wines. Malmsey, on the hand, is like a very special port.

PRICE: £9.79 [4 versions of Blandys].

AVAILABLE: Branches of Oddbins, wine merchants.

Bottle Sealers

Efficient, if you can't finish the bottle in one! Vacuvin wine savers pump the air out from the bottle so that the wine will not deteriorate through contact with the air; a champagne bottle sealer keeps in the fizz.

PRICE: Vacuvin £6.95; Champagne bottle sealers from £2.

AVAILABLE: Wine merchants, large kitchen shops and department stores.

Chocolate Truffle Sauce

Evil chocolate sauce from Charbonnel & Walker. Heat it up for puddings and ice-cream or just spoon straight from the pot.

PRICE: £5.75 for 12 oz pot.

AVAILABLE: Charbonnel & Walker, 28 Old Bond Street, London
W1X 3AB Tel: 071-491 0939; good delicatessens and large
department stores.

Chocolates

Real chocolate connoisseurs will have their palettes massaged by
the delights of Rococo Chocolates. Vegetable fat and sugary/
milky efforts don't get a look in. ... If the idea of Venus Nipples
makes your mouth water then a call to Sara Jayne is a priority
(her handmade chocolates are heaven); Bendicks Bittermints are
the apogee of after-dinner mints.

PRICE: e.g. Rococo's assorted truffles £6.95 a half-pound; Sara
Jayne's Venus Nipples £15 a pound; Bendicks Bittermints
£6.50 for 400g.

AVAILABLE: Rococo Chocolates, 321 Kings Road, London SW3
Tel: 071-352 5857 (Mail Order available); Sara Jayne, 517 Old
York Road, London SW18 1TS Tel: 081-874 8500.

Cookbook Holder

A clear acrylic bookstand which keeps the recipebook open at
the right page and protected from the fray.

PRICE: £6.95.

AVAILABLE: Branches of John Lewis Partnership, and other
department stores.

Good Housekeeping Diary and Account Book

Ever-popular aid to organizing the year – the diary features
excellent recipes for each month (all 'Tried, Tested, Trusted') and
an extensive accounts section for recording household
expenditure.

PRICE: £7.25.

AVAILABLE: *Good Housekeeping*, P O Box 325, London SW4 9JZ
Tel: 071-439 5000 (Mail Order).

Kitchen Bay Tree

A kitchen-sized bay tree from which to snip the freshest, most aromatic bay leaves. As evergreen plants they last all year. They grow equally well in the ground or in containers and can be clipped into shapes!

PRICE: Around £6.95.

AVAILABLE: Hollington Nurseries, Woolton Hill, Newbury, Berkshire RG15 9XT Tel: 0635 253908 (Mail Order).

Mail Order – Cheese

And no, they won't be able to guess from the smell! Neal's Yard cheeses represent the yardstick by which all traditional cheeses in Britain and Ireland are judged. They are supplied from small farms and diaries throughout the country and much of the stock is made from unpasteurized milk.

PRICE: e.g. Small Duckett's Caerphilly £8.50; Colston Bassett Stilton £25 for 5lb plus.

AVAILABLE: Neal's Yard Dairy, 17 Shorts Gardens, London WC2H 9AT Tel: 071-379 7646 (Mail Order available).

Mail Order – Clotted Cream

Genuine crusty thick Devonshire clotted cream.

PRICE: From £5.86.

AVAILABLE: Bowl O' Cream, PO Box 3, Salcombe, Devon TQ8 8QN (Mail Order).

Mail Order – Smoked Food

Smoked salmon is delicious and of all smoked foods, the most popular. People who are addicted to the nutty pungency may enjoy being adventurous and sampling a greater variety of smoked foods on offer: quails' eggs, spiced lamb and cashew nuts are but a few, and traditional kippers. Arbroath smokies (by Royal Appointment) are also available, delivered the day after your order.

PRICE: From £8.50; £9.05 for two pairs (Arbroath smokies).

AVAILABLE: Minola Smoked Products, Kencot Hill Farmhouse, Filkins, Lechlade, Gloucester. Tel: 0367 860391; The Spey Valley Smokehouse, Crombale, Grentown-on-Spey, Scotland PH26 3LN Tel: 0479 3078; Arbroath Smokies, 35 Seatgate Arbroath, Tayside DD1 1BG Tel: 0241 72023.

Menu Planner

A blank, lined book where you can keep a record of who ate what, when, with whom and where they were sitting. Essential for frequent hosts/hostesses who risk duplication unless they keep a constant record.

PRICE: From £7.95; (£59 Smythsons).

AVAILABLE: Stationers and department stores; Smythsons, 44 New Bond Street, London Tel: 071-629 8558 (Mail Order available).

Min/Max Cellar Thermometer

Gauges the fluctuations in temperature in the wine cellar – the single most effective factor in the successful storage of wine.

PRICE: £7.90.

AVAILABLE: Berry Bros & Rudd Ltd, 3 St James's Street, London SW1A 1EG Tel: 071-396 9600 (Mail Order available).

Parmesan Cheese Grater

Stores chunks of ungrated cheese in its integral airtight compartment. In longlasting acrylic that looks good enough to hand around the table.

PRICE: From £6.50.

AVAILABLE: Branches of Divertimenti; 45 Wigmore Street, London W1 Tel: 071-935 0689 (Mail Order available).

Rapid Ice

An ingenious invention for the times when the champagne/white wine hasn't got time to wait an hour in the fridge to cool. It looks like a muffler for a bottle – keep it in the freezer and just slip it over the bottle for fast chilling (about five minutes). Can be used again and again and again.

PRICE: £6.95.

AVAILABLE: Scotts of Stow, Admail 222, The Square, Stow-on-the-Wold, Gloucs GL54 1AF Tel: 0249 449111 (Mail Order).

Real Chocolate Hot Chocolate

Paradise for chocoholics. Charbonnel & Walker sell ready-flaked chocolate for drinking to go in the microwave.

PRICE: £7.25 for 500g canister of hot chocolate.

AVAILABLE: Selected delicatessens; Charbonnel & Walker, 28 Old Bond Street, London W1X 3AB Tel: 071-491 0939.

Rent a Fruit Tree

Choice of apple (cookers/desserts), or pear. One tree will yield approx 40 lbs of fruit. Rent the tree and the rest is done for you.

PRICE: £7 per tree.

AVAILABLE: Deborah and Jeremy Burns, Spindle Bush Farm, 1 Walnut Tree Cottage, High Street, Yalding, Kent MK18 6HX.

Screwpull

The easiest corkscrew of them all – and none better in the view of experts and non-experts alike. You only twist one way and the job's done.

PRICE: £9.95; (£115 for lever model with integral foil cutter).

AVAILABLE: Wine merchants, large department stores; call free on 0800 373792 for stockist details.

Tasting Spoon

Avoid burnt lips. This spoon allows hot liquid to run down a groove from large bowl to small, cooling as it goes.

PRICE: £6.96.

AVAILABLE: David Mellor, 4 Sloane Square, London SW1W 8EE and branches. Tel: 071-730 4259 (Mail Order available).

BETWEEN £10–£20

Adopt-a-Vine

Have a vine named after you, tend and harvest the grapes and produce your own English wine! (Or just collect the bottles.)

PRICE: £15 per vine.

AVAILABLE: St George's English Wines, Waldron Vineyards, Heathfield, East Sussex TN21 ORA Tel: 04353 2156.

Asparagus Steamer

Tall, stainless steel basket and pot combination. Stand the asparagus up and tips steam whilst stems boil.

PRICE: £13.50.

AVAILABLE: Kitchen shops and department stores.

Barbecue Cooking Sets

It's worthwhile having extra-long-handled implements to save singed eyebrows; and it looks far more professional. Also for anyone whose barbecue grill has the slats too far apart or who can't turn the sausages quickly enough to stop the last ones burning, these grills hold the food on both sides.

PRICE: £16.50 (three-piece cooking set); £3.45 (sausage/burger grill); £7.25 (fish broiler).

AVAILABLE: Branches of John Lewis Partnership.

BOOK CHOICE
Complete Cookery Books

The best and most comprehensive guides to cooking everything are by Delia Smith and Prue Leith. Clearly and simply written with excellent colour pictures. Delia's includes the secret of crunchy roast potatoes; Leith's recipes have all been tried and tested by students at her cookery school.

PRICE: £14.95 *Delia Smith's Complete Cookery Course* [BBC Books]; £20 *Leith's Cookery Bible* [Bloomsbury].

AVAILABLE: Bookshops, WH Smith.

BOOK CHOICE
French Provincial Cooking

Any book by Elizabeth David has become THE book on the subject.

PRICE: *French Provincial Cooking*: £12.99; *French Country Cooking* £8.99; *A Book of Mediterranean Food* £8.99 [Penguin].

AVAILABLE: Bookshops, WH Smith.

BOOK CHOICE
The Good Food Guide

Subjective reviews, but still the most thoroughly prepared guide to where to eat out in Britain. 1400 entries.

PRICE: £14.99 [Hodder & Stoughton].

AVAILABLE: Bookshops, WH Smith.

Booze – Flavoured Vodka

Vodka can be bought in a variety of flavours including lemon, pepper and the intriguing 'bison' variety. Alternatively add fruit or spices to a bottle of Absolut vodka – it will only take two days to mature and you will have your own particular brand.

PRICE: £12 per 70 cl bottle.

AVAILABLE: Supermarkets and off-licences.

Breakfast Set

A stunning lettered cream earthenware set from Emma Bridgewater, that tempts you with promise of bubble and squeak, toast and marmalade and steaming hot tea.

PRICE: From £8.95 (for a small mug) to £33.50 (teapot).

AVAILABLE: Emma Bridgewater, 739 Fulham Road, London SW6 5UL Tel: 071-371 9033 (Mail Order available).

Butcher's Steel

Knife sharpeners tend to wear away too much of the knife's edge; the blades should be sharpened using a wet stone or steel. Carborundum stone is the best.

PRICE: From £17.50 (Butchers Steel); From £5 (Carborandum).

AVAILABLE: Good kitchen shops and hardware stores.

Buy Someone a Meal Out

Most restaurants will let you book with a credit card authorized to a certain level, so you can pick up the tab even if you're not there. Plan in advance, the restaurant will need your signature.

PRICE: Entirely up to you!

AVAILABLE: Wherever you decide.

Chip Slicer

Home-made chips are light years away from 'oven chips'. Chopping completely dispensed with – these chips are ready for the pan at the press of a button.

PRICE: £18.50.

AVAILABLE: David Mellor, 4 Sloane London SW1W 8EE and branches. Tel: 071- 730 4259 (Mail Order available).

Coffee Grinder

A few seconds whizzing, and fresh coffee is available. Avoids 'ready-ground' losing its taste.

PRICE: £16.99 [Braun].

AVAILABLE: Electrical stores, and good kitchen shops.

Delicatessen Choice – Extra Virgin Olive Oil

The difference between virgin and extra virgin olive oil is expressed in degrees of acidity – the longer the olives are left after harvest time, the more acidic they will become. When you consider it takes 5 kg of olives to press a litre of good extra virgin olive oil it's not surprising it's expensive.

PRICE: £14.95 for 75 cl of Coltibuono oil from the Chianti Classico Estate.

AVAILABLE: The Oil Merchant, 47 Ashchurch Grove, London W12 9BU Tel: 081-740 1335 for stockists; The Fresh Olive Company of Provence, Morstore, Coronation Road, Park Royal, London NW10 7PG Tel: 081-838 1912 (Mail Order).

Electric Hand Blender

For small jobs and meals for one. A necessary back-up to a food-processor.

PRICE: £17.99.

AVAILABLE: Most electrical shops and kitchen shops.

Flower Cordials

Delicious, scenty drinks which are as delicate on the palate as flower fragrance is on the nose. A delicious alternative to fizzy water for non-drinkers. Elderflower, ginger, passion fruit, raspberry and lemon are just a few of the varieties available.

PRICE: £14.50 for a pack of three (Belvoir Fruit Farms); £3.80 Elderflower cordial from Oddbins.

AVAILABLE: Belvoir Fruit Farms, Belvoir, Grantham, Lincolnshire NG32 1PB Tel: 0476 870286 (Mail Order); wine merchants, off-licences and large supermarkets.

Game Shears

Strong dissection scissors for portioning game and the notoriously difficult duck – so the cook can avoid carving.

PRICE: £14.35 (tin scissor-action shears); £26.04 (stainless steel, spring-action shears).

AVAILABLE: Divertimenti stores; 45 Wigmore Street, London W1 Tel: 071-935 0689 (Mail Order available).

Gravy Separator/Sauceboat

Separates the fat (which rises to the surface) from the tasty residue which pours from the bottom of this clever sauceboat.

PRICE: About £11.

AVAILABLE: Kitchen shops.

Juice Press

The Citronmatic Juice Processor is an up-to-date juicer that starts squeezing automatically when fruit presses down on it. Design-conscious kitchens will love the Philip Starck juicer which looks like a very efficient cross between a spider and something from the War of Worlds.

PRICE: £17.99 (Braun Citronmatic Juice Processor); £41.50 (Philip Starck juicer).

AVAILABLE: Electrical stores, Boots; Braun (UK) Ltd, Dolphin Estate, Windmill Road, Sunbury-on-Thames, Middlesex TW16 7EJ Tel: 0932 785611; Philip Starck juicer from The Conran Shop, Michelin House, 81 Fulham Road, London SW3 6RD Tel: 071-589 7401 (Mail Order available).

Mail Order – Cakes

Meg Rivers Cakes are rich, fruity, (sometimes boozy) and all absolutely delicious! Her range includes traditional English cakes, cake gift packages (including tea or alcohol) and a Cake Club (members receive six 1lb cakes per year).

PRICE: e.g. Iced Celebration Cake £16.25 (1.2 kg); The Sailing Cake £11.50 (900g); Cake Club Membership £73.50 p.a.

AVAILABLE: Meg Rivers Cakes, Middle Tysoe, Warwickshire CV35 0SE Tel: 0295 688101 (Mail Order).

Mail Order – Foie Gras

Foie gras, whether you like it or not, is probably at the pinnacle of gastronomic aspirations. Available either half cooked in jars or in tins which can be stored (and will improve). Whole foie gras is the best (and most expensive), but pieces and a 'bloc' (made up of pieces) are a very acceptable second choice.

PRICE: e.g. Foie gras d'oie entier £30 per tin (200g); Bloc de foie gras d'oie £19.50 per tin (130g); Bloc de foie gras de canard £17.25 per tin (200g).

AVAILABLE: The Clark Trading Company, 17 Southbrook Road, Lee, London SE12 8LH Tel: 081-297 9937 (Mail Order).

Marrons Glaces

You either love or loathe these crystallized sweet chestnuts: those who love them would probably kill for them.

PRICE: £12.50 for 400g (by Fauchon, the Fortnums of France).

AVAILABLE: Branches of John Lewis Partnership; Selfridges, 400 Oxford Street, London W1A 1AB Tel: 071-629 1234 (Mail Order available).

Membership of The Pudding Club

Puddings are not unhealthy, just as long as you eat them with a clear conscience – according to the philosophy of this club! No messing around with sorbets or fruit – these puddings are of the traditional English variety and usually involve sponge or suet plus the mandatory custard. Membership is really just turning up at one of their meetings, which happen twice per month.

PRICE: £17 (includes wine, main course and your fill of about seven puddings).

AVAILABLE: The Pudding Club, Three Ways Hotel, Mickleton, Nr Chipping Camden, Glos GL55 6SB Tel: 0386 438429.

Membership of the Wine Society

Enables members to choose from well-priced wine selections and special offers (free delivery of a dozen or more bottles anywhere in the UK) and admits them to tastings and wine courses.

PRICE: £20 life membership.

AVAILABLE: The Wine Society, Gunnels Wood Road, Stevenage, Hertfordshire SG1 2BG Tel: 0438 741177.

Mezzaluna

Double-handled, 'half-moon'-shaped blade for high speed hand-chopping of meat, herbs, nuts, etc. Stainless steel with varnished wood handles.

PRICE: £10.95.

AVAILABLE: Good kitchen shops.

Pestle and Mortar

A very simple method of grinding and pulverizing small quantities. Traditional stoneware pestles are easier to clean and more impervious to lingering flavours (garlic!) than their wooden equivalents.

PRICE: £15.50 for 10 cm bowl.

AVAILABLE: Good kitchen shops.

Water Filter Jug

If your tap water has become practically unpalatable, these jugs become kitchen essentials rather than luxuries.

PRICE: £15.50 for Brita Jug, £3 for filter.

AVAILABLE: Large department stores, branches of John Lewis Partnership; for nearest stockist contact: Brita (UK) Ltd, Brita House, 62-64 Bridge Street, Walton-on-Thames KT12 1AP Tel 0932 228348.

BETWEEN £20–£50

Cafetière/Insulated Cafetière

Coffee experts now declare that the best coffee can be made in a pot. The cafetière is more elegant and easier. Add coffee and boiling water, wait, then press the plunger for perfect results every time. Insulated versions are now available which keep up to a litre of coffee piping hot for at least two hours.

PRICE: £27.95 for 3 cup (chrome finish); £31.95 for 6 cup; £34.95 for 8 cup; £36.95 for 12 cup; £19.95 (insulated version).

AVAILABLE: Kitchen specialists and departments; Scotts of Stow, The Square, Stow-on-the-Wold, Glos GL54 1AF Tel: 0793 706111 (Mail Order).

Cellar Book

By Hugh Johnson (author of the *World Atlas of Wine* and *Pocket Wine Book*), this includes complete buying plan for an ideal cellar and advice on choosing, storing and decanting. A perfect way to keep track of a home cellar.

PRICE: £25 [Simon & Schuster].

AVAILABLE: Good bookshops.

Chocolate Society Membership

A society formed with people in mind who start dribbling and twitching at the merest whiff of a slab of chocolate. Originally formed to promote awareness of good quality chocolate, there are frequent tastings and choc news for the dedicated.

PRICE: From £30.

AVAILABLE: The Chocolate Society, Norwood Bottom Farm, Norwood Bottom, Otley, West Yorkshire LS21 2RA Tel: 0943 851101.

Copper Egg Bowl

There is no substitute for the traditional method of beating egg whites – a flexible balloon whisk and copper bowl. The metal makes egg whites cling to the sides of the bowl, thus allowing more air to be beaten into them, for a lighter finish.

PRICE: £46.50 for 25 cm diameter bowl.

AVAILABLE: Good kitchen shops.

Decanting Funnel

An attractive funnel to ensure decanted wine ends up in the decanter.

PRICE: £45 (silver).

AVAILABLE: Jewellers, antique and silver shops.

Electronic Scales

Scales that can be used with or without the bowl – a flat surface for measuring large joints of meat, or the bowl to make it easier to weigh and mix several ingredients together.

PRICE: From £25.

AVAILABLE: Most electrical stores and large department stores, kitchen shops.

Fish Kettle

Long kettles for cooking trout, salmon, or whatever the fisherman brought home.

PRICE: From £30.

AVAILABLE: Kitchen shops and hardware stores.

Hampers

The more luxurious or original the better. Most department stores have standard varieties at Christmas and will deliver. For Ascot, Christmas, overseas or any occasion – from fruit and tinned ham, to Beluga caviar and Dom Perignon.

PRICE: From £22.50. £23–£2000 [Fortnum & Mason]; £16–£250 [Hay Hampers].

AVAILABLE: Major department stores; Fortnum and Mason, 181 Piccadilly, London W1A 1ER Tel: 071-734 8040. Hay Hampers, The Barn, Corby Glen, Nr Grantham, Lincolnshire NG33 4NJ Tel: 047684 420.

Harrods Gourmet Club Membership

Privileges of membership include six copies of *Table Talk* per year (full of food issues and special offers), opportunities to meet celebrities, dine at the best restaurants, taste the finest wines and generally come into contact with like-minded folk.

PRICE: £25 p.a.

AVAILABLE: Harrods Mail Order Dept, Grant Way, off Syon Lane, Isleworth, Middlesex TW7 5QD Tel: 081-479 9395.

Kitchen Tools for Left-Handers

Kitchen scissors, butterfly tin opener, corkscrew, left-hander spoon and a Lancashire potato peeler (the right-handed version is impossible for left-handers to use). Extremely useful for left-handers and hilarious when right-handers try to puzzle them out.

PRICE: £21.95.

AVAILABLE: Anything Left-Handed Ltd, 57 Brewer Street, London W1R 3FB Tel: 071-437 3910 (Mail Order available).

Le Creuset Cast Iron Pans

Pleasant, rather homely appearance. Except for terrines and pans with wooden handles, all pans can be used either on top of the stove or in the oven. Not for OAPs: they are heavy.

PRICE: Start at about £17.40 for gratin dish. Classic casserole with lid: 18 cm diameter £29.95; 22 cm diameter £43.85; 26 cm diameter £49.20.

AVAILABLE: All good kitchen shops, kitchen departments of large department stores.

MAGAZINE SUBSCRIPTION
Taste

Subcriptions to this glossy, mouth-watering magazine is an indulgence.

PRICE: £27 p.a. (monthly).

AVAILABLE: Lazahold, Freepost, P O Box 10, Sunderland SR1 1BR Tel: 091-510 2290.

Mail Order – Truffles

If you know what's what, you would only choose winter truffles, which although fearfully expensive, really show the far cheaper black summer ones up for the poor excuse they are! These are the only variety stocked by The Clark Trading Company.

PRICE: eg. whole black winter truffles (from France) £32.50 per 25g jar; stainless steel truffle slicer (for wafer-thin slices) £17.75.

AVAILABLE: The Clark Trading Company, 17 Southbrook Road, Lee, London SE12 8LH Tel: 081-297 9937.

Mandoline

Fast, efficient, traditional fine slicer for cucumber, potatoes, etc. Wooden frame, stainless steel blades. Only for the cook who doesn't have a Magimix.

PRICE: £20.65.

AVAILABLE: David Mellor, 4 Sloane Square, London SW1W 8EE Tel: 071-730 4259; and other good kitchen shops.

Membership of the Association of Restaurant Diners

People who eat out a lot and like to keep their finger on the pulse where new restaurants are concerned will appreciate the preferential booking service and monthly updates membership brings. The Restaurant Switchboard will make your reservation, arrange parties and offer advice on unusual restaurants.

PRICE: £35 p.a.

AVAILABLE: Association of Restaurant Diners, 108-114 Myddleton Road, London N22 Tel: 081-888 8080.

Membership of The Scotch Malt Whisky Society

Membership brings invitations to free tastings and an opportunity to buy the Society's own rare cask-strength single malts.

PRICE: £40 membership.

AVAILABLE: The Scotch Malt Whisky Society, The Vaults, 87 Giles Street, Leith, Edinburgh EH6 Tel: 031-554 3451.

The Truffle Lovers Kit

A rather optimistic kit for dreamers who hope to cultivate their own truffles. The kit includes a real oak tree sapling (their preferred haunt), culture details, a chocolate truffle-hunting pig, and ½ lb of chocolate truffles to enjoy while waiting (it may be quite a long time!).

PRICE: £25 per kit.

AVAILABLE: Fines Herbes, Freepost, London SW11 4BR Tel: 071-228 9672 (Mail Order).

£50 AND ABOVE

Caviar

One of the most luxurious presents money can buy. Possible to mail order Sevruga, Osietra or Beluga from Harrods in 50g, 125g or 250g pots or in a special Caviar Gift Set in a smart box with accompanying silver spoon.

PRICE: £68 (50g Beluga), £29 (50g Osietra), £24 (50g Sevruga).

AVAILABLE: Harrods, Knightsbridge, London SW1 Tel: 071-730 1234; Caviar Kaspa, 18 Bruton Place, London W1 Tel: 071-493 2612 (Mail Order).

Cookery Course

Send someone who would relish the prospect rather than someone whom you think would benefit from it! Evening, day, week and full-time courses available. Contact your local education authority which will run evening classes at very reasonable prices.

PRICE: Varies: Local evening classes may be £14 per term; Leith's ten-week evening lessons from £260; Cordon Bleu two day short course £120.

AVAILABLE: In London look in *Floodlight* for evening classes, elsewhere *Yellow Pages* under cookery schools; Leith's School of Food and Wine, 21 St Alban's Grove, London W8 BP Tel: 071-229 0177; Cordon Bleu, 114 Marylebone Lane, London W1M 6HH Tel: 071-935 3503.

Copper Bottomed Pans

Copper heats up almost instantaneously but also cools down very quickly. This makes it particularly good for cooking food fast, e.g. frying, sauteing. Buy the heaviest possible – to last for a lifetime.

PRICE: £31 (small saucepan by Prestige); £43 (large saucepan).

AVAILABLE: Branches of John Lewis Partnership.

Mail Order – Ham on the Bone

Succulent Wiltshire and traditionally York hams, specially cured for ten weeks are available mail order.

PRICE: £59 (whole York ham); £25 (half Wiltshire ham approx 7lbs).

AVAILABLE: Dukeshill Ham Company, Bridgnorth, Shropshire WV16 6AF Tel: 074 635519.

CHAPTER TEN

GARDENING

Two-thirds of us have a garden – but it's not all joy: 25% think of it as forced labour! That said, the British are now spending more on gardening products than ever before. Gardening has usurped our penchant for DIY. Personally, I get lost in a garden centre, but *Which?* believe they'll give you better plants than your average DIY superstore. It must save time and energy if you know what you're looking for in the first place.

UNDER £5

Ant Pen

Draw boundary lines across doorways and ants will cross at their peril.

PRICE: £2.29.

AVAILABLE: Branches of Sainsbury's Homebase.

Besom (Witches' Broom)

Still one of the best methods of clearing leaves and debris.

PRICE: £4.95.

AVAILABLE: Most good garden centres.

BOOK CHOICE
The 'Expert' Series

Simple step-by-step directions by Dr D G Hessayon in a series of well illustrated booklets. Excellent value and they sell in their thousands.

PRICE: £4.50 each for the *Lawns, Vegetables, Roses, Fruit, Flowers, Trees & Shrubs*; £5.95 for *The New Houseplant Expert*.

AVAILABLE: Gardening section of most large bookshops, garden centres.

Garden Flares

Wind-resistant torches for evenings al fresco. Lemon-scented candles also keep the midges at bay.

PRICE: From £2.50.

AVAILABLE: Most garden centres, large supermarkets and hardware stores.

Gardening Diary

Useful dates, names and addresses for those who may otherwise completely forget about the annual convention of The Hardy Plant Society.

PRICE: £4.95 [Charles Lett].

AVAILABLE: Large garden centres and good stationers.

Gardening Gloves

A thorny subject – not very exciting but essential. Avid gardeners get through lots.

PRICE: £1.50 upwards.

AVAILABLE: Garden centres, hardware and department stores.

Herbs

It is quite possible to create an entire herb garden for under £10. Small growing cuttings are available in the salad section of major supermarkets. Rosemary can grow into a large, decorative shrub.

PRICE: e.g. parsley 99p, tarragon £1.15, thyme £1, rosemary £1, basil £1.

AVAILABLE: Most garden centres and large supermarkets.

Houseplant Pest Deterrents

Phostrogen plant pins get stuck in the earth next to house and greenhouse plants, and keep them free from pests without spraying.

PRICE: £1.99 for 20 pins.

AVAILABLE: All good garden centres.

Houseplants

Greenfingers are often a prerequisite for healthy indoor as well as outdoor plants. Huge variety of choice – many can be planted outside during non-flowering season.

PRICE: From about £2.

AVAILABLE: Garden centres, nurseries, large supermarkets and department stores.

Pet Deterrents

A bugbear, particularly for the town and suburban gardener. To deter dogs and cats, scatter crystals called 'Get off my Garden!' or 'Scent off Buds'.

PRICE: £2.49.

AVAILABLE: All garden centres.

Plant Supports and Plant Ties

For under £5 you can provide a whole support network for climbers and ramblers.

PRICE: 89p for a clematis support, 99p for 100 paperwire twists, £1.60 for 60 adjustable ties.

AVAILABLE: Majority of garden centres.

Seeds – Bluebells

500 seeds will create a bluebell carpet in a wild patch of garden.

PRICE: £4.

AVAILABLE: Wild Seeds, Branae, Llanderfel, Balla, Gwynedd LL23 7RE Tel: 06783 427 (Mail Order).

Seeds – Giant Vegetable Seeds

Grow giant pumpkins and amusingly shaped turnips all of your own – then send pictures of the results to Esther.

PRICE: From £1.79 (marrow) to £2.49 (tomato/pumpkin).

AVAILABLE: Thompson & Morgan, Poplar Lane, Ipswich IP8 3BU Tel: 0473 688821 (Mail Order).

Seeds – Other

Create next year's herbaceous border or vegetable patch with the appropriate seeds. Coated seeds are more hardy and therefore more likely to germinate, but slightly more expensive. Phone major suppliers for free colour catalogues.

PRICE: From 60p per pack.

AVAILABLE: Suttons Seeds Tel: 0803 612011; Unwins Seeds Tel: 0945 588522; Mr Fothergill's Seeds Tel: 0638 751161; S E Marshall & Co Ltd Tel: 0945 583407.

Slug Pub

Harmless to the environment, children and pets. Place in ground and fill with beer, milk or yeast – greedy slugs fall in and die.

PRICE: £2.99 [Anthony Green & Co, Hull].

AVAILABLE: Sainsbury's Homebase; most large garden centres.

Soil Acidity Tester

Plants such as azaleas, camellias and rhododendrons need very low acid levels in the soil to thrive. A keen grower will need a tester to keep the soil at its optimum acidity level.

PRICE: £2.99.

AVAILABLE: Large gardening centres.

Spring Bulbs

Buy bulbs in autumn for spring flowering. Unless you have a great deal of space stick to simple varieties.

PRICE: From £1.39.

AVAILABLE: Sainsbury's Homebase, B & Q. Mail Order: Avon Bulbs, Burnt House Farm, Lambrock, South Petherton, Somerset, TA13 4HE (Unusual bulbs). J Parker Dutch Bulbs (W/S) Ltd, Dept 452, Chester Road, Old Trafford, Manchester M16 9HL Tel: 061-872 1700.

Terracotta Pots

Tubs, patio pots and plant holders. Even better, filled with plants. Machine-made terracotta is more porous and therefore more likely to suffer frost damage than the (slightly more expensive) hand-made terracotta which also acquires the patina which evades the smooth machine-made version.

PRICE: From £3!

AVAILABLE: All garden centres; Whichford Pottery, Whichford, Shipston-Upon-Stour, Warwickshire CV36 5PG Tel: 060884 416 (Mail Order available).

Waterproof Pen

To label everything and still be able to identify it after the storm.

PRICE: From 89p.

AVAILABLE: Garden centres; Also craft shops – ask for indelible pens.

BETWEEN £5–£10

Dandelion And Daisy Weeder

This is a V-shaped fork which whisks out the offending weeds without leaving great gashes in the lawn.

PRICE: £5.95.

AVAILABLE: All large garden centres.

Digital Thermometer

Records highest and lowest temperatures – essential for well run greenhouses.

PRICE: £9.95.

AVAILABLE: Maplin Electronics, PO Box 3, Rayleigh, Essex SS6 8LR Tel: 0702 552911 (Mail Order only).

Fruit Bushes

Gooseberry, strawberry, raspberry and blackcurrant bushes are all available mail order from garden fruit specialists. Each plant is also guaranteed for 12 months against possible failure.

PRICE: (reductions for multiples) – gooseberries £7.65 for 2 plants; strawberries £8.45 for 12 plants; raspberries £6.95 for 5 plants; blackcurrants £6.95 for 2 plants (plus £3.50 p&p).

AVAILABLE: Ken Muir, Honeypot Farm, Rectory Road, Weeley Heath, Clacton-on-Sea, Essex C016 9BJ Tel: 0255 830181; or any good nursery.

Garden Planner

What, when and where to plant next year? With a garden planner it can all be laid out in black-and-white.

PRICE: £7.95.

AVAILABLE: Large garden centres, good bookshops and stationers.

Kneeling Pads

No more soggy knees and aching joints.

PRICE: £7.50.

AVAILABLE: Most garden centres, department and hardware stores.

Tool Sharpener

To keep all shears and scissors, etc, up to scratch.

PRICE: £7.49 [Spear & Jackson].

AVAILABLE: Majority of garden centres.

BETWEEN £10–£20

Aerator Sandals

These are a cross between pattens and running spikes and strap onto wellies before taking a walk over compacted areas of lawn. The spikes open air passages and get water, air and nutrients down to the roots where they're needed.

PRICE: £15.99.

AVAILABLE: The Traditional Garden Supply Company Ltd, 22 Guildford Park Road, Guildford, Surrey GU2 5ND Tel: 0483 450080 (Mail Order).

Chelsea Flower Show Tickets

It's THE gardening event of the year, for which every variety of plant flowers in May. Non-members' day is Friday.

PRICE: Around £20 Friday; (RHS Members on Tues/Wed/Thurs).

AVAILABLE: Contact: The Royal Horticultural Society, PO Box 313, Vincent Square, London SW1P 2PG Tel: 071-834 4333.

Decorative Garden Taps

Charming transformations of outdoor taps come in the shape of mallards, squirrels, ducks, snails and frogs. Finished in verdigris they come looking like they have been around for years.

PRICE: £16.

AVAILABLE: Flora & Fauna Ltd, Orchard House, Patmore End, Ugley, Bishop's Stortford, Hertfordshire CM22 6JA Tel: 0799 88289 (Mail Order).

Fragrant Shrubs

Many shrubs bear sweet-smelling flowers and others have aromatic foliage. What warm summer evenings were made for. *Buddleia Davidii*: a hardy, strong-growing shrub that's attractive to butterflies and bees. Grows to between 4 and 8 feet. *Jasminum Communis* (Common Myrtle): the glossy leaves are aromatic, has profuse white flowers in July/August. Evergreen. *Wisteria Sinensis* (Chinese Wisteria): one of the most popular wisterias, long chains of mauve f flowers are produced during May to June; deciduous.

PRICE: Varies: from about £10.

AVAILABLE: Good garden centres and nurseries.

Garden Furniture

Prices vary enormously. Individual pieces work out quite inexpensively but a whole matching 'set' can add up.

PRICE: Stacking White Resin Furniture: chairs from £17 (children's £2.99); parasols from £39; bases £5.95; tables from £59; sunbeds from £69.99. White Aluminium Furniture: tables £89.99; chairs £39.99; deckchairs from £14.99.

AVAILABLE: Large garden centres, DIY, department and large furniture stores.

Garden Furniture Protective Covers

Hardwearing plastic covers for all garden furniture for protection during the winter or April showers.

PRICE: From £16.50 for patio set (from £10.99 for lounger).

AVAILABLE: Most good garden centres.

Garden Gnomes

Love them or loathe them, gnomes are a peculiarly British obsession and one which has obviously driven some people quite mad – at the Gnome Reserve all the visitors have to wear red winceyette hats so as not to embarrass the gnomes. It's by no means a small preoccupation either, in a recent survey by *Garden News* magazine 47% of readers admitted to owning a gnome.

PRICE: From £3 to £40 (about 3 ft tall).

AVAILABLE: The Gnome Reserve, West Putford, Nr Holsworthy, North Devon Tel: 0409 241435; selected garden centres.

Green Belt

A very useful way of carrying lots of gardening palaver – a gardener's apron with specially designed pockets to hold trowels, handforks, string, plant labels and seed packets, etc.

PRICE: £6–£20.

AVAILABLE: Good garden centres.

Handtools

'Cheap' tools are no good to anyone – they rust and they bend. Good quality tools, although more expensive, are an investment for the future. The Spear and Jackson Sovereign Range of premium tools (16 altogether) come with a ten-year guarantee.

PRICE: Start at £6.95 for hand tools to £34.95 for shears and loppers.

AVAILABLE: All garden centres and good hardware stores.

Instant Trees

It's possible to buy quite mature trees (from 10″ to 30″ high) and have them supplied and planted for you.

PRICE: From about £10 for a sapling – the more mature the tree, the more it will cost.

AVAILABLE: Argyll Landscapes, Drishaig, Inverary, Argyll Tel: 0499 2351.

MAGAZINE SUBSCRIPTION

Gardening news, tips and photographs to provide information or inspiration for the green-fingered.

PRICE: A year's subscription will currently cost you: *Gardeners' World* (monthly): £18.60; *Practical Gardening* (monthly): £14.50; *Organic Gardening* (monthly): £18; *The Gardener* (monthly): £16.80; *Garden Answers* (monthly): £12.

AVAILABLE: Contact the subscription departments for each magazine.

Membership Of The Herb Society

Annual membership includes four copies of *The Herbal Review* magazine, discounts on plants, information on herb courses, etc. Booklets on growing herbs.

PRICE: £14 p.a.

AVAILABLE: The Herb Society, PO Box 599, London SW11 4RW.

National Garden Gift Tokens

Redeemable at over 1500 garden centres and at any Interflora outlet.

PRICE: At your discretion.

AVAILABLE: From most garden centres (contact the Horticultural Trades Association, 19 High Street, Theale, Berkshire RG7 5AH for a stockist list – Tel: 0734 303998).

Propagator

To germinate seeds, roots and cuttings quickly, with vents for humidity/temperature control. A small propagator can fit on a windowsill or greenhouse shelf.

PRICE: From £19.99.

AVAILABLE: Most large garden centres.

Trugs

Useful, handy and good-looking baskets with supports – a traditional gardening accessory to gather long-stemmed flowers or weeds. Made in sweetchestnut and willow.

PRICE: From £18.

AVAILABLE: Most good garden centres; Hamptons of Bristol, New Street, Charfield, Wotton-Under-Edge, Glos GL12 8GS Tel: 0453 842889 (Mail Order).

BETWEEN £20–£50

Barbecues

These come in all shapes, sizes and pricebands. Start with a disposable (charcoal in what resembles a Chinese takeaway container); move on to a build your own version; or straight through to a Weber – the haute cuisine version (that looks like the Martians that starred in the Smash ad).

PRICE: £3.45 (disposable); £21.99 (build your own); £89.99 [Weber].

AVAILABLE: Most garden centres and DIY stores.

BOOK CHOICE
A Garden for All Seasons

Hundreds of ideas for spring, summer, autumn and winter. Over 1000 illustrations.

PRICE: £23.95 [Readers Digest].

AVAILABLE: Most good bookshops.

BOOK CHOICE
RHS Encyclopaedia of Gardening

Anything with The Royal Horticultural Society imprimatur is sure to be authoritative when searching for definitive gardening books. The 600-page volume has more than 3000 how-to-do-it photographs and explains and illustrates all the techniques a gardener is ever likely to wish to study.

PRICE: £29.95 [Dorling Kindersley].

AVAILABLE: All good bookshops.

BOOK CHOICE
Roses

Peter Beale's book is a guide to everything you need to know about roses, including histories, care, scent, frequency of flowering, etc.

PRICE: £35 [Harvill].

AVAILABLE: Most good bookshops.

Compact Apple Trees

Apple trees that grow straight up in columns and can be planted as close as two feet apart. Ideal for small gardens.

PRICE: £26.25 for two (plus £3.50 p&p).

AVAILABLE: Ken Muir, Honeypot Farm, Rectory Road, Weeley Heath, Clacton-on-Sea, Essex C016 9BJ Tel: 0255 830181.

Compost Makers

Get rid of garden rubbish and save on bought compost. Relate size of compost maker to size of garden. Also for anyone who doesn't particularly like doing the job by hand, a Black & Decker compost shredder.

PRICE: Around £35.99 (compost maker); £134.99 (Black & Decker shredder).

AVAILABLE: Large garden centres; The Organibox, Halifax Wineform Co, Calder Mill, Hebden Bridge, West Yorkshire HX7 6LJ Tel: 0422 842070 (Mail Order); shredder from large garden centres and hardware stores.

Fold-Away Cassette Hose

Neat and tidy way to store garden hose. Check cassette is robust and rewind system is easy to use.

PRICE: From £39.99 [Gardena].

AVAILABLE: Most garden centres.

Fruit Picker

Bring down fruit safely from trees.

PRICE: About £40.

AVAILABLE: Branches of Sainsbury's Homebase.

Garden Design Course

The Royal Horticultural Society run courses that are extremely reasonably priced, especially on weekdays.

PRICE: £22 (day schools).

AVAILABLE: Contact: The Royal Horticultural Society, PO Box 313, Vincent Square, London SW1P 2PE Tel: 071-834 4333.

Greenhouse Heater

An economical occasional heater, when you need to keep the frost at bay. The Parasene will heat a small greenhouse for three and a half days on one gallon of paraffin.

PRICE: £29.99.

AVAILABLE: Most garden centres and DIY stores.

Hammock

Lounging in a Brazilian pure cotton hammock must be one of the most comfortable ways to snooze on a summer afternoon. Ensure it is erected between two objects sturdy enough to bear your weight.

PRICE: £39.95.

AVAILABLE: Elmley Heritage, Stone House, Elmley Lovett, Droitwich, Worcs WR9 0PS Tel: 0299 23447 (Mail Order).

Molechaser

If you're of the Jasper Carrott school of thinking where the only way to get rid of the mole plague is with a shotgun, then welcome the molechaser which harmlessly and effectively clears them from the garden. Push the stake into the ground and every 15 seconds it will emit a deep vibrating sound which moles can't bear.

PRICE: £29.95.

AVAILABLE: Innovations Ltd, Euroway Business Park, Swindon SN5 8SN Tel: 0793 514666 (Mail Order).

Organic Gardening Course

For environmentally aware gardeners.

PRICE: £30 (day course including food).

AVAILABLE: The Drummuir & Park Trust Estate Office, Drummuir, Banffshire AB5 3JE Tel: 054281 225.

Plant Frames

Not canes, but galvanized metal grids through which herbaceous plants grow – you can't see them at all during the flowering season.

PRICE: From £24.

AVAILABLE: Power Garden Products, 3 Daytona Drive, Allesbury, Coventry CV5 9QG Tel: 0676 23062 (Mail Order).

Royal Horticultural Society Membership

Membership includes: lectures throughout the year, courses, free entry to their Westminster shows, advice on problems and projects and a good monthly magazine.

PRICE: £27 p.a.

AVAILABLE: The Royal Horticultural Society, PO Box 313, 1 Vincent Square, London SW1 P 2PE Tel: 071-834 4333.

Secateurs

Good tools are always welcome and rose growers and all pruners alike would welcome a pair of Felco secateurs – rather more expensive than other makes, but first-class (all parts replaceable; servicing available).

PRICE: About £30; Left-handed £35.95.

AVAILABLE: Good garden centres and hardware stores; or call Felco Burton McCall on 0533 340800 for stockists.

Sprayer

For applying foliage feed, insecticides etc. Useful to have more than one for different chemicals.

PRICE: £31 [Premier Plus].

AVAILABLE: Most good garden centres.

Strimmer

For grass trimming and lawn edging.

PRICE: From £21. 99 [Black & Decker]; £31.99 for a Flymo Multi-Trim for large amounts of lawn edge.

AVAILABLE: All large garden centres.

Weatherproof Lights

Gala outdoor lights for patios, barbeques, Christmas trees; ten different colour bulbs on 14.5m cable.

PRICE: £36.99.

AVAILABLE: Sainsbury's Homebase and other large garden centres.

Window Box

Filled with plants or herbs, perfect for those with little or no garden and anyone who loves a decorated windowsill and fragranced room.

PRICE: A terracotta box, overflowing with blooms would probably cost in all about £20–£50 depending on choice of plants (and time of year!).

AVAILABLE: Make up your own in garden centres and nurseries.

£50 AND ABOVE

Ball Barrow

Barrow with a difference – easy to use, creates ease of access.

PRICE: £51.

AVAILABLE: Large garden centres. (Not always in stock so may need to be ordered. Generally takes a week.)

Conservatory

Another room for the house. Very often become extensions to the livingroom, extra playroom etc. Also comes in handy for growing plants.

PRICE: From £3000 to £40,000 (average price £8000).

AVAILABLE: The Conservatory Association, 2nd Floor, Godwin House, George Street, Huntington, Cambs PE18 6BU Tel: 0480 458278 (free advisory leaflet).

Cordless Hedge Trimmer

The task of cutting, pruning and clipping hedges, vines and creepers need not be restricted to availability of a main power supply. A cordless hedge trimmer allows manoeuvrability without the possible dangers of a power cable.

PRICE: From £79 [Black & Decker].

AVAILABLE: Most garden centres, hardware stores; for nearest stockist contact: Black & Decker Ltd, Wespoint, The Grove, Slough, Berkshire SL1 1QQ Tel: 0753 511234.

Cordless Phone

This ceases to be a luxury for the avid gardener. Always check the range before you buy.

PRICE: From £69.50.

AVAILABLE: Boots, hardware and major department stores.

Garden Log Book

A service specifically for people with severe problems – either baffled by what's already in their garden, puzzled by a recently-acquired garden or have a well-developed garden that needs recording. Soil is tested, plants identified and labelled and problems diagnosed – then details recorded in a hardback book.

PRICE: Starts at £95 (based on number of different plants in garden).

AVAILABLE: Garden Log, Freepost, London SW11 4BR Tel: 071-228 9672.

Garden Shed

Is any garden really complete without one? Consider size of garden, location of shed and how much equipment is actually going to be stored before buying. Usually in kit form.

PRICE: From £115.

AVAILABLE: Large garden centres and furniture stores.

Garden Vac

Hoover the lawn and flower beds just like they were the carpet – this ingenious invention by Flymo picks up grass cuttings, leaves and empty cans leaves the soil behind.

PRICE: £79.99.

AVAILABLE: Most DIY and garden centres.

Greenhouse/Mini-Greenhouse

A serious investment, but it is possible to buy anything from a self-assembly kit upwards. A mini-greenhouse fits against a wall and is only 5 ft deep.

PRICE: £150 upwards.

AVAILABLE: Access, Crick, Northants NN16 7BR Tel: 0788 822301 (Mail Order).

Growing Bench

Is to the gardener what the Workmate is to the DIYer. Pop this workbench in the greenhouse and use it for potting – or station it on the lawn and use for barbecues.

PRICE: £125 [Black & Decker].

AVAILABLE: Most gardening centres; for nearest stockist contact: Black & Decker Ltd, Westpoint, The Grove, Slough, Berks SL1 1QQ Tel: 0753 511234.

Lawnmower

Deciding on a lawnmower may turn out to be Pandora's box of delights. Bear in mind the size of the garden plus the pros and cons of each mower i.e. the traditional cylinder-type collects the clippings but really needs a level surface to function properly; a rotary copes best with long grass, but is not as manoeuvrable as a hover.

PRICE: From £69.95 Flymo hover mower (reasonable on all lengths of grass – does not collect clippings); £300 Qualcast Suffolk Punch 35s; (cylinder mower with finely-tuned adjustable height settings).

AVAILABLE: Garden machinery suppliers.

Sawbench

Smoke-producing logs can only be burned in the country and if they are going to be sawn rather than chopped, a good sawbench is essential. The secret is stability and good grip on the log.

Agriframe's version has a unique bracing feature which secures logs up to 10″ in diameter – and offers a money-back satisfaction guarantee.

PRICE: £63.95.

AVAILABLE: Agriframes Ltd, Charlwoods Road, East Grinstead, West Sussex RH19 2HG Tel: 0342 328644 (Mail Order).

Steamer-Style Chair

Foldaway teak chair in old-fashioned steamer style. Can winter outside as it is made with rust-resistant bolts and hinges.

PRICE: £495.

AVAILABLE: The General Trading Company, 144 Sloane Street, London SW1 Tel: 071-730 0411.

Tractor-Style Lawnmowers

Ideal for large lawns as it is possible to sit down on the job. Also extremely useful for heavy towing and transporting jobs.

PRICE: About £1000 to £2000.

AVAILABLE: Paice & Sons Ltd, Parkwood, Byers Lane, South Godstone, Surrey RH9 8JJ Tel: 0342 893894.

Watering Systems

Continuing water shortages and extended water metering make these systems increasingly popular and practical. They can deliver precisely the right amount of water for each area of the garden.

PRICE: £53.99 for Greenhouse Set; approximately £150 upwards for Garden System.

AVAILABLE: Gardena UK Ltd, 7 Dunhams Court, Letchworth Garden City, Herts SG6 1BD Tel: 0462 686688.

CHAPTER ELEVEN

HEALTH & BEAUTY

THERE'S an image we hold in our heads of glowing vitality – Jane Fonda et al have a lot to answer for! In reality three-quarters of us risk reduced life-expectancy because we under-exercise, and 95% of those who diet will eventually put back all that weight again. The answer is to turn a blind eye and pamper ourselves with some of life's little luxuries. Despite the recession the sales of cosmetics and beauty products seem to be healthier than those who wear them, with the expensive end of the market holding up best!

UNDER £5

Block of Alum

Crystal alum is the oldest form of aftershave and antiseptic. A block of it is one of the cheapest things you can buy at Trumper! PRICE: £4.90.

AVAILABLE: Geo F Trumper, 9 Curzon Street, London W1Y 7FL Tel: 071-499 1850/2932; 166 Fairbridge Road, London N19 3HT Tel: 071-272 1765 (Mail Order).

BOOK CHOICE
'Diet' Books

A new genre of weight-control guide writers have realised that we hate being hungry. Instead of calorie pinching, losing weight and being healthy depends not on how much you eat but what it is you're eating, and in the case of The Hay Diet, don't eat it with potatoes. Highly recommended apart from The Hay Diet (which avoids eating protein and carbohydrates together) are Rosemary

Conley's 'Hip and Thigh Diet' (low fat) and Leslie and Susannah Kenton's 'Raw Energy' (fresh, uncooked, high energy foods).

PRICE: *Food Combining for Health* (The Hay Diet) £7.99 [Thorsons]; *The Complete Hip and Thigh Diet* £4.99 [Arrow]; *Raw Energy* £5.99 [Arrow].

AVAILABLE: All good bookshops.

Cosmetics – Eyebrow Definers

All well-dressed faces are wearing well-defined eyebrows. This new shaped brow can be enhanced with all manner of pencils, powders and brushes – for the most natural results choose a shade as close as possible to the natural hair colour.

PRICE: e.g. from £2.40 (No 7) to £11 (Chanel Precision Brow).

AVAILABLE: Boots and all good chemists.

Cosmetics – Liquid Eye Liner

If you want to avoid looking like a panda, Chanel produce a gel/fluid that is foolproof and spillproof, and which actually comes off. It comes with a fine brush for even application and is suitable for contact lens wearers.

PRICE: £14 (Chanel – black only); £3.40 (brush) £4.35 (pen).

AVAILABLE: All good chemists and department stores.

Essential Oils

Essential oils are extracted from plants and are known for their healing and therapeutic qualities. By heating the oils, dabbing them on pulse points or putting a couple of drops in the bath, the beneficial effects can be felt. The oils can be used for anything from indigestion to nervous tension; though do take proper advice in case of contraindications (side-effects).

PRICE: From £1.75 for 10 ml.

AVAILABLE: Boots, The Body Shop, health food stores; Aromatherapy Products Ltd, The Knoll Business Centre, Old

Shoreham Road, Hove, East Sussex BN3 7GS Tel: 0273 325666; Aromatherapy Hotline: Tisserand have set up a helpline for advice on using essential oils Tel: 0273 412139.

False Eyelashes

The seventies revival has repopularized falsies (what they don't realize is that some women have never been able to live without them – Nancy Sinatra claimed to sleep in hers). Available in whole lids or as individual lashes which should be applied using tweezers.

PRICE: e.g. £3.95 (Elegant Touch Fashion Lashes); £3.45 (Elegant Touch Dura Lash Individual Lashes); £24 (Eurolash individual lashes).

AVAILABLE: Boots and all good chemists.

Footcare Creams

The foot is independently acknowledged to be one of the most erogenous zones in the body, containing about 72,000 nerve endings. Foot massagers, lotions and nourishing creams are therefore likely to be very welcome and enjoyable presents.

PRICE: From £1.15 (Peppermint Foot Lotion – The Body Shop).

AVAILABLE: Cosmetics To Go, Freepost BH15 1BR Tel: 0800 373366 (Mail Order); The Body Shop; all good chemists and department stores.

Fridge Lock

A safety gadget for toddlers which can be given in jest to make midnight foragers think twice before raiding the fridge!

PRICE: £2.99.

AVAILABLE: All good baby equipment stockists; Early Learning & Baby Centre, South Marston, Swindon SN3 4TJ Tel: 0793 832832 (Mail Order).

Garlic Tablets

One a day, they say, keeps the vampires away and also keeps the blood flowing smoothly.

PRICE: £4.95 [Kwai]; £10.99 [Kyolic 350 mg tablets].

AVAILABLE: Holland & Barratt branches and other health food shops.

Handbag Atomizer

A favourite scent as accessible as a lipstick.

PRICE: £4.45–£25.

AVAILABLE: John Lewis Partnership, H Samuel, most department stores.

'Keep in the Fridge' Creams

Products with a limited life (from three to six weeks) that should be kept in the fridge because they really are 'natural'. All products are made freshly each day from fresh fruit and natural ingredients with no preservatives – hence their short life. The problem is not using them in time – but trying not to eat them – they smell so good.

PRICE: e.g. Kiwi Shampoo £3 (four week fridge life); Strawberry and Ginger Body Mask £4.20 (four weeks); Cucumber Cleanser £3 (three weeks).

AVAILABLE: Cosmetics To Go, Freepost, Poole, Dorset BH15 1BR Tel: 0800 373366 (Mail Order).

Loofah

The fibrous pod of the luffa plant which is used as a natural skin exfoliant in the bath (rubbing away the dead skin cells so skin is soft and can breathe) or just as a back scratcher.

PRICE: From £2.85 for a whole loofah; £3.95 (Loofah mitt).

AVAILABLE: Boots and all good chemists.

Make-Up Brushes

Shu Uemera, the Japanese artist turned businessman, understandably makes brushes rather well. His are the most sought after by make-up professionals with a range that includes every shape and size imaginable. Most make-up ranges have a selection of brushes available.

PRICE: £4–£100 [Shu Uemera].

AVAILABLE: Shu Uemera, Harvey Nichols, Knightsbridge, London SW1 Tel: 071-235 2375 (Mail Order available).

Massage Roller

When faced with a grooved stick you may well wonder what you're going to do with it! Roll it with your feet or on the back of the neck where it is particularly good.

PRICE: £2.20–£3.10 (Footsi); £8.50 (wooden back strap).

AVAILABLE: Body Shop stores nationwide; The Body Shop International plc, Hawthorn Road, Wick, Littlehampton, West Sussex BN17 7LR Tel: 0903 717107 (Mail Order).

Protector Razor

Worlds away from the cut-throat, this is an affordable design classic (it had a brief sojourn as an exhibit at The Design Museum). A protective covering over the blades prevents any nicks whilst not impeding the closeness of shave.

PRICE: £3.08 [Wilkinson Sword].

AVAILABLE: Boots and all good chemists.

Shampoo Bars

Exclusive to Cosmetics To Go, shampoo in a solid soap-like bar. Rub once or twice over the head, or lather in the hands – novel and lasts for ages. Varieties include Bronx Blonde, Wax & Clam-Baked Vanilla, Coconut, and Dead Sea Salt (for fine, flat hair).

PRICE: £2.60.

AVAILABLE: Cosmetics To Go, Freepost, Poole, Dorset BH15 1BR Tel: 0800 373366 (Mail Order).

Travel Bottles

Small plastic bottles and pots are unendingly useful for travellers who don't wish to take their family-size shampoo or moisturizing cream away just for the weekend.

PRICE: From 55p per bottle.

AVAILABLE: Chemists and department stores.

BETWEEN £5–£10

BOOK CHOICE
Allen Carr's Easy Way to Stop Smoking

Allen Carr's uniquely intelligent approach developed from years of counselling work doesn't rely on scare tactics and it actually works! You're allowed to smoke while you're reading it! The book is not a miracle worker however, and is for people who genuinely want to kill the weed.

PRICE: £6.99 (video also available £14.95).

AVAILABLE: All good bookshops.

BOOK CHOICE
Organic Gardening

Geoff Hamilton's pocket encyclopedia on how to turn your patch into an area of aromatic herbs and wonderful vegetables and enjoy dishes cooked with home-grown ingredients.

PRICE: £8.99 [Dorling Kindersley].

AVAILABLE: All good bookshops.

Cholesterol Tests

High cholesterol is now recognized as one of the primary contributors to heart disease. Check out what the damage is.

PRICE: £7.99 [Boots].

AVAILABLE: Branches of Boots.

Dumbells/Ankle and Wrist Weights

You are likely to end up resembling an orang-utan if you attempt taking these home on the bus. Wiser to order them by mail.

PRICE: From £6.20 (neoprene soft dumbell); from £5.20 (mini hand weight); from £7.30 (2 × 1lb ankle/wrist weights) plus delivery.

AVAILABLE: Energy Express, Chaconia, 36 Beech Lane, Kislingbury, Northants NN7 4AL Tel: 0604 832843 (Mail Order).

Exercise Mat

Aerobics mat which can used at home to offer protection from the shag pile, and which incorporates handles so can also be taken to classes. Moisture-resistant and washable.

PRICE: £6.55.

AVAILABLE: Sports shops; Energy Express, Chaconia, 36 Beech Lane, Kislingbury, Northants NN7 4AL Tel: 0604 832843 (Mail Order).

Left-Handed Manicure Scissors

Scissors are the trickiest piece of equipment for a left-hander to manoeuvre and the problem is accentuated with delicate handiwork. Manicure scissors or a manicure set would make the job a whole lot easier – and also remember that right-handers have to cut the nails on their right hands so they would be useful for anyone!

PRICE: £7.25 (straight or curved manicure scissors); £14.95 (set of two scissors, one right, one left); Manicure sets from £12.95.

AVAILABLE: Anything Left-Handed Ltd, 57 Brewer Street, London W1R 3FB Tel: 071-437 3910 (Mail Order).

Men's Skin Products

A man's skin is usually oiler and tougher than a woman's, but it still needs careful attention. 'Grooming products' for men are becoming more widely available – go for designer Chanel, or own-label 'Mostly Men' by The Body Shop.

PRICE: e.g. Chanel from £16.50 (aftershave moisturizer); Body Shop 90p (shaving gel).

AVAILABLE: Chemists and department stores; The Body Shop branches nationwide.

Natural Sounds Tape

The 'ultimate listening situation experience' – which has no melodies or words, i.e. nothing you can sing along to and distract you from the meditation the music is designed to promote.

PRICE: e.g. *Ocean Waves at Sunset* £6.95.

AVAILABLE: New World Cassettes, Paradise Farm, West Hall, Halesworth, Suffolk IP19 8RH Tel: 098 681682 (Mail Order).

Non-Allergic Products

Sensitive skins can react violently to make-up and creams that contain for example alcohol and abrasives, or are highly perfumed, as well as harsh alkaline products. Baby products are renowned for their gentle care of skin, but grown-ups may prefer the more sophisticated ranges of hypoallergenic products by Almay, Clinique or Lancôme.

PRICE: From: £7.95 [Almay].

AVAILABLE: Chemists and department stores.

Snoring Silencer

Essential to prevent fractiousness during the day due to lack of sleep at night, the snorer is a rather nasty-looking plastic clip which hooks onto the bottom of the nostrils and allows 50% more air to pass freely in and out of the nost and throat, reducing vibration of the palate, the most common cause of snoring.

PRICE: £5.99.

AVAILABLE: Harbingers, Bowerhill, Melksham SN12 6SR Tel: 0225 790777 (Mail Order).

Tongue Defurrer

You'd better believe it! Omano Products has come to the rescue of an orally unhygenic world with its tongue cleanser which can clear debris from a furry mouth – leaving you with a squeaky clean tongue and fresh breath.

PRICE: £6.95.

AVAILABLE: Harrods; OM Products, PO Box 2826, London N10 3HZ Tel: 081-883 5828 (Mail Order).

Treatment – Manicure/Pedicure

Wax manicures and pedicures are especially good for aching joints and dry skin when the hands or feet are coated in warm paraffin wax; try also hand-softening treatments where the hand is massaged with essential oils and then aromatherapy cream. Even a scrub and polish is a pampering session.

PRICE: Manicures start from £7 (pedicures are a few pounds more expensive); French manicure around £11; sculptured (acrylic) nails around £45.

AVAILABLE: Contact local hair and beauty salons.

Water-Filled Insoles

Plastic, water-filled insoles that act as shock and heat absorbers. The insoles also act as continuous masseurs on the soles of the feet as the water flows from one part of the foot to another.

PRICE: £5.95.

AVAILABLE: The Natural Shoe Store, 21 Neal Street, London WC2 Tel: 071-602 2866 (Mail Order available).

BETWEEN £10–£20

BOOK CHOICE
BMA's Family Doctor

Dr Tony Smith's encyclopedia of common ailments and how to diagnose and treat them and when to call the doctor.

PRICE: £12.99 [Dorling Kindersley].

AVAILABLE: All good bookshops.

BOOK CHOICE
Eat Your Greens

A single-handed vegetable crusade by Sophie Grigson (the books of the Channel 4 programme). Sophie takes in hand the long-neglected vegetable with its diverse colours, tastes and hues and transforms its various forms into exotic and everyday dishes.

PRICE: £15.99 [Network].

AVAILABLE: All good bookshops.

BOOK CHOICE
Natural Pharmacy

Pick flowers and plants with confidence: infuse your own herbal teas. Fascinating reading if you'd like to make it a hobby.

PRICE: £14.99 [Dorling Kindersley].

AVAILABLE: All good bookshops.

Cosmetics – Bronzing Powder

Instant radiance which doesn't streak, doesn't look orange and costs less than a week in Majorca. Available in a variety of shades to suit all skin tones, bronzing powders are the lightweight alternative to foundation.

PRICE: e.g. Bronze No 7 Pressed Powder £5.50; Ultraglow Loose Powder £9.95; Clarins Bronzing Powder Duo £15.

AVAILABLE: Boots, good chemists and department stores.

Cosmetics – Custom Blended Make-Up

Obviously the present cannot be a complete surprise as the receiver will need to be colour matched – either by Prescriptives or Cosmetics à la Carte – two ranges that tailor-make foundation and powder to the exactly right skin tone (including black skin). After finding the exact shade one of five adjustors will be added to also match skin type.

PRICE: £38 foundation [Prescriptives]; £30 foundation, £20 powder [Cosmetics a la Carte].

AVAILABLE: Prescriptives – counters in large department stores; Cosmetics a la Carte, 102 Avro House, Havelock Terrace, London SW8 4AS Tel: 071-622 2318 (Mail Order).

Fitness Video

A rash of videos have appeared featuring men and women with unnaturally good figures. Many involve accessories e.g. Cher's elastic bands, Reebok's Step, but others can be embarked upon with just a mat (to make the floor exercises more comfortable). There has been a swing from highly aerobic exercise which can jiggle your joints to a low impact regime, which promises the same results.

PRICE: e.g. *Cher Fitness* £10.99; *Rosemary Conley* £8.99.

AVAILABLE: All good video stockists.

Hair Straightening Irons

Ideally for someone who bemoans their frizzy/curly ends – and for achieving the sleek silhouette with a centre parting that will remind everyone of a supermodel.

PRICE: £19.95 (Boots Convertible – straightener and crimper in one).

AVAILABLE: Branches of Boots.

Hairbrush

Mason Pearson hairbrushes are firm and strong – every girl's dream. They come in four sizes and four colours.

PRICE: £10–£45.

AVAILABLE: Most good chemists and department stores.

Heated Rollers

Carmen rollers are a blast from the past – but they are still right up-to-the-minute, setting soft and glam curls – very Charlie's Angels!

PRICE: £21.75 [Carmen].

AVAILABLE: All good electrical appliance stores and department stores.

MAGAZINE SUBSCRIPTION
Health and Fitness

More than a slimming magazine, news and views on all aspects of nutrition, health and fitness!

PRICE: £20 p.a.

AVAILABLE: *Health & Fitness* Subscriptions Manager, 120-126 Lavender Avenue, Mitcham, Surrey CR4 3HP Tel: 081-646 1031.

Magnifying Mirror

Not for the faint-hearted – these show up every nook and cranny. Frightening the morning after the night before, but excellent for applying make-up.

PRICE: Around £14 for reasonably sized, brass-framed mirror.

AVAILABLE: Most good chemists and department stores.

Natural Sponge

As big as a boulder for luxurious bathing – or small pebbles for applying make-up.

PRICE: From 75p for a very small sponge to £25 for a very large one.

AVAILABLE: All good chemists.

Royal Jelly

Magic honey which keeps the likes of Barbara Cartland and Cliff Richard buzzing. The fresher the better.

PRICE: e.g. £13.25 for 30 capsules [Regina].

AVAILABLE: Holland and Barrett stores nationwide; other health food stores, most chemists.

Seaweed Bath Salts

Very smelly and rather unpleasant-looking stuff. According to the secrets of thalassotherapy, however (*thalassa* is Greek for 'sea') the ocean and its minerals have extremely potent healing powers and cosmetic benefits, particularly seaweed because the proteins, fats and sugars it contains are similar to those in our bodies.

PRICE: £16.15 for 10 sachets (Thalgo's Micronized Marine Algae Powder).

AVAILABLE: Thalgo Salons; for nearest stockist contact: Thalgo House, Tranquil Passage, Blackheath Village, London SE3 0BJ Tel: 081-852 7472.

Self-Tanning Creams

Ever since the 1920s when Coco Chanel returned from the South of France sporting a tan we have associated bronzed flesh with beauty and health. Prolonged sun exposure is now acknowledged to be dangerous for your skin and also leaves it like a wrinkled prune; but we haven't managed to kick the psychological effect of well-being a tan produces. Create it at home with the very good self-tanning creams that are now on the market.

PRICE: e.g. For the face: Lancome's Espirit de Soleil £18; for the body, Clarin's Self Tanning Milk £10.25; Boots' Easitan Duo Pack £5.99.

AVAILABLE: All good chemists and department stores.

Sterile Medical Kit

With increased foreign travel, especially to the more remote corners of the world, GPs are advising anyone anticipating a trip to carry sterile medical kits so as to avoid contact with contaminated equipment. The Medical Advisory Service for Travellers Abroad recommends the kit should contain hypodermic needles, syringes, swabs and sutures.

PRICE: £13.50 [MASTA].

AVAILABLE: MASTA London School of Hygiene & Tropical Medicine, Keppel Street, London WC1E 7HT Tel: 071-631 4408 (Mail Order).

Treatment – Facial

Facials available are many and varied; from the basic cleanse-tone-massage-mask-moisturize option right up to the use of galvanic and high frequency equipment to treat specific problems. Men enjoy them too!

PRICE: Around £15–£60 upwards.

AVAILABLE: Local beauticians.

Treatment – Massage

The images evoked by 'Swedish massage parlours' have finally been dispelled and massage and massage-related techniques are increasingly being recognized by the medical profession as an effective therapeutic system. Techniques not only relieve painful joints and muscles but because it is so relaxing it can also be an effective combatant to stress.

PRICE: Around £15–£30 per hour.

AVAILABLE: The only state registered therapists using massage are physiotherapists but a list of reputable practitioners can be obtained from the Institute for Complementary Medicine, P O Box 194, London SE16 1Q2 Tel: 071-237 5165.

Trumper Cologne

Established in 1875, Trumpers has been dispensing masculine colognes, masculine hair-oils and ever so masculine haircuts for the last 100 years. Their Extract of Limes is a classic which can be used in the bath and for all toilet purposes.

PRICE: £19.

AVAILABLE: Geo F Trumper, 9 Curzon Street, London W1; 20 Jermyn Street, London SW1 Tel: 071-272 1765.

Wave Webs Glove

If you remember *The Man From Atlantis*, then you'll appreciate what these are all about. A webbed glove that improves muscle tone by increasing resistance if worn in the water during exercise.

PRICE: £13.58 per pair [Polaris].

AVAILABLE: Polaris, Unit 10, Parker Centre, Mansfield Road, Derby DE2 4SZ Tel: 0332 381853 (Mail Order).

Yoghurt Maker

The healthy alternative to an ice-cream maker – it is simple to make your own, guarantees additive-free results and will save a fortune over time.

PRICE: £14.99 [Salton].

AVAILABLE: Electrical appliance shops; Antiference Ltd, Aylesbury, Bucks HP19 3BJ Tel: 0296 82511.

———————————————————————

BETWEEN £20–£50

———————————————————————

Air Ionizer

Mountain Breeze ionizers not only clean the air but also emit invigorating negative ions – just like those on mountain tops that don't quite make it into our homes and offices. Should perk anyone up, but particularly hayfever, asthma and bronchitis sufferers.

PRICE: £29.99.

AVAILABLE: Boots, Currys, Electricity Board Shops, John Lewis Partnership and other department stores; for nearest stockist contact: Mountain Breeze Tel: 0695 21155.

Anti-Cellulite Cream

Doctors would have us believe it doesn't exist – we all know it does, but if you believe by rubbing cream onto problem areas it's going to miraculously disappear then you probably believe in the tooth fairy. By combining cream, plus diet, plus exercise, you may stand more of a chance of shifting it.

PRICE: e.g. £18 Clarins Body Contouring Oil; £25 Christian Dior Svelte Body Refining Gel.

AVAILABLE: All good chemists.

Cosmetics – Les Meteorites

Launched by Guerlain in 1987, much imitated but never matched, 'Les Meteorites' are multicoloured pastel balls which are brushed onto the face and designed to enhance and 'illuminate' the complexion. The success of the powder ball has launched a whole range by Guerlain including lipsticks, and bronzing powder balls.

PRICE: £21.

AVAILABLE: All good chemists and department stores.

Cosmetics – Powder Compact

The cosmetic qualities of the case are as important as the product. Ideally it should be smart enough to be seen in public and have a satisfying snap shut. The chicest compact around is the Chanel Poudre Facette (lovely black lacquer case).

PRICE: £22 [Chanel].

AVAILABLE: Large chemists and department stores.

Dental Plaque Remover

Wizard gadgets which clean teeth far more effectively than the average person can be persuaded to – hence less plaque and sparkling smiles.

PRICE: £49.95 (Bausch & Lomb Interplak); £1.99 (Boots anti plaque mouthwash).

AVAILABLE: Larger chemists.

Epilator

A variation on a ladies' shaver that plucks each hair out at the root. The process takes a while but the effects last for three to four weeks. No pain, no gain.

PRICE: £30–£40.

AVAILABLE: Boots, most good chemists, department stores.

Eye Treatments

The skin around the eyes is the first to show the signs of ageing because it is finer here. Smile lines are attractive and full of character, but cosmetics companies have invested enough time and money developing more and more sophisticated products to feed the paranoia.

PRICE: e.g. £29.50 Ceramide Eyes Time Complex Capsules [Elizabeth Arden]; £6.25 Performance Firming Eye Cream [Pond].

AVAILABLE: All good chemists, department stores.

Inflight Comfort Kit

Top models swear by it – so for the top model in your life, get him/her this moisturizer which keeps skin perfectly lubricated while flying in dry aircraft cabins.

PRICE: £30 (Comfort kit, including cooling eye-compress, rehydration gel, nasal freshener and concentrated mouth wash); £5 (rehydration gel).

AVAILABLE: Aromatherapie, Park Lane Hotel, 107B Piccadilly, London W1 Tel: 071-499 6321 (Mail Order available).

Infra-Red Lamp

To be used with care, but helps poor skins as well as acting as a pick-me-up. With your eyes shut it could be the warmth of the sun on your back. Just reach out for your pina colada.

PRICE: £27.95 [Beurer].

AVAILABLE: Large chemists; John Bell & Croyden, 50 Wigmore Street, W1 Tel: 071-935 5555 (Mail Order available).

Treatment – Aromatherapy

An ancient healing art which combines body and face massage using oils extracted from plants and which are absorbed quickly into the bloodstream. Most therapists take time detailing personal and medical histories before treatment to ensure the best oils to use for each individual. Aromatherapy, in common with other holistic therapies, seeks to treat the patient as a whole rather than just the symptom.

PRICE: From £20 to £35 per session.

AVAILABLE: Contact: International Federation of Aromatherapists, 4 East Mearn Road, West Dulwich, SE21 8HA Tel: 081-846 8066.

Treatment – Flotation

Probably the closest we can get to a transcendental experience whilst bound in our mortal coil. The tanks are lightproof, sound insulated and full of salty water and when inside the floater loses the pull of gravity leaving the mind completely at rest and cleared for creative and non-stressful thought. Some people find the idea ridiculous – others rave about its re-balancing effects.

PRICE: From £20 per session.

AVAILABLE: Send SAE to: Float Tank Association, 29 Sunbury Lane, London SW11 3NP for details of nearest tank.

Treatment – Reflexology

Reflexology treats symptoms of stress, back pain and digestive complaints amongst others, by massaging specific areas or 'reflex points' of the foot and hands which correspond to different organs and functions of the body.

PRICE: From £15 to £20 per session.

AVAILABLE: Contact: British Reflexology Association Tel: 0886 21207 for list of practitioners.

Treatment – Shiatsu

Bless you. Shiatsu helps build up the body's natural network of energy according to ancient Chinese medicine and is really like all-over reflexology. Fingers instead of the needles used in acupuncture are used to stimulate points all over the body.

PRICE: Around £25 a session.

AVAILABLE: Contact: Shiatsu Association, c/o Oakdene Road, Redhill, Surrey RH1 6BT for practitioner lists; British School of Shiatsu Tel: 071-251 0831.

Vanity Case

For all the clobber girls love to take on holiday. A terribly useful way of keeping all the bottles together (and ensuring they arrive intact). Its contents tends to be weighty so the case should be sturdy enough to cope.

PRICE: e.g. Samsonite £66; Antler £34.95.

AVAILABLE: Selected luggage shops and department stores.

Vegetable Juicer

A heavy-duty juicer that will cope not only with soft fruit but will also pulverize any carrot that crosses its path.

PRICE: e.g. £39.99 Kenwood Centrifugal Juice Extractor.

AVAILABLE: Electrical appliance shops and department stores.

£50 AND ABOVE

Aerobics Shoes

High impact aerobics is known to rattle joints such as knees and hips. You need shock-absorbing shoes.

PRICE: £49.99 (Reebock step shoe).

AVAILABLE: Olympus Sport stores nationwide.

Digital Blood Pressure Reader

Insert left index finger into the ring (which has an integral pneumatic cushion) and you are given a reliable reading of minimum and maximum blood pressure values and number of beats.

PRICE: From £74.99 [Ormon].

AVAILABLE: Selected branches of Boots, and other chemists.

Exer Skier

Doyen of the Sunday supplements, this exercise machine actually works! Designed for total body fitness, it duplicates the cross-country skiing sensation, builds stamina, strengthens heart and lungs and burns loads of calories.

PRICE: From £319.

AVAILABLE: NordicTrack (UK) Ltd, 3 Collins Road, Heathcoate Industrial Estate, Warwick CV34 6TF Tel: 0926 430090 (Mail Order).

Extending Shaving Mirror

Classic shaving mirror which can be adjusted, concertina fashion, to get the best light and most comfortable shaving angle. Czech & Speake are the chicest suppliers, but it is available less chic and more cheap from department stores.

PRICE: e.g. £189 (chrome); £215 (brass or nickel) [Czech & Speake]; £34.95 [Science Museum Brainwaves catalogue].

AVAILABLE: Czech & Speake, 39c Jermyn Street, London SW1 Tel: 071-439 0216; Science Museum Brainwaves, Freepost SU361, Dept 5317, Hendon Road, Sunderland SR9 9AD Tel: 091-514 4666 (Mail Order).

Futon

'Futon' is Japanese for 'bed roll' and these cotton-filled mattresses can be rolled straight onto the floor or onto a low pallet bed to become a hard but extremely supportive sleeping surface. Very good for bad backs. Traditional Japanese futons are slim (unlike any imitations) and because of this the air can circulate properly so they stay springy.

PRICE: From £89 (single); any size can be made to suit requirements.

AVAILABLE: Futon Company (five branches in London and one in Bristol); 654 Fulham Road, London SW6 5RU Tel: 071-736 9190 (Mail Order available).

Home Sauna

This is about as good as it gets – a luxurious, fully-equipped cabin in the glorious privacy of your own home.

PRICE: e.g. Celebration £999 (family size – 4 ft × 5 ft, includes heater, benches and all accessories, VAT, delivery and installation); £645 (2 ft × 4 ft).

AVAILABLE: Amber Leisure Ltd, Pearson Street, Wolverhampton WV2 4HP Tel: 0902 871301.

Introduction to Massage Course

A very popular skill! In an introduction weekend you can learn and master the basic techniques including a neck and shoulders routine for reducing stress as well as sequences for the back, face and head.

PRICE: £90.

AVAILABLE: Contact: London College of Massage, 5-6 Newman Street, London W1P 3PF Tel: 071-323 3574.

Muscle Training Multi-Gyms

Pumping weights has long been a public and private obsession for men and women, but free weights don't offer the range of exercises multi-gyms can. Resistance is adjustable and at least ten exercises can usually be executed, sometimes as many as 40. Permanent space often needed if you are going to set up a gym in the privacy of your own home.

PRICE: From about £500–£4000; e.g. Tunturi Muscle Trainer £480.

AVAILABLE: Contact: Leading Lifestyles (specialist suppliers of fitness equipment) 5 Palace Place, Brighton, East Sussex BN1 1EF Tel: 0273 821968.

Power Shower

My father swears his shower is the cause of his tonsure-like bald patch. Unlike traditional showers, power showers are multi-functional i.e. they can be used for all over body massage with a hard spray or for a softer aerated flow. Units are available quite reasonably, but must always be fitted in conjunction with a pump unit which means a basic price of £300.

PRICE: From £360 to £1600 plus pump and installation.

AVAILABLE: Bathroom specialists and builders merchants; for nearest stockist contact: Hans Grohe Ltd, Unit 2D, Sandown Park Trading Estate, Royal Mills, Esher, Surrey KT10 8BZ.

Punch Bag

The ultimate stress reliever?

PRICE: From £55 to £115 (canvas and leather).

AVAILABLE: Title Sports, 241 Southwark Park Road, London SE16 Tel: 071-231 1519.

Reebok Step System

The lastest fitness craze. A solid, well designed step – on and onto which you perform a series of exercises. The accompanying video shows a formidable group of perfect bodies working out to a catchy relentless beat.

PRICE: Step System £59.99; Video £9.99.

AVAILABLE: Branches of Olympus Sport.

Relaxmate

An example of New Age gadgetry, the Leahy Relaxmate is a pair of goggles which seals off external vision and instead submerges the wearer in rhythmic patterns of light designed to relax the brain. The idea is to reduce stress and induce sleep.

PRICE: £79.99.

AVAILABLE: American Retro, 35 Old Compton Street, London W1 Tel: 071-734 3477 (Mail Order available).

Serious Scales

Speak-Your-Weight scales are safer if confined to seaside postcards. Serious scales based on balancing weights are the sort you see in medical environments and allow for absolutely NO cheating.

PRICE: £270.25 [Seca]; £129.25 [Seca Electronic Scales].

AVAILABLE: Larger chemists, medical suppliers.

Trip to a Health Farm

Many health 'resorts' now offer one-day, weekend and short-week breaks as well as the traditional week's stay. The main aim of the health farm is that whoever has been should return home rejunvenated and revitalized; the stay becomes more like a retreat. A short break at a health farm is the perfect treat for a woman because she'll not only be pampered from head to foot but she'll be in one of the only places she can go on her own without feeling self conscious.

PRICE: e.g. Champneys from £150 per night; Ragdale Hall from £89.50 per night; Brooklands Health Farm £68 (prices include treatments).

AVAILABLE: Champneys, Wiggington, Tring, Herts HP23 6HY Tel: 0442 873155; Ragdale Hall, Ragdale, Nr Melton Mowbray, Leics LE14 3PB Tel: 0664 434831; Brooklands Health Farm, Calder House Lane, Garstang, Preston, Lancashire PR3 1QB Tel: 09952 5162.

Vegetarian Cookery Course

Not just veggies but anyone keen on reducing meat in their diet could improve their range of dishes by attending a short mid-week or weekend course run by the Vegetarian Society. Advice on sound nutritional planning for meatless diets plus hands-on cookery and demonstrations on all things wholefood and vegetarian.

PRICE: e.g. £296 (four-night midweek course with full board).

AVAILABLE: The Cordon Vert Cookery School, The Vegetarian Society, Parkdale, Dunham Road, Altrincham, Cheshire WA14 4QG Tel: 061-928 0793.

CHAPTER TWELVE

DIY/Interior Design

As a nation we are extremely practical. Come Spring, 74% of us admit to painting, wallpapering and assembling unit furniture. However, DIY is still a bit hit and miss: 90,000 self-inflicted injuries were bad enough to end up in the casualty departments last year. It's obviously a good thing to invest in the right tools!

UNDER £5

Box of Biscuits

Essential for dunking in mugs of hot sweet tea whilst on the job.
PRICE: From £4.99.
AVAILABLE: Supermarkets, branches of M&S.

Fuse and Bulb Tester

A quick way to check if the fuse is dead before you chuck it and replace it.
PRICE: £4.99 [Plasplugs].
AVAILABLE: DIY shops; for stockists contact: Plasplugs, Wetmore Road, Burton-on-Trent, Staffs DE14 1SD Tel: 0283 30303.

Leak Treatment

New from the people who gave us velcro is a first-aid kit for leaks called Velseal; bandage up plumbing problems or garden hoses until more help arrives.
PRICE: From £2.99.

AVAILABLE: DIY stores; for stockists contact: Healy Williams, Kings Business Centre, Vale Road, Windsor SL4 5JW Tel: 0753 841458.

Nail Holder

A magnetic strap which grasps nails and tacks, etc, when you're up the ladder; saves a mouthful of nails.

PRICE: £2.99.

AVAILABLE: DIY and hardware stores.

Radiator Roller

A long-handled paint roller to go down the backs of radiators and into corners if your hand's too big to fit.

PRICE: £3.99.

AVAILABLE: DIY and hardware stores.

Retractable Tape Measure

Metal tapes which are easy for one person to use, and include an instant return mechanism, are a DIY essential.

PRICE: £2.99–£7.45.

AVAILABLE: All DIY stores.

Set of Paint Brushes

The avid painter may not ever be faced with clogged brushes, but for most people new brushes are more than welcome.

PRICE: From £3.29 (2″ Harris); £10.75 (6″ Harris).

AVAILABLE: All DIY outlets.

Spirit Level

Eyes are deceiving. It's only afterwards you realize the shelf is squint! A spirit level comes under the heading of DIY essential, and so can be bought at basic and luxury prices.

PRICE: £4–£25.

AVAILABLE: DIY, hardware stores.

Strip and Fit

A handy all-in-one screwdriver and cutter for cutting and stripping outer insulation and flex for bionic plug changes.

PRICE: £4.29.

AVAILABLE: DIY and hardware stores.

Tool Shelf

A shelf with loads of pre-cut holes, in which to tidy away screwdrivers, hammers, et al.

PRICE: £2.49.

AVAILABLE: All large DIY stores.

Tools

The better and stronger tools are inevitably in the more expensive ranges. Hammers, chisels, screwdrivers and spanners are hoarded by workmen and they can never have too many.

PRICE: Stanley and Draper tools start from under £5.

AVAILABLE: DIY stores.

Utility Rail

A steel rail with six hooks and five pinch clips to keep handles of mops and brooms from crashing to the floor and hold long dusters etc.

PRICE: £4.90.

AVAILABLE: Branches of Ikea.

WD-40

Miracle spray that lifts scuffs off paintwork, loosens limescale, eases stiff doors – when the car breaks down you could do far worse than squirt a bit of this under the bonnet and hope for the best.

PRICE: From £1.39 (100, 200, 400 ml cans).

AVAILABLE: Hardware, DIY and supermarkets.

BETWEEN £5–£10

4-Way Socket

Less dangerous than an adaptor which can so easily cause electrical fires. An extended socket is less likely to be knocked, and will often include an overload protector for added safety.

PRICE: From £5.

AVAILABLE: Department stores, hardware and DIY shops.

BOOK CHOICE
The Ideal Home Design Sourcebook

Although this only sources companies in the south-east, practically all the goods can be supplied by mail order. Packed with information on where to get what for all interior design and DIY needs, how much it costs, and when the shop's open.

PRICE: £9.95 (by Barbara Chandler).

AVAILABLE: *The Ideal Home Design Sourcebook*, PO Box 66, London E15 1DW Tel: 081-503 0589 (Mail Order).

Drain Declogger

Problems with the drains? Is someone sensitive about their plumbing? This romantic present is an aerosol pressure plumber which clears clogged drains up to ten times from one can – with minimal effort on the user's part.

PRICE: £6.99.

AVAILABLE: Selected DIY stores; for nearest stockist contact: Worldwide Marketing and Promotions, Unit 1, Coulsdon, Surrey Tel: 081-763 2480.

Dust/paint sheets

Unless there's an endless supply of old sheets or the furniture is in that extraordinary paint-splattered effect, decorating can be difficult. Large storage bags especially for the job could be the answer, or try tear-and-puncture-resistant cover-up sheets.

PRICE: £5.95 each (storage bags 8″ × 4″; sheets 10.5″ × 9.75″).

AVAILABLE: Innovations International, Euroway Business Park, Swindon SN5 8SN Tel: 0793 514666 (Mail Order).

Extension Cable

The wall and the machinery fail to make contact more often than would seem possible. Extension cables come in a variety of lengths, the longer the better, and when not used for power drills are just as handy for radios or TVs in the garden.

PRICE: £8.49 (5m); £20 (10m).

AVAILABLE: DIY/hardware stores.

First Aid Kit

For minor cuts and grazes and accidents with a hammer.

PRICE: £7.99–£14.35.

AVAILABLE: Boots and other chemists.

Rolling Ruler

A must for designers and DIY enthusiasts who need to get their lines and edges straight. Accurate measurement and drawing is simple with the parallel motion this enables.

PRICE: £7.50 [Staedtler Mars].

AVAILABLE: DIY and hardware stores; London Graphics, 9-10 McKay Trading Estate, Kensal Rd, London W10 5BN Tel: 081-969 6644 (Mail Order).

Silver Polishing Gloves

Specially impregnated silver-polishing mitts don't really make the job any easier – but certainly more fun. Especially gratifying on large areas, polishing not only restores shines but helps keep tarnish at bay.

PRICE: £5.41 a pair.

AVAILABLE: Liberon Waxes, Mountfield Industrial Estate, Learoyd Road, New Romney, Kent Tel: 0679 67555 (Call for stockists and Mail Order).

Slapsticks

Brilliant idea – large transfers of Beatrix Potter, Disney, Teddy Bears' Picnic, etc, which you can smooth on to a wall and peel off at a later date.

PRICE: £9.95.

AVAILABLE: Branches of John Lewis Partnership.

Stencil Kit

Creativity without too much risk but a great deal of satisfaction as the end result really brightens up a room. Stencils and paint are available separately or as a kit, although the desired shade of paint can be achieved if you mix your own.

PRICE: From £7.95 (stencil), £1.95 (paints), £1.95–£2 (brushes).

AVAILABLE: Branches of Laura Ashley, Stencilitis from Homebase, department stores, etc.

Tool Box

Very professional toolboxes are available surprisingly cheaply. There is aserious version in metal with cantilever trays displaying its wares when the box is opened.

PRICE: £7.69.

AVAILABLE: All DIY stores.

———————————————————————————

BETWEEN £10–£20

———————————————————————————

Anti-Cut Glove

Safeguard against cuts and grazes when handling glass or metal by wearing these stainless steel-based gloves. The wire core is sheathed in nylon and 'kevlar' (a space age material used in sails), the glove is cuffed and fits either hand.

PRICE: £19.95.

AVAILABLE: Modern Originals, 8 Forge Court, Reading Road, Yateley, Camberley, Surrey GU17 7RX Tel: 0252 878785 (Mail Order).

BOOK CHOICE
Conran's Beginners Guide to Decoration

From the man who brought us back the Michelin Building, tips and ideas about how to make your house just that little bit extraordinary.

PRICE: £12.99 (hardback); £8.99 (paperback) [Conran Octopus].

AVAILABLE: Bookshops.

BOOK CHOICE
The Government Auction Handbook

A rather nasty, but incredibly useful book listing sales of property and possessions seized by HM Customs and Excise, Liquidators, Bailiffs and Collectors of Taxes. There are no reserve prices and it is possible to bag real bargains.

PRICE: £12.95.

AVAILABLE: Carnell Ltd, Main Road, Alresford, Nr Colchester Essex CO7 8AP.

Cordless Drill Charger

You have got the drill now you have to charge it. Rapid charges are more expensive (and more desirable) than their less speedy flow charge versions.

PRICE: From £18.99 (Black & Decker two-hour charger) to £105 [Bosch].

AVAILABLE: Branches of Texas, B&Q, Homebase, etc.

DIY Safety Kit

Goggles, nose and mouth mask, protective gloves and earplugs – armour in which the Knight of the Kitchen Shelves can do battle.

PRICE: £14.

AVAILABLE: DIY stores.

Ear Protectors

To block off noise of shrieking drills so the wearer can later have a normal conversation in the pub.

PRICE: £11.

AVAILABLE: Branches of Do-It-All, Texas, Homebase and other DIY outlets.

Festoon Blind Kit

These are the blinds that pretend to be curtains but use much less material. The kit has everything you need to create one except the fabric and thread.

PRICE: £14.95 (two sizes; includes tape, cords, cleats, etc).

AVAILABLE: Branches of Laura Ashley.

Fire Extinguisher

Kitchen fires can start in an instant and spread alarmingly fast. An extinguisher or fire blanket to hand saves panic and gives peace of mind.

PRICE: £17 fire extinguisher; £18.50 fire blanket.

AVAILABLE: Branches of John Lewis Partnership.

Flexible Screwdriver

Designed to allow access to the tightest nooks and crannies, it has a flexible 'nose' with a comfortable ratchet action handle and is supplied with four bits, three socket wrenches and a rigid shaft for normal use. A bit of a gimmick but useful nonetheless.

PRICE: £12.95.

AVAILABLE: Science Museum Brainwaves, Freepost SU361, Dept 5317, Hendon Road, Sunderland SR9 9AD Tel: 091-514 4666 (Mail Order).

Low Energy Lightbulbs

If all households used two low energy lightbulbs, the energy saved would be equivalent to the output of a large nuclear station. They use 75% less electricity than an ordinary lightbulb and last eight times as long.

PRICE: £13.50 (100W Philips – 8000 hour life).

AVAILABLE: All good electrical appliance and lighting shops, department stores and DIY outlets.

Overalls/Boiler Suit

For the man/woman who has run out of old shirts and jeans to ruin.

PRICE: From £15.99; disposable boilersuits from £7.99.

AVAILABLE: Larger DIY outlets.

Subscription to Which?

The consumer magazine that gives you the lowdown on an enormous variety of goods and services – often hilarious and always guaranteed to save time, trouble and money.

PRICE: £12.75 a quarter (41 reports).

AVAILABLE: *Which?*, Freepost, Hertford X, SG14 1YB Tel: 0992 589031.

Terribly Useful Storage Units

The Elfa System consists of a frame into which you slot trays and baskets of different depths. Add castors, a solid top surface, etc. Stores almost everything in a variety of sizes and can transform an empty cupboard into an invaluable store – but you have to put it together yourself.

PRICE: From £12.90 (starter kit).

AVAILABLE: Branches of John Lewis Partnership.

The Silver Solution

An almost magic treatment which replates silver treasures showing through to the core. The price reflects its real silver content.

PRICE: £14.50.

AVAILABLE: Branches of John Lewis Partnership and hardware stores.

Vice

Needs to be clamped onto a workbench, but will then grip anything – from tiny screws, to large pieces of wood, piping and metal.

PRICE: From £16 [Draper].

AVAILABLE: DIY stockists.

Yankee Screwdriver

Anyone prone to losing the different screw heads will appreciate this: they are stored within the clear handle.

PRICE: £15.50 [Stanley].

AVAILABLE: Branches of John Lewis Partnership, and DIY stores.

BETWEEN £20–£50

BOOK CHOICE
Reader's Digest Complete DIY Manual

A bible to guide the amateur in everything from bricklaying and plumbing to making rabbit hutches and perspex toastracks. Loose leaf, so you can take the relevant page under the sink unit with you.

PRICE: £32.95.

AVAILABLE: Reader's Digest, 25 Berkeley Square, London W1X 6AB Tel: 071-409 5131.

Cordless Screwdriver

Ask any DIYer for their fantasy tool and a hungry look will come into their eyes when they mention a cordless screwdriver. Life made easy – an electric screwdriver does all the work, is rechargeable and will also go in reverse.

PRICE: From £27 (Bosch and Black & Decker).

AVAILABLE: All good DIY and hardware stores.

Drill Bit Set

You've got the drill – now you just need all the bits to go with it. Sets of attachments are available for specific jobs – e.g. carpentry – but a 'handyman' set should cover general needs.

PRICE: £22.40 (16 pieces – including five wood bits, six high speed steel bits and five masonry bits).

AVAILABLE: Most DIY stores; for nearest stockist contact: Black & Decker Ltd, Westpoint, The Grove, Slough, Berks SL1 1QQ Tel: 0753 511234.

Mitre Kit

It's funny how corners never fit when you attempt the DIY route. The mitre kit solves the problem by guiding the saw at the right angle (45 degrees) for perfect joints.

PRICE: £25.

AVAILABLE: Major DIY outlets.

Nail, Screw etc Storage Cabinet

Essential to avoid 2″ screws becoming jumbled with 1″ nails or tacks, or up to 42 other items.

PRICE: £24.49 (25 drawer); £40.69 (43 drawer).

AVAILABLE: DIY and hardware stores.

Paintstripper

Available in gas or hot air versions, neither of which are idiotproof – turn your head for a moment and you'll have char-effect woodwork.

PRICE: e.g. £38 [Bosch], £82 [Black & Decker].

AVAILABLE: DIY outlets; Contact Robert Bosch Ltd, Broadwater Park, North Orbital Road, Denham, Uxbridge UB9 5HJ Tel: 0895 838383 (Mail Order).

Pastemate

A luxury for a wallpaperer. Saves glueing and cutting up on the dining table by giving an alternative surface to work on.

PRICE: £33.
AVAILABLE: Texas, B&Q, Homebase, etc.

Strong Point Safe

An undetectable small DIY safe. Once you've fitted it into the wall it looks like a double plug socket and you can even plug something into it for effect.

PRICE: £34.99.
AVAILABLE: Security firms, large department stores.

Telescopic Feather Duster

Proud houseowners' lives can be made a misery by out of reach cobwebs that keep catching their eye. A feather duster which extends to eight feet can reach the furthest recesses of the sitting-room.

PRICE: £22.50.
AVAILABLE: Authentics, 42 Shelton Street, London WC2 Tel: 071-240 9845 (Mail Order).

Wire, Pipe and Stud Detector

An electronic device which locates cables and pipes when drilling and so prevents avoidable floods and fireworks. It also pinpoints joists and studs to give firm fixings.

PRICE: £21.49 [Rapitest].
AVAILABLE: All good DIY and hardware stores.

£50 AND ABOVE

Bandsaw

Woodwork enthusiasts will be able to knock up a tray or two with this one. Cross-cutting, mitre/bevel cuts as well as common contour cuts are all made easy – but the machine really requires a workshop to house it.

PRICE: From £240.

AVAILABLE: For nearest stockist contact: Black & Decker Ltd, Westpoint, The Grove, Slough, Berks SL1 1QQ Tel: 0753 511234.

Black & Decker Workmate

The firm base on which to build the empire, or the shelves. This is a must – easy storage, easy to carry with lots of vices to grip any size or shape.

PRICE: £58.95 [Black & Decker WM 536].

AVAILABLE: All good DIY and hardware stores.

Cordless Drill

Offers the solution to never having a socket when you need one. It has a hammer action, 10 mm chuck capacity and its own charging unit.

PRICE: £66.95 [Black & Decker BD 602].

AVAILABLE: All good DIY and hardware stores.

Cordless Phone System

Invaluable for those who spend quality time up ladders, under cars or with their heads in cupboards – a phone will always be at hand. The Rabbit system has been found to overcome the problem of interference experienced with many phones and you can add up to six handsets all working from one unit.

PRICE: £200.

AVAILABLE: Argos, British Telecom shops, Dixons.

Design and Decoration Course

Terribly smart course for people with plans for terribly smart houses – this teaches you everything you'll need to know.

PRICE: £2950 (ten week course).

AVAILABLE: Inchbald School of Design, 7 Eaton Gate, London SW1 Tel: 071-730 5508.

Intruder Alarm System

A wireless version which means the minimum disruption when installing (which they claim takes less than an hour). Transmitters are powered by batteries so there are no wires ruining the woodwork.

PRICE: £249.95 (Response Wireless Intruder Alarm System).

AVAILABLE: Response Electronics Plc, Unit 1, First Quarter, Longmead Industrial Estate, Epsom, Surrey KT19 9QN Tel: 0372 744330.

Jig Saw

Fix-Its will know that this doesn't come in 500 or 1000 piece options but is a saw which allows curves and complex cuts. Some versions have a variable speed range and can also be used for mitre cuts, holding the tool constant at any angle between 0 and 45 degrees.

PRICE: £75 [Hitachi].

AVAILABLE: For stockists contact: Hitachi Power Tools (UK) Ltd, Precedent Drive, Rooksley, Milton Keynes, MK13 8PJ Tel: 0908 660663.

Mitre Saw Kit

For the DIY king who is master of his realm, a portable mitre kit will enable seamless joins.

PRICE: From £270.

AVAILABLE: For nearest stockist contact: Black & Decker Ltd, Westpoint, The Grove, Slough, Berks SL1 1QQ Tel: 0753 511234.

Power Planer

Variable cutting depth means you can either just lightly skim over the surface or deeply shave the wood.

PRICE: From £73.30 [Black & Decker, and Bosch].

AVAILABLE: Most DIY stores.

Socket Set

High on the objects of desire list – a complete set of sockets in a quality chrome veranium, neatly packaged in a plastic carry case.

PRICE: £63.99 [Draper].

AVAILABLE: DIY stores; for nearest stockist contact: Draper Tools, Hursley Road, Chandlers Ford, Eastleigh, Hants SO5 5FY Tel: 0703 266355.

Wallpaper Stripper

Really takes away the fun of scraping – this literally steam irons the paper so it lifts off a treat. Suitable for right or left-handed paperers with an unclippable water tank.

PRICE: £53.10 [Black & Decker].

AVAILABLE: Most DIY stores; for nearest stockist contact: Black & Decker Ltd, Westpoint, The Grove, Slough, Berks SL1 1QQ Tel: 0753 511234.

Wet and Dry Vacuum

Where normal vacuums blow up with too much litter, the wet and dry version will take leaves, spills and small bits of rubbish in its stride.

PRICE: £149.

AVAILABLE: John Lewis Partnership and hardware stores.

CHAPTER THIRTEEN

MUSIC, ARTS & THEATRE

PAVAROTTI in the Park, the Bolshoi Ballet at the Albert Hall and a burgeoning number of arts festivals have all done their bit to increase our cultural leanings. The Arts Council help by funding over 20 regional organizations. Almost twice as many people now visit a cinema or theatre every week than in 1985, but three times as many can still be found in the pub!

UNDER £5

Antiquarian Novels

First editions of books by favourite authors are likely to cost a small fortune, but quality antiquarian books need not be so expensive. Always keep your eyes peeled at jumble sales and secondhand bookshops.

PRICE: Anything from 50p.

AVAILABLE: Secondhand bookshops (if in London you couldn't do better than Charing Cross Road); Bell, Book & Radmall, 4 Cecil Court, London WC2N 4HE (Catalogue (free) Mail Order).

BOOK CHOICE
Beginner's Guide To ...

Playing the guitar, piano, saxophone, or just about any instrument you care to mention. No musical knowledge necessary as the books take you step by step through finger-positioning, etc. Idiot proof.

PRICE: £4.95 [Wise Publications] £14.95 for beginners' 'set' of books 1, 2 and 3.

AVAILABLE: All music shops; Boosey & Hawkes, 295 Regent Street, London W1R 8JH Tel: 071-436 2850 (Mail Order).

Calendars

These are almost as good as the real thing. Beautiful glossy art calendars featuring reproductions from a particular artist or period of painting.

PRICE: From £3.95.

AVAILABLE: WH Smith, stationery shops, or gallery shops: The National Gallery Trafalgar Square, London WC2N 5DN Tel: 071-839 3321 (Mail Order available).

Canvases

Make sure you know what it is they want – not just any old piece of canvas will do.

PRICE: From £1.55 per metre.

AVAILABLE: Russell & Chapple, 23 Monmouth Street, London WC2 Tel: 071-836 7521 (Established 1770 – specializes in canvas, offering an extensive range of primed and unprimed canvases.)

Daylight Simulation Bulbs

For artists and craftsmen who need a constant and uniform source of light especially during winter, and also for general reading for tired old eyes. May help those suffering from Seasonal Affective Disorder!

PRICE: £4.50.

AVAILABLE: Graphic supplies shops; or contact Daylight Studios, Dept LP, 223 Portland Road, London W11 Tel: 071-229 7812.

Diaries

For music or art lovers, highlighting special diary dates e.g. The Proms, The Summer Exhibition, etc; for those who would be keen to attend.

PRICE: e.g. £4.95 Boosey & Hawkes Music Diary; £7.50 leather version.

AVAILABLE: All music shops. Galleries also produce glorious hardback diaries featuring colour plate reproductions from their collections.

Paint Stain Devil

Useful to remove the stubborn stains created by energetic oil painting.

PRICE: £1.45 (50 ml).

AVAILABLE: Boots, large supermarkets and hardware stores.

Plastic Palette

A plastic (less expensive) version of the traditional wooden artist's palette, designed by Roberson to give a wide mixing area, brush holder and maximum portability.

PRICE: £4.

AVAILABLE: All good artists' supply shops; L Cornelissen & Son, 105 Great Russell Street, London WC1B 3RY Tel: 071-636 1045 (Mail Order available).

Proms Tickets

Easily available for the series if you book well in advance. Tickets for the last night are limited to two per person and when applying tickets for FIVE other concerts must be bought at the same time!

PRICE: From £4.

AVAILABLE: Promenade Concerts Ticket Office, Royal Albert Hall, London SW7 2AP Tel: 071-589 8212.

Sheet Music

Either single pieces or collections from particular composers or periods. 'Easy' versions are also available and arrangements for different instruments.

PRICE: From £2.05 (average about £3 for single piece).

AVAILABLE: Boosey & Hawkes, 295 Regent Street, London W1R 8JH Tel: 071-436 2850 (Mail Order available) – Over 53,000 titles. The Coliseum Shop (opera from all centuries), English National Opera, London Coliseum, St Martins Lane, London WC2N 4BR Tel: 071-836 0111.

Tickets to TV and Radio Shows

Do you know anyone who's mad enough to want to see *Top of the Pops* or *Keeping Up Appearances*? Most television shows are only booked one or two months in advance; the most popular ones however (comedy and light entertainment) can be booked as far ahead as the next season.

PRICE: FREE.

AVAILABLE: TV shows: BBC Ticket Unit, Centre House, 56 Wood Lane, London W12 7SB Tel: 081-743 8000. Radio shows: BBC Ticket Unit, BBC, London W1A 4WW Tel: 071-580 4468. Information available from the Ticket Units. You must apply in writing to obtain tickets.

Watercolour Paper

The brightness of a watercolour painting comes from the reflection of light back through the paint from the white paper and different effects can be achieved by using rougher paper which will retain more pigment. Most of the papers produced for watercolourists are also made into pads or blocks which vary in size from 7″ x 5″ to A2.

PRICE: Pads from £3.10; Sheets from 80p.

AVAILABLE: All good artists' supply shops.

BETWEEN £5–£10

Artist's Brush Roll

Canvas brush-holder which rolls up to carry artist's brushes while travelling and avoids damage to the hair/bristle.

PRICE: £6.95.

AVAILABLE: Artists' supply shops.

Blank Video Tapes

Ideal for someone who always drops off during the programme they've been staying up to watch, or has to work while their favourite black-and-white afternoon movie is on.

PRICE: £5.25 (TDK 2 × 180 minute tapes).

AVAILABLE: Record shops and audio departments.

BOOK CHOICE
Biographies

The life story of a favourite painter/poet/composer/singer/musician, etc, will mean happy anticipation of new snippets of information by the recipient. Make sure to buy either the most recent or the most controversial.

PRICE: Paperbacks start at about £5.

AVAILABLE: All good bookshops.

BOOK CHOICE
Eyewitness Art Series

Fascinating series of books on the lives and techniques of the great artists packed with photos of paintings, people, materials, and general ephemera which offer real insights into the artist's life and times. Series includes Manet, Van Gogh, Post-Impressionism.

PRICE: £9.99 [Dorling Kindersley].

AVAILABLE: All good bookshops.

BOOK CHOICE
Oxford Dictionary of Art and Artists

Pocket-size guide to the great and good in the art world. Informed and informative – ideal for taking on gallery trips.

PRICE: £5.99 [Oxford University Press].
AVAILABLE: Most bookshops, art shops and gallery shops.

BOOK CHOICE
Pocket-Sized Classics

Hardback classics that are small enough to fit into a pocket or handbag and, unlike paperbacks, survive the journey remarkably well.

PRICE: About £9.95 [Bloomsbury and Chatto].
AVAILABLE: All good bookshops.

Books on Tape

Books recorded onto tape/CD; modern authors often read their own works and other classics are read by honey-voiced story tellers.

PRICE: From £5 to £10.
AVAILABLE: Large record stores, book stores and department stores; Hammick's Customer Service, Unit 1, Rosevale Business Park, Newcastle-under-Lyme, Staffordshire, ST5 7QT Tel: 0782 626625 (Mail Order).

CD Cleaner

Either manual or battery-powered, a CD cleaner will maintain crystal-clear sound and leave any dusty old collection sparkling.

PRICE: From £6.99.
AVAILABLE: Music and hi-fi stores, large department stores.

CD Storage System

Stacking system for rationalization of any CD collection. Can be wall-mounted.

PRICE: From £7.99 (holds 20 CDs).
AVAILABLE: All CD stockists.

Covent Garden Mailing List

Advance programme details mean that those on the mailing list have the opportunity to book before the general public (though offers no guarantee of success!).

PRICE: £9.

AVAILABLE: Membership Secretary, The Friends of Covent Garden, Royal Opera House, London WC2E 9DD Tel: 071-240 1200.

Exhibition Catalogues

Having made do with a few postcards, an exhibition lover would delight in the full glossy catalogue, usually packed with information and clear reproductions. Galleries usually stock catalogues well after the exhibition itself.

PRICE: From about £5.

AVAILABLE: Gallery shops and large art bookshops (for major exhibitions); Zwemmers Ltd (specialists on books on the arts) 24 Litchfield Street, London WC2H 9NJ Tel: 071-240 4158 (Mail Order available).

Instrument 'Care Kit'

Organized kits of brushes, dusters and solutions which will care specifically for clarinets, trumpets, etc.

PRICE: £10.

AVAILABLE: All good music shops.

Posters And Prints

Prints of old masters, pop groups and exhibition/concert posters – catalogues are available from The Poster Shop for £9.95 and £12.95. Limited edition prints are available from most local galleries.

PRICE: From £5.

AVAILABLE: Record shops, gallery shops and The Poster Shop, 109 Kings Road, London SW3 Tel: 071-376 5569 (Mail Order available).

Record Tokens

Dull? Smacks of last-minutism? On the other hand the recipient will buy what he or she actually wants to listen to!

PRICE: Up to you (tapes start at about £8).

AVAILABLE: All good record shops.

Sable Brushes

Roberson sable brushes are high-quality watercolour brushes; they're the sort used by Prince Charles and recommended by him for use when travelling.

PRICE: Small brushes available for under £10.

AVAILABLE: All good artists' supply shops; L Cornelissen & Son, 105 Great Russell Street, London WC1B 3RY Tel: 071-636 1045 (Mail Order).

Sketch Books

Hardbacked sketch books are a glorious necessity for anyone with 'an eye'. Good acid-free paper is essential, landscape and portrait shapes available. Good art shops name block their own sketchbooks.

PRICE: From £1.20 to £10.

AVAILABLE: All art and craft shops.

Sketching Pencils

Sketching pencils that range from very soft to very very soft which can be used quickly and blend easily.

PRICE: £7.50 (12 blacklead pencils).

AVAILABLE: Art and graphic supply shops.

Spirit Level

A pocket-size spirit level with a built-in tape measure – invaluable for someone who takes their picture hanging and framing seriously.

PRICE: £9.95.

AVAILABLE: RA Enterprises Ltd, 8 Forge Court, Reading Road, Yateley, Camberley GU17 7RX Tel: 0252 861113 (Mail Order).

BETWEEN £10–£20

BOOK CHOICE
Film Guides

Eighth edition of *Halliwell's Film Guide* – the world's most authoritative film guide – includes more than 1000 new entries. Also, Barry Norman's personal choice of the *100 Best Films of the Century* – some people think he never gets it wrong!

PRICE: £12.99 (*Halliwell's Film Guide*); £16.99 (*100 Best Films of the Century* – Chapmans).

AVAILABLE: All good bookshops.

BOOK CHOICE
Guinness Book of British Hit Singles

Reference book for pop-pickers of all ages. Every hit since the 1950s compiled by Paul Gambaccini, Tim Rice and Jonathan Rice.

PRICE: £10.99 each.

AVAILABLE: Most good bookshops.

BOOK CHOICE
The Art of Conducting

If anyone you know starts waving their arms in the air like Magnus Pyke at the slightest provocation, could they perhaps do with some professional guidance? Give in conjunction with a conductor's baton?

PRICE: £12.95 (+ £1.50 p&p) [Rhinegold Publishing]; Conductor's baton from £4.15.

AVAILABLE: Rhinegold Publishing Ltd, 214 Shaftesbury Avenue, London WC2H 8EH Tel: 071-240 5749 (Mail Order); baton from most music shops.

Coloured Pencils

Anyone who likes to draw would relish a set of Karisma pencils. The design of the box is award-winning and the coloured pencil leads are uniform in texture so blend perfectly – used by many professional illustrators.

PRICE: £21.60 (24 coloured pencils).

AVAILABLE: Graphic supplies stores.

English Folk Dance and Song Society

If you know anyone whose particular penchant is folk song, morris or clog dancing, then this is the society for them! Benefits include, society magazine, library privileges at HQ, a vote at the annual AGM and, of course, the opportunity to meet other enthusiasts.

PRICE: £20 annual membership.

AVAILABLE: EFDSS, Cecil Sharp House, 2 Regents Park Road, London NW1 7AY Tel: 071-485 2206.

Evening Classes

There are thousands of part-time and evening classes throughout Britain for the artisitic and musical. It is possible to learn pottery, paint watercolours, write creatively, or play the cello or the banjo.

PRICE: From about £14 for eight classes.

AVAILABLE: Details of courses in your area should be available from local education authority and/or library. In London, *Floodlight* is published every Autumn and lists over 16,500 different classes covering a truly extensive range of hobbies and interests.

film Script

From their favourite movie, whether *Citizen Kane*, *Conan the Barbarian* or *Godfather III*. They'll love it 'maybe not tomorrow, maybe not next week . . .'.

PRICE: £18 (+ £1.50 p&p).

AVAILABLE: Hollywood Scripts, Palladium House, 1–4 Argyll House, London W1V 1AD Tel: 071-978 2706 (Mail Order).

Friendship of an Orchestra

Would benefit any earnest concert-goer – Friendships can include 10% discount on single tickets, magazine, priority booking, rehearsal passes and recording offers.

PRICE: £10–£49.

AVAILABLE: Friends of London Symphony Orchestra, Tel: 071-588 0205; Royal Philharmonic Orchestra, London Tel: 071-608 2381; Royal Scottish Orchestra, Glasgow Tel: 041-226 3868; Halle, Manchester Tel: 061-834 8363.

Friendship Of National Arts Collection Fund

The NACF helps museums buy and RETAIN works of art in this country. Benefits include: FREE entry to all galleries in Britain, reductions on entry to major exhibitions, quarterly magazine, specially arranged views, lectures, concerts, etc.

PRICE: £15 p.a. (£250 life membership – 1993; £500 in 1994).

AVAILABLE: Membership Secretary, NACF, 20 John Islip Street, London SW1P 4JX Tel: 071-821 0404.

Itty-Bitty Book Light

A mini flashlight that clips onto the cover of a book and allows you to read at night without encouraging the huffs and puffs of a partner who is being dazzled.

PRICE: £12.95.

AVAILABLE: Innovations (Mail Order) Ltd, Euroway Business Park, Swindon SN5 8SN Tel: 0793 514666 (Mail Order).

Jazz Concert Tickets

Jazz Services, a central services unit which provides national touring, education, marketing and media information. Together with regional jazz organizations, it forms a national network for jazz in the UK. Alternatively, contact Ronnie Scotts – to see all the famous names; there's practically no-one who hasn't played here. Membership available for one evening.

PRICE: From £12.

AVAILABLE: Ronnie Scotts, 47 Frith Street, London W1 Tel: 071-439 0747; Jazz Services, 5 Dryden Street, Covent Garden, London WC2E 9NW Tel: 071-829 8352/3/4.

'Learn To Play' Videos

The Music Makers Video series gives the beginner a thorough grounding in their chosen instrument, be it drums, clarinet, bass guitar or saxaphone. Tuition by expert musicians, aided by computer graphics.

PRICE: £14.95–£33 each.

AVAILABLE: Music shops, video outlets.

Literary Society Membership

Societies exist for fervent followers of literary and poetic figures. For example, The Brontë Society, The Daresbury Lewis Carroll Society (who elect an honorary Alice each year), and The Byron Society.

PRICE: e.g. £10 p.a. The Byron Society (includes Society Journal).

AVAILABLE: See the *Arts Address Book*, available from local libraries.

Mahl Stick

If you don't know what it is you don't need one, but you may know a man who does. The elegant, traditional stick-rest on which the artist rests his wrist while painting above and around wet or smudgeable areas. Screws apart into three lengths.

PRICE: Around £13.

AVAILABLE: Artists' supply shops.

Membership Of British Film Institute

Benefits include priority booking, monthly programme booklet and the BFI's *Film and TV Handbook*. There is also be the chance to meet a favourite celeb who may come and talk in person to NFT audiences about their career.

PRICE: £13.50 p.a.

AVAILABLE: Membership Secretary, Membership Department, BFI, South Bank, London SE1 8TL Tel: 071-928 3535.

Music Society Membership

Societies brought into existence from the keen interest in and devotion to particular composers. Amongst these is The Elgar Society, The Chopin Society, The Haydn Society, The Jose Carreras Society.

PRICE: A nominal membership fee.

AVAILABLE: See *The Music Yearbook* (Published by Rhinegold) available in local libraries.

Music Stand

Stentor music stands are bestsellers – as well as being light and having a wide desk to cope with lots of music, their quintessential charm is the fact that they are easily collapsible – there is only one direction in which it will snap shut. A Conductor's Stand is much more substantial but not so portable and can cope with heavier scores.

PRICE: £12.95; £49.50 (Rosewood Conductor's Stand with spring-loaded legs).

AVAILABLE: All good music shops.

Music Videos

Live recordings of anyone from Ashkenazy to INXS – usually includes interviews and background information as well as concert.

PRICE: From £11.99.

AVAILABLE: Large record stores, video retail outlets, large department stores.

Stage Pass

A superb national arts card available to anyone between 14 and 30. Savings of up to 50% in theatres, concert halls and arts centres across the country.

PRICE: £14 London & Home Counties, £7.50 everywhere else.

AVAILABLE: Youth & Music, 28 Charing Cross Road, London WC2H ODB Tel: 071-379 6722.

Tickets To 'Must See' Shows

A night out for two to an 'always wanted to see' show is a real treat. Make sure you research what THEY want to see and that they're free that night! West End Theatre tokens are an easy way to give tickets – used just like record or book tokens they can be exchanged at 65 London theatres plus several regional theatres.

PRICE: Seats in the stalls usually start at about £10. West End Theatre tokens available in £1, £5, £10, £20 vouchers.

AVAILABLE: From the venue; Ticketmaster Tel: 071-413 1453.

Watercolour Set

The Cotman Complete Watercolour Set includes everything needed to get started – pad, paint, palette, etc.

PRICE: From £12.60; £26.50 (Cotman Set).

AVAILABLE: Most good artists' suppliers; for nearest stockist contact: Winsor & Newton, Whitefriars Avenue, Wealdstone, Harrow, Middlesex HA3 5RH Tel: 081-427 4343.

Wooden Mannequin

Jointed models which will assume any standing position humanly possible (and humanly impossible) for reference when sketching.

PRICE: From £14.50.

AVAILABLE: Artists' supply shops.

BETWEEN £20–£50

BOOK CHOICE
Kobbe's Complete Opera Guide

All you ever wanted to know about opera but never dared to ask. The definitive and indispensable guide.

PRICE: £30.

AVAILABLE: Good music and bookshops.

BOOK CHOICE
Oxford Companion to English Literature

Dictionary of writers and books with salient figures, works and movements highlighted and discussed.

PRICE: £22.50 (hardback); £6.99 (concise edition) [Oxford University Press].

AVAILABLE: All good bookshops.

'Boxed Set'

Entire series of composer's and writer's works, or classic TV series are available as 'boxed sets', e.g. *The Beethoven Collection* (the nine symphonies on six CDs), Jane Austen, *The Collected Works* (selection of three in each box). Also classic TV series e.g. *Brideshead Revisited* are available in their entirety.

PRICE: e.g. Beethoven Collection £32.95; Jane Austen £11.95; the entire works of Mozart from Philips Classics on 180 CDs(!): £1200.

AVAILABLE: Major record shops; all good bookshops; video stockists. Ring Philips on 081-846 8515 for details. Compact Classics, 56 Chepstow Villas, London W11 2QX Tel: 071-221 1735.

Friendship of Opera Company

The ENO performs its operas in English! It also offers a great variety of work, tries to keep ticket prices reasonable and 'de-dinner jacket' opera generally. Friendship of the Royal Opera House is for real opera aficionados – and how many people can afford to go as a habit? Friendships include open rehearsals and advance booking details.

PRICE: ENO: £23 p.a.; RNO: £40 p.a.; £28 Junior (under 26).

AVAILABLE: Friends of the English National Opera, London Coliseum, St Martins Lane, London WC2N 4BR Tel: 071-836 0111; Membership Secretary, The Friends of Covent Garden, Royal Opera House, London WC2E 9DD Tel: 071-240 1200.

Friendship Of The Royal Academy

Excellent exhibitions including their annual Summer Exhibition. Benefits include: free entrance, private previews, free quarterly magazine. Friends may also take a guest to to any exhibition they visit, also free of charge (guess who?).

PRICE: £35 p.a. (Reductions for Junior (under 26) and Country (more than 75 miles from London Friends.)

AVAILABLE: The Royal Academy, Piccadilly, London SW1 Tel: 071-439 7438.

Local Theatre Membership

Local repertory theatres and arts centres are in all the major towns and cities and the local repertory company is quite often excellent. The theatres themselves often act as try-outs for West End productions.

PRICE: Could be about £30 depending on local theatre (though many offer concessions).

AVAILABLE: Local council offices.

Metronomes

Electronic metronomes have rather a nasty digital tick, but nonetheless are cheaper than the traditional variety and easily portable. Small credit card-sized metronomes can be clipped onto the top pocket. Traditional 'pyramid' metronomes come in a variety of woods – to match the piano and with or without a bell to signal bar endings.

PRICE: £15.95–£79.95 (electronic); £25–£80 (traditional – a bell tends to add £10 to price).

AVAILABLE: All good music shops; Boosey & Hawkes, 295 Regent Street, London W1R 8JH Tel: 071-436 2850 (Mail Order available).

MAGAZINE SUBSCRIPTION
Leisure Painter

Many artists start as amateurs and develop their style as they go along, so leisure painting can be quite professional!

PRICE: £20.50.

AVAILABLE: The Artists Publishing Co Ltd, Caxton House, 63-65 High Street, Tenterden, Kent TN30 6BD Tel: 0580 763315.

Opera Glasses

For the very short-sighted or very nosy. Prices start at about £20 – though an increase in price tends to mean an increase in the quality of casing rather than lens. Alternatively, a good pair of binoculars.

PRICE: £40–£220.

AVAILABLE: The Royal Opera House Shop, Covent Garden, London WC2E 9DD Tel: 071-240 1200 Ext 343 (Mail Order); field sports shops.

£50 AND ABOVE

A Trip to the Edinburgh/Eisteddford/Aldeburgh Festivals

Edinburgh is the all-encompassing arts festival, held in August. Opera, theatre, dance and music draw performers from far and wide – tickets themselves are terribly cheap; but it pays to make friends with a native Edinburgher to secure accommodation. The Eisteddford is set amongst the rolling hills of Northern Wales, with music and dance from contestants from 50 countries.

PRICE: Under £10 for ticket; over £100 including accommodation for a weekend.

AVAILABLE: The Edinburgh International Festival, 21 Market Street, Edinburgh EH1 1BW Tel: 031-225 5756; Aldeburgh Festival Box Office, High Street, Aldeburgh, Suffolk IP1 5AX Tel: 0728 453543; International Musical Eisteddford, Llangollen, Clywd LL20 8NG Tel: 0978 860235.

Art Appreciation Holiday

Art and archaeology tours whose destinations include most of the world, from Aphrodite's Isle (Cyprus) to the Deep South of the USA. They can provide tailormade arrangements for museum friends and other groups concerned with visual arts.

PRICE: From £445 to £1300 plus.

AVAILABLE: Specialtours Ltd (organizes tours on behalf of the NACF), 81A Elizabeth Street, London SW1W 9PG Tel: 071-730 2297; Prospect Music & Art Ltd, 454-458 Chiswick High Road, London W4 4PH Tel: 081-994 6477.

Christie's/Sotheby's Catalogues

Beautifully produced details of forthcoming sales (in England and throughout the world). Would appeal to someone with a particular interest – anything from old master paintings to Chinese snuff bottles. Prices vary according to number of sales per year. The rock and pop memorabilia sales are fascinating for all ages.

PRICE: £40 (London Prints category – three sales per year) £2260 (all London categories – 177 sales per year).

AVAILABLE: Sotheby's Catalogue Subscription Dept, 34-35 New Bond Street, London W1A 2AA Tel: 071-408 5129 Christie's Subscriptions Dept, Unit 1 Stockholm Road, London SE16 3LP Tel: 071-231 5240.

Drum Machine

Drum 'banks' with either four or eight touch sensitive pads and up to 75 backing voices.

PRICE: £89.99 (four pads) £169.99 (eight pads).

AVAILABLE: Yamaha stockists. For stockists contact: Yamaha-Kemble Music (UK) Ltd, Sherbourne Drive, Tilbrook, Milton Keynes MK7 8BL Tel: 0908 366700.

Keyboard/Synthesizer

From a basic keyboard, to what reasembles a mini-space station. A keyboard is more for home-use while professionals use synthesizers for their 'gigs'. It is absolutely incredible what expert sounds can be achieved with a little tinkering.

PRICE: From £120.

AVAILABLE: Yamaha stockists including Chappell of Bond Street, 50 New Bond Street London W1Y 9HA Tel: 071-491 2777.

MAGAZINE SUBSCRIPTION
The Burlington

Magazine for art historical studies concentrating on unpublished research. Extensive international exhibition coverage and book reviews. A glorious publication – indispensable for students and those with a keen interest in art historical banter.

PRICE: £127 p.a. (£89 introduction offer for new subscribers only).

AVAILABLE: The Burlington Magazine, 6 Bloomsbury Square, London WC1A 2LP Tel: 071-430 0481.

Personal CD/Car CD

The 'Discman' has superseded the 'Walkman' and though slightly larger than the cassette player, it can still fit into a pocket and the sound quality can be enjoyed whilst jogging, or on the bus. A carstack system is available which holds ten CDs and can be pre-programmed to play tracks from each for up to 12 hours continuously.

PRICE: From £135 (personal CD); £649 [Sony] Car CD – alternatively a dashboard extractable car CD/stereo £349.

AVAILABLE: Leading electrical stores and Sony stockists.

Portable Artist's Easel

An aluminium artist's easel which weighs just 3 lbs 8 oz when dismantled. For artists who enjoy painting *en plein air* – can also be used as a table easel. Holds canvases up to 48".

PRICE: £62.50.

AVAILABLE: Artists' supply shops.

Summer Schools

There are myriad practical courses for artist improvement and inspiration. Summer schools are also offered by some of the country's most prestigious art colleges. Central St Martins offers new residential painting courses in Florence, Venice, France and Dartmoor as well as the courses at its base.

PRICE: From £30 to £700 plus, depending on length of course.

AVAILABLE: e.g. The Development Unit, Central St Martins, Southampton Row, London WC1B 4AP Tel: 071-753 0388.

The New Grove Dictionary of Music and Musicians

The musical equivalent of *The Encyclopedia Britannica* – it is HUGE! Twenty volumes, each with 900 pages – 'the greatest musical dictionary ever published'.

PRICE: £1190 [Macmillan].

AVAILABLE: Christopher Enticknap, *The Grove Dictionary of Music*, FREEPOST, Brunel Road, Houndmills, Basingstoke, RG21 2XS Tel: 0256 817245.

Tickets to Opera Festival – Glyndebourne/Garsington

Glyndebourne remains the international opera festival par excellence and tickets are famously elusive. Don't give up; you can telephone for returns or queue on the day – although with prices at £750 or £1000 you can't be half-hearted. (1992 was the last year in the old theatre and the new enlarged Opera House opens in 1994.) At Garsington (mini Glyndebourne) the thrill and spill (and opera) can be just as good and the setting as magical.

PRICE: From about £90.

AVAILABLE: Glyndebourne Opera Festival, Glyndebourne, Lewes, Sussex Tel: 0273 812321; Garsington Manor, Garsington, Oxford OX9 9DH Tel: 0865 791629.

CHAPTER FOURTEEN

SPORTS & SPORTING ACTIVITIES

Sports can be divided into the couch potato variety – more kindly described as 'spectator sports' – and those where participation is essential. Spectator sports' popularity tend to follow their media exposure (Jilly Cooper rather than the Prince of Wales being accredited with the increased interest in polo). For the more energetic it's amazing how cheaply a new experience can be tried, with many clubs lending equipment to get you started. Nowadays there's no need to be competitive: it's quite acceptable to glide or motor race simply for the experience, camaraderie and joie-de-vivre.

UNDER £5

After Swim Shampoo Bar

Shampoo in a convenient bar for lathering on hair after swimming. Removes the smell of chlorine and leaves hair soft and shining.

PRICE: £3.10.

AVAILABLE: Cosmetics To Go, Freepost, Poole, Dorset BH15 1BR Tel: 0800 373366 (Mail Order).

Balls

Most people playing sport will have the necessary equipment. All of of them will welcome a new set, or a spare set of balls to replenish those battered or lost.

PRICE: e.g. Squash £1.50 each [Dunlop]; Tennis £3.99 for three [Slazenger]; Golf £6.50 for three [Maxfli]; Cricket £3.99 [Match]; Rugby £9.99 [Umbro]; Soccer £12.99 [Mitre].

AVAILABLE: Branches of Olympus Sport and First Sport.

BOOK CHOICE
Know the Game

Inexpensive illustrated first step guides to over 50 games from American Football to Women's Hockey. Includes all the popular sports, e.g. golf, soccer, etc, as well games like rounders and scrabble.

PRICE: £1.99 [A & C Black].

AVAILABLE: Good sports shops and bookshops.

Grass Stain Remover

For removing grass stains from cricket trousers, after diving to make the winning catch.

PRICE: £1.50 (Stain Devil).

AVAILABLE: Boots, other chemists, some hardware stores.

Zinc Sunblock

The white paste seen on the noses of surfers, skiers and Australians has gone psychedelic. The creams are now available in pinks, yellows, greens – essential for anyone out in strong sunlight for long periods.

PRICE: Zinc Stick £3.95.

AVAILABLE: Most good sports shops.

BETWEEN £5–£10

Baseball Caps

The teams from the major league teams such as the LA Dodgers, Miami Dolphins, Chicago Bears.

PRICE: £8.99.

AVAILABLE: Branches of Olympus Sport.

Learn to ... in a Weekend

Sailing, golf, windsurfing, rockclimbing, etc. First class beginners' guides with excellent colour illustrations.

PRICE: £7.99 [Dorling Kindersley].

AVAILABLE: Good bookshops.

Darts

If you leave out the cost of 'your round', darts is one the least expensive sports around. The best darts are made from tungsten.

PRICE: £9.99 (Harrow's Assassin); £19.99 (Harrow's Eric Bristow).

AVAILABLE: All good sports shops.

Luminous Tape

Late-night joggers and cyclists should not go out without it. This luminous self-adhesive tape can be used on clothes, trainers, back packs or bikes.

PRICE: £5.95 (3m).

AVAILABLE: Good sports shops and department stores.

Snow and Ice Grips for Shoes

If you're going to break your leg at least stand an outside chance of doing it on the slopes rather than on the road in the resort. Chromed springs are held over shoes with rubber loops to allow safer walking on ice or packed snow.

PRICE: £8.65 per pair (large or small).

AVAILABLE: Chester-Care, Low Moor Estate, Kirkby-in-Ashfield, Notts NG17 7JZ Tel: 0623 757955 (Mail Order).

Swimming Goggles

Keeps water and chlorine from the pool or the sea out of your eyes.

PRICE: e.g. £5.99 Speedo Pro Plus goggles; £17.99 Speedo Pro Focus Anti Fog goggles.

AVAILABLE: All major sport shops.

Telescopic Golf Ball Retriever

One of those tools which is useless for 99.99% of the population, but for small number of people who have amphibious golfballs this tool will be a life and money-saver. A telescopic 6′ handle with clever steel wire-basket that rescues balls from murky depths (or leafy heights).

PRICE: £9.95.

AVAILABLE: Innovations Ltd, Euroway Business Park, Swindon SN5 8SN Tel: 0793 514666 (Mail Order).

—————————————————————
BETWEEN £10–£20
—————————————————————

A Day at the Races

An opportunity to put a fiver to win on any horse 'that's got a pretty face' or whose name has some whimsical link. Daily membership will include entry to the Members' Enclosure opposite the winning post and enable you to go anywhere on the course including the parade ring.

PRICE: e.g. From £13 to £22 according to the day's events.

AVAILABLE: Sandown Park Racecourse, Portsmouth Road, Esher, Surrey KT10 9AJ Tel: 0372 483072 and other racecourses throughout the country.

Basketball Set

The ball and hoop together in this set. You are responsible for the actual jumping, slam dunks, etc.

PRICE: £13.99.

AVAILABLE: Larger branches of Olympus Sport.

BOOK CHOICE
Nautical Almanac

Macmillan and Reed publish the two definitive guides to all things nautical – each has their own devotees, but either *should* be seen on the chart-table of every boat afloat. Detailed information on tides, port entries, plus sections on radio, weather, basic navigation and ship and boat recognition. Updated annually.

PRICE: £19.95 [Thomas Reed Publications Ltd]; £22.99 [Pan Macmillan Ltd].

AVAILABLE: Bookshops and chandlers.

BOOK CHOICE
Rothman's Football Yearbook

Indispensable companion to the football season, the clubs, the competitions, the cups, the leagues, the results from last season, plus next season's fixture list.

PRICE: £14.99 [Headline].

AVAILABLE: Sports shops and bookshops.

BOOK CHOICE
We Learned to Ski

Eight years on and now in its fourth edition this excellent guide to skiing is still the one to buy.

PRICE: £13.99 [Collins].

AVAILABLE: Published by the *Sunday Times* and Harper Collins.

BOOK CHOICE
Wisden Cricketer's Almanac

1993 is the 130th edition of John Wisden's unrivalled cricketer's 'bible'. Includes test match reviews, reports on English country games, plus the fixture lists for the coming season.

PRICE: £19.50 (paperback) [Gollancz].

AVAILABLE: All good bookshops.

Dartboard

In the office, on the back of the garage door, in the staffroom – see if you can hit the board, much less 'a double top'.

PRICE: £19.99 (Harrow's Official Competition Board).

AVAILABLE: All good sports shops.

Flags

National flags of England, Scotland, Wales and all the other countries of the world in all sizes. Also flags for companies made to order and flagstaffs.

PRICE: Depends on size and countries; e.g. £13.95 United Kingdom 6 ft × 3 ft.

AVAILABLE: Zephyr Flags and Banners, Midlands Road, Thrapston, Northamptonshire NN14 4LX Tel: 0832 734484.

Floating Fin

Flippers to most of us! Enables speedy chasing or retreat from fish, men-of-war etc.

PRICE: £19.99.

AVAILABLE: Olympus Sport branches in the UK.

Horse of the Year Tickets

The culmination of thousands of events held throughout the country. Over 3000 horses and riders take part in competitions ranging from driving and dressage to the final National Showjumping Championships. Ends with the top 24 riders competing in the International Grand Prix.

PRICE: Seats from £10 to £35.

AVAILABLE: The Horse of the Year Show Office, P O Box 100, Kenilworth, Warwickshire CV8 2XS Tel: 0203 693088. Tickets from Wembley Box Office Tel: 081-900 1234.

Lessons – Dry Slope Skiing

A few lessons spent on a dry slope before a holiday can help beginners grasp the sport more quickly and remind keen skiers that pre-ski exercises are needed urgently.

PRICE: Varies: from £4 per hour for the use of the slope to £15 per hour for a lesson.

AVAILABLE: Contact: British Ski Slope Operators Assocation, 258 Main Street, East Calder, West Lothian E4530EE Tel: 0506 884343.

Lessons – Gliding

Alone in the sky with no engine. Most clubs have introductory lessons – after that there are day- or week-long courses. To go solo demands a minimum of 20 flights – you may need more!

PRICE: Introductory lessons from £15 for 20 minutes.

AVAILABLE: Contact: The British Gliding Association, Kimberley House, 47 Vaughan Way, Leicester LE1 4SG Tel: 0533 531051.

Lessons – Golf

A good idea for both beginners and 'experts' who need to improve their driving etc.

PRICE: £15 – £20 for half an hour.

AVAILABLE: Golf course professionals or driving ranges.

Lessons – Land Yachting

A land yacht can reach 50 mph before a first timer has fully grasped the plot. Initially hairaising – ultimately good fun. Organised on a friendly and informal basis with 16 'clubs' throughout the country happy to give lessons.

PRICE: Approx £12 per half day.

AVAILABLE: British Federation of Sand and Land Yacht Clubs, 23 Piper Drive, Long Whatton, Loughborough, Leics LE12 5DJ Tel: 0509 842292.

Lessons – Rowing

Perceived as a male-dominated expensive sport. Untrue! Increasing numbers of women-only teams, and very inexpensive to try out. Most clubs will give first lessons for a nominal fee to see whether you like it. Most also have boats to loan/rent.

PRICE: According to club.

AVAILABLE: Details of local clubs from Amateur Rowing Association, 6 Lower Mall, London W6 9DJ Tel: 081-748 3632.

Lessons – Tennis

Dreams of playing at Wimbledon or gentle sociable games on a summer afternoon? Beginners might have more fun joining a group. A ten-week course should master the basics of the game. Lessons at three levels.

PRICE: Elementary from £8.20 per hour; Intermediate from £10.50 per hour; Professional from £14.75 per hour.

AVAILABLE: Details of local clubs from The Lawn Tennis Association, Queens Club, West Kensington, London W14 9EG Tel: 071-385 2366.

Mask and Snorkel

Jacques Cousteau fans and those on their holidays can explore the underwater world with this colour mask and snorkel.

PRICE: £14.99.

AVAILABLE: Olympus Sport branches in the UK.

Membership – Cyclists' Touring Club

Cycling is one of the healthiest forms of exercise and a wonderful way to discover the countryside. The Cyclists' Touring Club organizes rides, plans touring itineraries, gives technical advice and includes insurance for members. For mountain bike folk, The British Mountain Bike Federation does much the same and is the governing body for sport and recreation.

PRICE: Around £20.

AVAILABLE: Cyclists Touring Club, Coterell House, 69 Meadow Row, Goldaming, Surrey GU7 3HS Tel: 0483 417217; The British Mountain Bike Federation, 36 Buckingham Road, Kettering, Northants NN16 8HG Tel: 0536 412211.

Membership – Football Club

Let them cheer from the stands not the sofa. Membership usually includes ticket discounts, priority bookings, official yearbook etc.

PRICE: Varies according to club; e.g. Manchester United £10; Chelsea £22.

AVAILABLE: The club of your choice or The Football Association, 1B Lancaster Gate, London W2 3LW Tel: 071-402 7151.

Microwaveable Gel Pads

A special gel pack covered in towelling fabric that can be cooled in the fridge and used on different parts of the body – ideal for sprains and strains.

PRICE: £16.65 (leg/arm), £21.50 (back/thigh), £33.75 (shoulder/back).

AVAILABLE: Chester-Care, Low Moor Estate, Kirkby-in-Ashfield, Notts NG17 7JZ Tel: 0623 757955 (Mail Order).

Pedometer

Devices which automatically monitor the distance walked, run or hit. They are small and light and easily attach to clothing, arms or ankles.

PRICE: From £14.95 to £135.

AVAILABLE: Pedometers International Ltd, 1 Whittle Close, Drayton Fields, Daventry, Northants NN11 5RQ Tel: 0327 706030.

Rugby Ball

James Gilbert's rugby balls are used all over the world. The grown-up version called the Barbarian is this year's 'World Cup Ball'. Their most popular seller is the Murrayfield.

PRICE: £21.50 the Barbarian; £14.99 the Murrayfield.

AVAILABLE: Sports shops; James Gilbert, 5 St Mathew Street, Rugby CV21 3BY Tel: 0788 542426.

Ski Videos

Three videos for skiers of all standards – bad, not so bad, and not at all bad – to improve fitness and skills before hitting the slopes.

PRICE: £19.95 each or £49.95 for the set.

AVAILABLE: *Sunday Times* Video Library, PO Box 169, Horsham, West Sussex RH13 5YL Tel: 0403 242727 (Mail Order).

Sportsbag

For those who still carry their sports kit under their arm, and drop bits on the way from the car to the court. A stylish decent size sportsbag will be much used and appreciated.

PRICE: Around £16.

AVAILABLE: Anywhere.

'Wet and Dry' Sportsbag

A sportsbag specially designed to keep wet and dry sports kit separate. Has four leak-resistant zippered compartments, while muddy and smelly shoes go in the large central section.

PRICE: £12.95.

AVAILABLE: Innovations (Mail Order) Ltd, Euroway Business Park, Swindon SN5 8SN Tel: 0793 514666.

BETWEEN £20–£50

Archery Set

Anyone from eight to eighty can learn archery and you don't have to be that fit. Quicks, the archery specialist, have three shops in London, the South and the Midlands. Their staff are very helpful and they have an excellent mail order magazine.

PRICE: e.g. £22.95 The Forester Set (includes bows and arrows).

AVAILABLE: Quicks, 18-22 Stakes Hill Road, Waterlooville, Hants PO7 7JF (Mail Order available).

Comfort Saddle

Bike saddles are now cushioned for comfort and specially designed to fit the different bottoms of men and women. The ritzier versions include an inflated pocket of special gel.

PRICE: From £19.95; Avocet £29.95.

AVAILABLE: All good bicycle shops.

Cricket Club Membership

Gentle summer days enjoying the complexities of the game as a spectator or playing? Club memberships offer a host of benefits from free entry to matches to busy social programmes.

PRICE: Varies – approximately £50.

AVAILABLE: Your local cricket ground or The Test and County Cricket Board, Lords Cricket Ground, London NW8 8QZ Tel: 071-286 4405.

Lessons – Fencing

Erol Flynn, The Three Muskateers, The Scarlet Pimpernel. If you want to know how to emulate the famous folk enrol for a class of sensible and safe lessons at a fencing club. Fencing combines fitness, competition, discipline and emphasis on executing the classic movements correctly. Most clubs will lend epees and foils to novices.

PRICE: £30–£50 for ten-week course of lessons.

AVAILABLE: Contact: The Amateur Fencing Association, 1 Barons Gate, 33/35 Rothschild Road, London W4 5HT Tel: 081-742 3032.

Lessons – Waterskiing

Exhilarating and exhausting to learn, so beginners must be reasonably fit. Wet suits are essential to prevent hypothermia. Most clubs have learn-to-ski days and you'll usually 'be up' by the end of the day.

PRICE: £30–£35.

AVAILABLE: Details of 160 clubs, some of which are in the most unusual places from: The British Waterski Federation, 390 City Road, London EC1V 2QA Tel: 071-833 2855.

Lessons – Windsurfing

Beginners should be able to swim, be reasonably fit and have a grim determination to persevere in the face of adversity. The beginners' course lasts one day (approximately six hours). By the end a pupil should be able to sail away, turn round and come back. The next level involves sailing round a triangle.

PRICE: £35–£50 for a day's course.

AVAILABLE: Details of approved schools from: The Royal Yachting Association, RYA House, Romsey Road, Eastleigh, Hampshire SO5 4YA Tel: 0703 629962.

MAGAZINE SUBSCRIPTION
Golf World

Packed with news, reports and articles on how to improve your game.

PRICE: £32.50 (12 issues).

AVAILABLE: Tel: 071-538 1031.

MAGAZINE SUBSCRIPTION
Rugby World and Post

Rugby has been marketed much more aggressively during the past few years, witness the World Cup etc … and as a result has become much more popular.

PRICE: £26 (12 issues).

AVAILABLE: Subscriptions Tel: 0622 721555.

Runner's World

You don't have to run marathons to read this magazine, but if you do it helps.

PRICE: £25.40 (12 issues).

AVAILABLE: Tel: 071-972 9119.

Monogrammed Tennis Bag

Side pocket large enough to hold a large-headed racket plus zipper compartment for balls, shoes, socks, etc. Serious court-side chic which may mean looking better off-court than on. Monogrammed with up to four initials.

PRICE: £34.50.

AVAILABLE: Eximious, 10 West Halkin Street, London SW1R 8JL Tel: 071-235 7828 (Mail Order available).

Racquets

The various brands and prices can seriously confuse anyone who just wants to take up the game. Beginners should avoid paying too much initially until they've decided it's the sport for them. The following names and prices were gathered one day at a major branch of Olympus Sport to give guidance only.

PRICE: e.g. Badminton – average price £40 [Carlton]; Squash – average price £40; Tennis – £50 plus [Head].

AVAILABLE: Olympus Sport stores nationwide.

Rugby Shirt

Versatile and hardwearing shirts that can be worn on or off the field. Also popular with sailors and skiers. The major international shirts, England, Wales, New Zealand, Australia, etc are all available by mail order.

PRICE: From £24.99.

AVAILABLE: Cotton Traders, 9/12 Dale Street, Broadheath, Altringham, Cheshire WA14 5EH Tel: 061-926 8185 (Mail Order).

Ski Goggles

'Cool' and very practical, these goggles have a double lens and are large enough to wear glasses underneath.

PRICE: £24.99.

AVAILABLE: Alpine Sports and other ski shops.

Snooker/Billiard Cue

Budding World Champions will want one of Riley's impressive range of cues.

PRICE: From £21 to over £400.

AVAILABLE: Sports shops, department stores or E J Riley Tel: 0282 772500.

Tickets – Wimbledon

Plan in advance and apply to the public ballot. Send a stamped addressed envelope before December 31st for the following summer's tournament. There is a one in five chance of getting tickets which are limited to two per household. One of the 'guests' must be the applicant which makes it an especially enjoyable present. A limited amount of tickets are reserved for the public, but this may involve use of the sleeping bag for popular matches.

PRICE: Tickets £10–£50.

AVAILABLE: The Secretary, All England Lawn Tennis Club, PO Box 98, Wimbledon SW19 5AE Tel: 081-946 2244 (Tickets), 081-944 1066 (Office).

Water Resistant Stopwatch

Ideal for sailors at the start of races or anyone else who's into wet split-second timings.

PRICE: £34.99 [Casio].

AVAILABLE: Branches of H Samuel.

£50 AND ABOVE

A Balloon Trip

A trip of approximately one hour floating over the English countryside will leave you breathless with exhilaration! For once the brochure copy is accurate. Very good fun; people have even hired one to propose marriage!

PRICE: Around £135 per person in an eight person balloon. Alternatively hire your own for a day for between £500 and £700 (you can have two trips: one morning and one in the evening).

AVAILABLE: Flying Pictures (Balloons) Ltd, Montgolfier House, Fairoaks Airport, Chobham, Surrey GU24 8HU Tel: 0276 855111.

Activity Holidays

Athletics, bowls, gymnastics, mountaineering, skating, triathalon – coaching in all these and many other sports is available for all those who've always wanted to try '...'. The Sports Council publishes an annual guide to coaching courses and activity holidays.

PRICE: Varies according to course: e.g. cricket – two weekends £70, one week £195–£295.

AVAILABLE: The Information Centre, Sports Council, 16 Upper Woburn Place, London WC1H Tel: 071-388 1277 (FREE guide with a SAE).

A Lifejacket

You shouldn't go out on the water without one on, and in many clubs you're not allowed to sail or windsurf unless you wear one. Forget memories of traditional lifejackets. Modern versions can be lighter and much less cumbersome.

PRICE: e.g. Crewfit range £82.95 – £147.65.

AVAILABLE: Crewsaver Ltd, Mumby Road, Gosport, Hants PO12 1AQ Tel: 0705 528621.

An Outward Bound Course

The principles of an outward bound course are to develop self confidence and learn the value of teamwork. Most people thoroughly enjoy a week of well-planned physical challenge, and return to normal life slightly the better for it. An ideal present for all the family!

PRICE: Courses start at £225 per week.

AVAILABLE: Outward Bound, Chestnut Field, Regent Place, Rugby CV21 2PJ Tel: 0788 560423. There are five centres round the country.

Cricket Bat

For sixes and centuries! A proper bat fashioned from mature naturally seasoned willow. The bat must suit the batsman i.e. heavy or light, right handle length – so make sure you can exchange it if necessary.

PRICE: e.g. £120 (Maestro original).

AVAILABLE: Gunn & Moore, 119/121 Stanstead Road, Forest Hill, London SE23 1HJ Tel: 081-291 3344.

Cricket Trousers

Smart traditional-looking trousers that are as close to flannels as you will find anywhere. The wool-polyester mix is machine-washable.

PRICE: £55.

AVAILABLE: Boden, 2 Pembroke Buildings, Cumberland Park, Scrubs Lane, London NW10 6RG Tel: 081-964 2662 (Mail Order).

Golf Clubs

Amber alert time. Keen players will have their own (and most of the other required kit). A beginner should consider buying a second-hand set to start with. Alternatively go to a recommended local golf pro, or shop with a large selection.

PRICE: A new set £149 (will include trolley, putter, nine irons, three woods, bag and a few balls!).

AVAILABLE: Local professionals or American Golf Discount Shops throughout the UK. For nearest branch call 0925 823299.

Lessons – Flying

'Almost anyone can learn to fly'. An initial lesson at a local airfield will cover an introduction to flying, the club and the airfield and a flight during which you will get a chance to take the controls. The resulting exhilaration could lead to a wonderful new interest and serious damage to your bank balance. To fly solo a minimum of 12-15 hours must usually be spent in the air. Getting a pilot's licence will take between 50 and 55 hours. Then there's the plane …

PRICE: From £75.

AVAILABLE: Acone Air Sports operate a nationwide voucher at over 50 airports throughout the UK. Just choose the course and the location. They will send you full details, together with a voucher to be presented at the relevant airbase: Acorne Sports Tel: 0494 451703.

Lessons – Motor Racing

An excellent day of serious fun for grown ups! The day starts with a briefing session and safety tips and ends with timed laps in a Formula First Racing Car. Choose from circuits in Norfolk, Kent, Cheshire and Lincolnshire.

PRICE: £79.

AVAILABLE: Details from Brands Hatch Racing, Fawkham Longfield, Kent DA3 8NG Tel: 0474 872367.

Lessons – Parachuting

The world seems quite clearly divided into those who would love to and those who wouldn't under any circumstances. A two-day course includes an introduction to the subject, fitness training, parachuting and landing techniques and one static line jump from an aircraft flying at 3000 ft. Good luck!

PRICE: £159 for two days.

AVAILABLE: Acorne Sports, P O Box 1057, Marlow, Bucks SL7 3XT Tel: 0494 451703.

Lessons – Sailing

One of the most addictive sports and possibly one of the most expensive. The trick is to get addicted in someone else's boat! Or to stick to dinghies. Enormous fun for both kids and adults. Sailing courses vary from complete beginners to Yachtmaster Offshores, in boats from dinghies to ocean-going cruisers, for periods from a weekend to 5 days.

PRICE: Dependent on course-length and boat – e.g. around £150 for a five-day residential beginners' dinghy saling course.

AVAILABLE: A list of approved schools and courses is available from The Royal Yachting Association, RYA House, Romsey Road, Eastleigh, Hampshire SO5 4YA Tel: 0703 629962.

Lessons – Scuba Diving

SCUBA (Self-Contained Underwater Breathing Apparatus) allows a diver to stay under water for sustained periods and is incredibly exciting. To dive in open water it is necessary to undergo a rigorous training period, easier now since many clubs have introduced lessons at local swimming pools.

PRICE: Intensive 15 hour courses available either over a weekend or five evenings during the week from £235 (BSAC novice course); club membership around £150 p.a.

AVAILABLE: For details of local schools and clubs and programme of courses and events contact: British Sub Aqua Club, Telfords Quay, Ellesmere Port, South Wirral, Cheshire L65 4FY Tel: 051-357 1951.

Membership of the MCC

The waiting list for full membership is currently 24 years. You can't be put down until your 16th birthday and you must be proposed by four full members who have known you for three years. This means you can't be a member of the MCC until you're 40 years old UNLESS you play cricket to a high standard i.e. county level. Still worth it if your son is a budding Test star.

PRICE: Currently £142.

AVAILABLE: MCC Membership, Lords Cricket Ground, St Johns Wood Road, London NW8 8QZ Tel: 071-289 1611.

Personal LCD Colour TV

For Test Match and Wimbledon fanatics, enabling them to watch the action in the office, car, etc. The quality of the pictures is surprisingly good – the size of the screen determines the price.

PRICE: From £129.99 (2″) to £169.99 (4″) [Casio].

AVAILABLE: Dixons, Electrical equipment shops.

Powakaddy

Calls itself 'The Golf GTI'. Seen on golf courses all over the UK, this powered golf trolley carries your clubs, balls, brolly, etc, round the course leaving you the energy to concentrate on your game.

PRICE: £429.

AVAILABLE: Call 0795 47355 for nearest stockist.

Pulsemeter Watch

A watch which monitors your pulse and therefore allows you to adjust your pace whilst you exercise. Modern, digital, liquid-crystal, saver of heart failure?

PRICE: £139.95.

AVAILABLE: Large chemists; John Bell & Croyden, 50 Wigmore Street, W1 Tel: 071-935 5555 (Mail Order available).

Sky Sports Subscription

Test matches live from the subcontinent at 4 a.m. Premier League football games as they're played. Big fights A great present for sports fans but their 'partner in life' might well polaxe you.

PRICE: £6.99 per month subscription; Dish receiver £220 plus £40 installation.

AVAILABLE: Ask television dealers for details.

Snooker/Billiard Table

First you need a good size spare room – the full size table is 12 ft x 6 ft and you need 5 ft of space round the table. If you've the space this is one of the best after-dinner games around. The Aristocrat is one of Riley's bestsellers and they also supply all the necessary accessories from cues to marking boards.

PRICE: £4105 Aristocrat (full size) including delivery and installation.

AVAILABLE: E J Riley, Riley House, Station Road, Padiham, Burnley BB12 7AR Tel: 0282 772500.

Sports Walkman

The bright yellow box complete with auto-reverse and anti-rolling enables joggers and exercisers to skip through their session elated or informed.

PRICE: £57.99 (tape only); £74.99 (tape + radio).

AVAILABLE: All hi-fi shops and department stores.

Sports Watch

Tag Heuer, now found on the wrists of the fashion conscious, are more usually found in sporting events ranging from the Olympics to the Formula 1 Motor Racing World Championships.

PRICE: From £160 to £1760.

AVAILABLE: Brochure and stockists from Tag Heuer, 16/18 Harcourt Street, Worsley, Manchester M28 5GN Tel: 0204 861168.

Table Tennis Table

Enormous fun for all the family. These full size table tennis tables are cleverly designed to foldaway and rollaway after use. For a serious game you need 10 ft x 18 ft of clear space for the table.

PRICE: £149.99 Standard (9 ft × 8 ft); £299.99 All Weather (9ft × 5 ft).

AVAILABLE: Petworth House Ltd, Polesden Lane, Ripley, Woking, Surrey GU23 6LR Tel: 0483 225222.

The Cricket Bag

'Unless you are a helmet-wearing wicket keeper with two sets of pads, this bag will take everything'. Also looks 'the part' and is waterproof.

PRICE: £85.

AVAILABLE: Boden, 2 Pembroke Buildings, Cumberland Park, Scrubs Lane, London NW10 6RG (Mail Order).

CHAPTER FIFTEEN

PETS & ANIMAL LOVERS

ALL pet owners are convinced that a pet is therapeutic. A third claim to prefer their pets to people; the majority give them birthday presents and know their four-legged friends are highly intelligent – possibly linked to the animal's ability to dote on their owners. So when buying for pets you need to be most careful. Owners want only the best. Forget about scraps, bring on the gourmet meals! Humans may rely on the National Health, but private pet psychiatrists will be paid for. Pet owners know where their priorities lie!

UNDER £5

Anti-Tangle Grooming Spray

Even owners who adore grooming admit that a pump-spray 'stay-on' conditioner helps untangle and condition coats, especially long-haired breeds which often take on the appearance of bindweed.

PRICE: £2.95 (250 ml).

AVAILABLE: Good pet shops; Companion Care, Freepost, PO Box 99, Swadlincote, Derbyshire DE12 6BR Tel: 0283 761110 (Mail Order).

BOOK CHOICE
Tear Jerkers

Animal-loving softies' eyes can brim with tears at the mere mention of *Tarka the Otter*. Videos are just the same – *Bambi* has been know to reduce grown men to blubbering wrecks!

PRICE: From £4.

AVAILABLE: All good bookshops.

Brite White Shampoo

For grubby pets who have lost their snowy whiteness! Any yellow discolouration disappears from light coloured coats as well as whites and creams; pH balanced.

PRICE: £4.50 (12 oz).

AVAILABLE: Petcetera etc Ltd, PO Box 112, Henley-in-Arden, Solihull, West Midlands B95 5HD Tel: 092 684 3030 (Mail Order).

Cat Mint

Very pretty, scented flowering shrub which cats adore! One sniff and a roll and they're transported to feline heaven. It's also a decorative addition to any garden.

PRICE: About 95p for a clipping.

AVAILABLE: Most garden centres.

Chocs and Chews

Simple! In lots of supermarkets as well as pet shops from only 12p!

PRICE: From 12p.

AVAILABLE: All pet shops, some supermarkets.

Dog Hat

When you thought you'd seen it all. A cap designed in America (!) is available in camouflage or bright orange for the trendiest and most stylish leader of the pack.

PRICE: £4.50.

AVAILABLE: The Leading Edge stores; The Leading Edge (Retail) Ltd, Euroway Business Park, Swindon SN5 8SN Tel: 0793 436648 (Mail Order).

Dog Toothbrush

'Dog breath' may become an insult of the past! One brush a week is plenty, using a toothpaste which helps prevent odour and plaque-forming bacteria.

PRICE: £1.60 (toothbrush); £4.35 (malt flavoured toothpaste).
AVAILABLE: Large pet shops; Companion Care, Freepost, PO Box 99, Swadlincote, Derbyshire DE12 6BR Tel: 0283 76111.

Fish Tank Castle

All manner of paraphernalia available to clog up the aquarium. Goldfish have a memory span of three seconds so his new furniture will be a constant source of surprise.
PRICE: From £1.65.
AVAILABLE: All pet shops.

Flea Collar

Whether given in jest or not, flea collars will prevent the excessive scratching and biting that may develop amongst a family and their pet. The agent in the collar kills existing fleas and any new fleas that may jump onto the animal.
PRICE: £1.95 [Zodiac – cat] £2.25 [Zodiac – dog].
AVAILABLE: All good pet shops.

Food Bowl

Unembellished stainless steel or earthenware food bowls are available very cheaply – and even personalized they are not expensive. The base should be broader than the top if you want to avoid spills. Also, the Water-Well travel bowl which has an integral non-splash and non-spill lid – ensures animals have access to water when travelling.
PRICE: From £2.25 (stainless steel); from £4.25 (earthenware).
AVAILABLE: All pet stores.

Food Supplement

High calorie vitamin concentrate designed to stimulate the appetite and increase weight gain. Ideal for finicky eaters and toy breeds.
PRICE: £2.80 [Vicon].
AVAILABLE: Good pet stores.

Nesting Box

Endless delight for families with trees in the garden – different varieties are available for different breeds of bird. Keep it small or you may find squirrels taking over.

PRICE: £2.46 (finch nesting box); £11.50 for five.

AVAILABLE: Pet shops; Grange Pet Centre, Hillier Garden Centre, Woodhouse Lane, Botley, Southampton S03 2EZ Tel: 0489 781260 (Mail Order).

Poopa Scoopa

Pet mess pick-up device; if pets embarrass in public the evidence can be removed. Snap-actioned scoop.

PRICE: £2.49.

AVAILABLE: Most pet shops.

Security Collar Tag

The least expensive investment for greater peace of mind. The owner's name/phone number inside a small metal cylinder which attaches to the collar.

PRICE: 95p (metal cylinder).

AVAILABLE: All pet shops.

Taste Deterrent

Bitter Apple could be the answer to nibbled furniture, nibbled coats and nibbled cage mates. Break the habit by painting with this nasty-tasting liquid. Highly successful when used on horses, dogs, cats, even guinea pigs.

PRICE: £2.50 (90g).

AVAILABLE: Many pet stores.

BETWEEN £5–£10

BOOK CHOICE
The Life Trilogy

The books of the David Attenborough series – *Life on Earth, The Living Planet, The Trials of Life*. Photographs and narrative taken from the series and are just as stunning.

PRICE: £9.99 each [Collins – paperback].

AVAILABLE: All good bookshops.

Clothes Brush

Many animal lovers spend a good deal of their time impersonating their pets and pet hairs are really anti-social in company. A Pet Hair Pic-Up is an adhesive roller which picks up pet hairs from clothing and upholstery.

PRICE: £5.50.

AVAILABLE: Cat Claws (Basco), PO Box 71, Croydon CR0 2ZZ Tel: 081-683 1000 (Mail Order).

'Crowning Glory'

An inner cosmetic for cats – a new evening primrose oil (reputedly works wonders on humans) lives up to its promise to perk up puss.

PRICE: £5.95 for 60 capsules.

AVAILABLE: Cambridge Veterinary Sciences Ltd, Henry Crabb Road, Littleport, Ely, Cambs CB6 1SE Tel: 0353 861911.

Dog Stop Alarm

A screeching alarm, similar to a personal protection device, which assists in training dogs not to bark at whim. Could be sent anonymously to neighbours?

PRICE: £5.95.

AVAILABLE: Large pet stores; Companion Care, Freepost, PO Box 99, Swadlincote, Derbyshire DE12 6BR Tel: 0283 761110 (Mail Order).

Head Collars

A kinder way to walk the dog than a choker chain. Slips over the dog's muzzle in the same way as a horse's head collar. Six sizes available.

PRICE: £3.50–£8 [Halti].

AVAILABLE: Most pet stores.

Nail Clippers

Some owners take their pets to the vet, but the Miller Safety Cutter has a safety stop to prevent over-clipping and bleeding so it makes it quite safe for anyone who's afraid they might get bitten.

PRICE: £5.50.

AVAILABLE: Most pet stores: Petcetera etc Ltd, PO Box 112, Henley-in-Arden, Solihull, West Midlands B95 5HD Tel: (092) 684 3030 (Mail Order).

Photo Coasters, Jigsaws

Jigsaws, coasters, giant posters, T-shirts – the sky's the limit for pet photo opportunities. One of the cheapest and most popular options is a set of six coasters.

PRICE: From £6.99 (six).

AVAILABLE: Boots photo shop; most photo labs.

Reflective Collar and Lead

To ensure a pet is seen and less likely to get hurt. Made from woven fluorescent polyester with reflective strip.

PRICE: £7.99–£10.99.

AVAILABLE: From pet shops or direct from CANAC, Becks Mill, Westbury, Wilts BA13 3SD Tel: 0373 864775.

Retractable Leash

Long-range leads. You can keep them short or allow up to five metres of freedom. Definitely an easier option for walker and walked.

PRICE: £9.95 [Flexi 16ft], £11.95 [Flexi 5m].
AVAILABLE: All good pet shops.

Scratching Pad

Ideal for stay-at-home cats who play havoc with the furniture and the curtains. Designed with a honeycomb corrugated material, they scratch it, roll on it, sleep on it and just can't leave it alone.

PRICE: £6.95.

AVAILABLE: Pet shops; Cat Claws (Basco), PO Box 71, Croydon CR0 2ZZ Tel: 081-683 1000 (Mail Order).

—————— BETWEEN £10–£20 ——————

Adopt-a-Whale

Adoptive parents receive a certificate, photo and information about their whale's latest activities. The adoption fee enables the Whale and Dolphin Society to further its work – making the ocean a safer place for whales.

PRICE: From £12.50.

AVAILABLE: WDCS, Freepost, Bath, Avon BA1 1XR Tel: 0225 334511.

Aquarium

Aquaria-to-order is a service offered by specialist shops in which tanks can be arranged in all kinds of shapes and designs. Tanks not only for fish, but reptiles, spiders, rats and other creatures that are best kept behind glass.

PRICE: From £12.95.

AVAILABLE: Aquaria available from most pet shops; Aquaria-to-order, Aqua Plan Crystal Palace Aquarium, 54 Westow Street, London SE19 Tel: 081-771 1349.

BOOK CHOICE
Animal Watching

Desmond Morris, the zoologist who most famously turned his eyes to watching the human animal, gives an amazing insight into the life and behaviour of other animals – from lions in the Serengeti to hedgehogs in the garden.

PRICE: £12.99 [Arrow].

AVAILABLE: All good bookshops.

BOOK CHOICE
Dog/Cat Care Manuals

Endorsed by the RSPCA, these manuals help owners understand and care for their pets. Illustrated throughout with photographs, diagrams and flowcharts.

PRICE: £12.99 each [Dorling Kindersley].

AVAILABLE: All good bookshops.

BOOK CHOICE
Magnificent Menagerie

Lucinda Lambton offers reassurance for the animal crazy – they are not the only potty pet owners.

PRICE: £20 [HarperCollins].

AVAILABLE: All good bookshops.

Cat's Cradle

Literally a fur-fabric bed on a metal frame which can be hooked over the radiator – to cradle snug cats.

PRICE: £12.99.

AVAILABLE: 91 Kings Road, Sutton Coldfield, B79 5AL Tel: 021-354 4715.

Dog Coat

Raincoats, waxcoats or fleecy-lined tartan coats – for dashing dogs-about-field. Thirty standard sizes available (based on back length); or made-to-measure. Many include reflective strips and all have optional name/initial embroidery.

PRICE: From £19.

AVAILABLE: Most pet stores.

Dog Dri Bag

A zip-up washable towelling bag into which you pop wet, muddy and smelly dogs after walks. It may look silly, but the head stays out and the rest of his body gets warm, clean and dry in no time.

PRICE: From £13.50 (small) to £23.50 (large).

AVAILABLE: Comfy Pet Products, 2-4 Parsonage Street, Bradninch, Nr Exeter, Devon EX5 4NW Tel: 0392 881285.

Ducks/Hens

Free-range eggs for breakfast every day! Ducks do like a bit of water to swim on, but hens seem to fit into any secure environment. (Both need a nesting shed which can be closed to deter foxes.) The Domestic Fowl Trust can supply hatching eggs, day-olds, growers and point of lay birds, plus feedstuffs, equipment and housing.

PRICE: e.g. day-old-chicks from £3; adult from £16 (half grown = half adult price); Ducks e.g. Aylesbury £25 each; Poultry Housing £41–£1210.

AVAILABLE: Michael and Victoria Roberts, The Domestic Fowl Trust, Honeybourne, Nr Evesham, Worcestershire WR11 5QJ Tel: 0386 833083; see also local press classified sections.

Greenpeace Subscription

Greenpeace campaigns to save the whales, save the rainforests and protect seals, dolphins, porpoises and sea turtles, etc. Become a member and keep informed.

PRICE: £14.50 p.a.

AVAILABLE: Greepeace, Freepost, Canonbury Villas, London N1 2BR Tel: 071-354 5100.

Grooming Brushes

Some dogs whinny with delight when they see their brush – others cower under the sofa; Groomex pure bristle brushes should make the prospect more enjoyable for either. Handmade from wild hog-hair. De-matting combs and rakes are also available and 'slickers' for creating coats as sleek as otters.

PRICE: £16.95 (Medium-sized stiff white bristle), £16.25 (bristle and nylon mix), £4.25 (coned matt remover).

AVAILABLE: Pet stores; Petcetera etc Ltd, PO Box 112, Henley-in-Arden, Solihull, West Midlands B95 5HD Tel: 092 684 3030 (Mail Order).

Grooming Vouchers

Vouchers for brushing, bathing, clipping, trimming and general pet pampering in animal salons. Available for dogs, cats and long-haired rabbits.

PRICE: From about £12 for a cut and blow dry.

AVAILABLE: Check phone book or ask vet for nearest groomer.

MAGAZINE SUBSCRIPTION
Cat World

Grooming, products, features.

PRICE: £18 p.a. (monthly).

AVAILABLE: Cat World Ltd, 10 Western Road, Shoreham-by-Sea, West Sussex BN43 3WD Tel: 0273 462000.

MAGAZINE SUBSCRIPTION
Dogs Today

A magazine for pet lovers (rather than animal breeders). Full of cutesy pictures of dogs, and articles generally about their health and well-being.

PRICE: £13 p.a. (six issues).

AVAILABLE: *Dogs Today*, Pet Subjects Ltd, 6 Station Parade, Suningdale, Berks SL5 0EP Tel: 0344 875442.

National Geographic Society Membership

Membership of the world's largest nonprofit scientific and educational organization, the fees of which help support worldwide research, exploration and geography education. Membership includes 12 monthly issues of *National Geographic* magazine – a glorious publication, crammed with information, reports and the most wonderful photographs from our doorstep to the remotest corners of the world. An inspiration!

PRICE: £19.75 p.a. (monthly).

AVAILABLE: National Geographic Society, Freepost, PO Box 19, Guildford, Surrey, GU3 3BR Tel: 0483 33161.

Pet Bed

Bean bag beds for dogs can be waterproof, thermal, therapeutic, or all three and come in all shapes or sizes to cope with all shapes or sizes of pet. Alternatively, traditional wicker pet baskets are available in small to huge sizes.

PRICE: From £10.

AVAILABLE: All good pet shops; Creature Comforts, The Sidings, Mitton Road, Whalley, Blackburn, BB6 9SE Tel: 0242 890224 (Mail Order).

Pet Toilet

A sanitation contraption that disposes of the unwanted piles that collect in the garden. Install into the ground, collect mess with scoop provided, drop into the toilet and treat with powder which is odourless and environmentally-safe.

PRICE: £19.45.

AVAILABLE: Doreens Pet and Garden Centre, 33-37 Morning Lane, London E9 7AL Tel: 081-985 1616.

Pet Vac

Looks like a hairdryer, but is actually a battery-operated vacuum cleaner for use directly on pets! Picks up loose hair at source and prevents hair balls. Quick, safe and silent.

PRICE: From £14.95.

AVAILABLE: Direct Choice, Euroway Business Park, Swindon SN5 8SN Tel: 0793 513946.

Riding Lessons

This could be the beginning of a very expensive hobby! Ideal for horse-crazed youngsters or adults who haven't ridden since childhood and may have forgotten how good it feels.

PRICE: From about £13.50 for one hour lesson (less for conducted hacks).

AVAILABLE: Contact local riding stables.

RSPB Membership

Membership includes unlimited entry to the Society's 100 plus nature reserves, saving up to £3 per person; and award-winnng quarterly mag.

PRICE: £19 p.a.

AVAILABLE: The Royal Society for the Protection of Birds, The Lodge, Sandy, Beds SG19 2DL Tel: 0767 680551.

RSPCA Membership

On joining the RSPCA you receive a 'package' including the annual report, rulebook and membership card. Throughout the year you are kept in touch with a quarterly magazine.

PRICE: £15 full annual adult membership (£250 life membership).

AVAILABLE: RSPCA, Causeway, Horsham, West Sussex RH12 1HG Tel: 0403 264181.

Studded Collar

Brass stud embellished heavy duty dog collar – for all butch dogs, and would-be butch dogs.

PRICE: About £17.

AVAILABLE: Most pet shops.

Tetra Club Membership

For fishy people – who may be keen to learn how to succeed from the experts. Advice, newsletters, offers and seminars for those interested in keeping tropical fish or goldfish.

PRICE: £10 annual membership.

AVAILABLE: Tetra Fish Care, Lambert Court, Chestnut Avenue, Eastleigh, Hampshire S05 3ZQ.

Timed Feeder

Wonderful devices whereby owners can leave for nights/weekends secure in the knowledge that their pet is adequately provided for. Timed release lid is programmed to open after designated period to serve pre-prepared meal.

PRICE: £16.95 one meal; £29.95 two meals [Petmate].

AVAILABLE: All good pet shops.

Travel Basket

The Pet Voyageur is a development on the wicker travelling basket insofar as it is made of strong plastic that's easy to clean and disinfect – if pets don't travel too well! Air vents provide adequate ventilation and easy-open fasteners lock securely for transit.

PRICE: From £14.99 (four sizes available).

AVAILABLE: Most pet stores; for nearest stockist contact: Rolf C Hagen (UK) Ltd, Castleford, West Yorks Tel: 0977 556622.

———————————————————————————

BETWEEN £20–£50

———————————————————————————

Adopt-an-Animal

An amazing scheme devised by London Zoo whereby ANY animal can be adopted – from a scorpion to a giraffe. The scheme is based on what it costs to keep and feed an animal for a year (for the more expensive animals it's broken down into £30 adoption units). The adoptive parent's name will appear on a plaque near the animal's enclosure, and you also receive adoption certificates, photos and complimentary entrance tickets.

PRICE: e.g. cockroach £20, Chilean flamingo £60, Chinese alligator £750, chimpanzee £750, tiger £3000, Asian elephant £3000.

AVAILABLE: Adopt an Animal, The Zoological Society of London, Regent's Park, London NW1 4RY Tel: 071-722 3333 Ext 234/235.

Bird Table

Tree-mounted, hanging or free-standing, The Nuttery is an award-winning bird-feeder designed to prevent squirrels and larger birds reaching the nuts while smaller birds can squeeze through the heavy gauge PVC-coated steel wire frame.

PRICE: £20.

AVAILABLE: The Natural History Museum Collection, Freepost SU361, Dept 5315, Hendon Road, Sunderland SR9 9AD Tel: 091-514 2777 (Mail Order).

Dog Training Lessons

If you've tried lessons at home 'The Woodhouse Way', and failed – then drastic action may be called for. Enrolment in private or group dog training lessons should sort out the problems.

PRICE: From about £30 for set of lessons.

AVAILABLE: Contact vet who should put you in touch with local groups.

Home Delivery Food/Litter

Delivery direct to the cat flap would save endless time and energy.

PRICE: Often free delivery on orders over a certain value.

AVAILABLE: Obliging pet shop proprietors.

Infra-Red Lamp

Warmth for outdoor animals. Low filament temperature to elimate fire risk and very economical to run. This is a 'dull emitter' rather than a 'bright emitter' – therefore easier for animals to sleep.

PRICE: £24.90.

AVAILABLE: Grange Pet Centre, Woodhouse Lane, Botley, Southampton S02 2EZ Tel: 0489 781260 (Mail Order).

Insect Vacuum

From America and the inventive mind of Victor Kiam comes the insect vacuum which allows you to suck up insects without squashing them and then release them unharmed.

PRICE: £49.95.

AVAILABLE: Modern Originals, 8 Forge Court, Reading Road, Yateley, Camberley, Surrey GU17 7RX Tel: 0252 878785 (Mail Order).

MAGAZINE SUBSCRIPTION
BBC Wildlife Magazine

Runs concurrently with BBC Wildlife TV and radio programmes so you can study the stills of pygmy elephants and learn how to grow your own roof garden.

PRICE: £26 p.a.

AVAILABLE: BBC Wildlife Subscriptions, PO Box 125, Tonbridge, Kent TN9 1YP.

Magnetic Cat Flap

The magnetism keeps the flap from flapping and therefore helps prevent the draughts and debris that are so often present at ankle level.

PRICE: £49.

AVAILABLE: Most good pet shops.

Microchip Tracking

Pettrac provides a microchip implant which is linked to the National Pet Register for which dog wardens and animal welfare homes have microchip scanners. Would give peace of mind for pet owners whose animals who have a tendency to go a-wandering.

PRICE: About £20.

AVAILABLE: Contact local vet, or phone Pettrac direct for nearest clinic. Tel: 0825 791069.

Personalized Dog Blanket

Soft, warm and incredibly plush, this blue dog blanket is piped in red and personalized with the dog's name (up to 12 characters). Completely washable it can be thrown on the pet's bed or on the back seat of the car.

PRICE: £27.

AVAILABLE: Eximious, 10 West Halkin Street, London SW1R 8JL Tel: 071-235 7828 (Mail Order available).

Songbird Cage

Most pet birds in France live in much grander style than their British equivalents, so that is where Number Nineteen acquires much of its stock, along the lines of palaces and chateaux! Alternatively, the Chinese architecture of pagodas and mandarin palaces is reflected in the cages available from Neal Street East.

PRICE: From £23.99 [Neal Street East]; From £200 [Number Nineteen].

AVAILABLE: Number Nineteen, Camden Passage, London N18EA Tel: 071-226 1126; Neal Street East, 5 Neal Street, London WC2H 9PU Tel: 071-240 0135.

Terrier Tunnel

A pet bed designed for animals who like to burrow – looks just like a bed with the duvet tucked in. Cover and lining fully washable.

PRICE: £21.95 (small); £24.95 (large).

AVAILABLE: Comfy Pets Products, 2-4 Parsonage Street, Bradninch, Nr Exeter, Devon EX5 4NW Tel: 0392 881285 (Mail Order).

£50 AND ABOVE

Animal Behaviour Referral Service

Dr Mugford is the only qualified psychologist to work as an animal behaviourist. If an unruly pet is driving his owners to their wits' end then he will need to be referred by a vet.

PRICE: £60 per consultation for dogs.

AVAILABLE: Dr Roger Mugford & Associates, PO Box 23, Chertsey, Surrey Tel: 0932 566696. Vets should be able to recommend any local groups that can deal with the behavourial problems of pets.

Aviary

Indoor or outdoor timber constructed bird houses which include flight areas and sleeping quarters. An overall size of about 8′ × 6′ is ideal for canaries, finches, budgies, parakeets and small parrots; a larger aviary with a greater 'flight size' would be needed for larger birds.

PRICE: e.g. Swanmore Octagonal Aviary (heavy duty – timber plus boarding) £474.00; Beaulieu Aviary (planed timber) £131; Indoor aviary from £189.93 (metal with sloping roofs and integral perches and feeders) plus carriage.

AVAILABLE: Grange Aviaries and Pet Centre, Woodhouse Lane, Botley, Nr Southampton, Hants S03 Tel: 0489 781260 (Mail Order available).

Bee Hive

The only thing not possible to get through the post are the actual bees. Essential equipment includes hives, honey extractors, comb containers and protective clothing!

PRICE: About £150 to get started.

AVAILABLE: Robert Lee (Bee Supplies), Willows Garden Nursery, Maidenhead Road, Windsor, Berks SL4 5UB Tel: 0753 830256 (Mail Order).

Cataerobic Centre

Offers cats the chance to climb, scratch and sleep off the ground as they would in nature. Either floor-to-ceiling models, or various corner and free-standing variations.

PRICE: From £49.99 to £169.99.

AVAILABLE: The Aviary, 45 Tachbrook Street, London SW1 Tel: 071-834 3711.

Dovecote

Six-sided wooden dovecote with accommodation for six pairs of doves. On top of a very elegant doric column (in total, just over 11 ft high).

PRICE: £1017.

AVAILABLE: Chilstone, Sprivers, Lamberhurst Road, Horsmonden, Kent TN12 8DR Tel: 0892 723266.

Exotic/Non-Exotic Pets

Pets should always be welcome additions to the family and therefore tend to be requested rather than surprise presents. Snakes or chinchillas could make an exotic change from rabbits or guinea pigs. Always check any special living conditions that may be required.

PRICE: Rescued animals may be given away free to very good homes; pedigree breeds can cost hundreds of pounds.

AVAILABLE: Pet shops, classified ads in local press; vets will have details of special breeders; contact the RSPCA who can put you in touch with local animal centres which have rescued all types of animals and will give them away to very good homes.

Invisible Fence

Keeps roving pets within designated boundaries. A thin antenna wire is buried underground transmitting a harmless signal which is received by the dog's collar. In combination with the training programme, this system works effectively with 97% of all dogs.

PRICE: Transmitter, from £179; Receiver £129 per dog; Installation kit, £59.

AVAILABLE: Westwood House, Bradford Peverell, Dorchester, Dorset, DT2 9SE Tel: 0305 889716/718 (24-hour).

Pet Insurance

For an annual premium cats, dogs, horses and birds can be covered against vet and boarding fees, cost of advertising and reward if the animal goes missing plus death benefit and third-party cover.

PRICE: From £69.95 p.a.

AVAILABLE: Pet Protect, 15 Knightsbridge Green, London SW1X 7QL Tel: 071-823 9449; Pet Plan Ltd, Pet Plan House, 10-13 Heathfield Terrace, London W4 4BR.

Pet Portrait

Immortalization in any medium from oil to bronze, from life or from a photo.

PRICE: Varies enormously depending on the artist's reputation and medium. Starts at about £50 for a small, framed pastel.

AVAILABLE: Check the small ads in local newspapers and animal magazines; Sara Davenport's Gallery is devoted to paintings, drawings and sculptures of dogs and can put you in touch with artists: 206 Walton Street, London SW3 Tel: 071-225 2223.

Safari Trip

A fantasy for most people, most particularly big-animal lovers.

PRICE: e.g. 15 day Zambia Safari £1965 to £2075 (includes five nights in Kapani Camp and five nights in a bush camp, all accommodation and game viewing activities).

AVAILABLE: Twickers World Ltd, 22 Church Street, Twickenham TW1 3NW Tel: 081-892 8164/7606; Wildlife Safari, The Old Bakery, South Road, Reigate, Surrey RH2 7LB Tel: 0737 223903.

Terrier Finder

If pet terriers still follow their hunting instincts and spend a good deal of time down holes, it can be a worry to find them. This Terrier Finder receiver comes with either an 8 ft or 15 ft transmitting collar.

PRICE: £54.75 (8 ft); £59.75 (15 ft).

AVAILABLE: William Powell & Son Ltd, 35 Carrs Lane, Birmingham B4 7SX Tel: 021-643 0689 (Mail Order).

CHAPTER SIXTEEN

SPECIAL FAMILY OCCASIONS

Look through the photo album and all the highlights of the years will be there; Christenings, going away to college, passing a driving test, getting through the dreaded GCSEs – but it's often appropriate to register the event with a bit more than a party and photos in the album. Family gifts – large or small – become treasured heirlooms; mother's day memories bring a smile to her face long after the event. It's definitely worth the effort to make it special.

ANNIVERSARY

1st – Paper

An exquisite writing set made from hand-marbled Italian paper will encourage anyone to smarten up their written English and take a calligraphy course!

PRICE: Blotters from £25, letter rack £32.75, pen stands £7.45.

AVAILABLE: The Italian Paper Shop, 11 Brompton Arcade, London SW3 1DY.

5th – Wood

For the memoirs – a teak or green maple fountain pen with gold lid.

PRICE: £25.25.

AVAILABLE: The General Trading Company, 144 Sloane Street, Sloane Square, London SW1X 9BI Tel: 071-730 0411.

10th – Tin/Steel

An antique-finish steel table and chairs will instil the romance of The Left Bank into the breakfast room or patio.

PRICE: £99 (table); £49 (chairs).

AVAILABLE: Branches of Habitat.

15th – Crystal

Weighty water jugs from Waterford; crystal tumblers for less.

PRICE: £112 (Icelip); £15 (tumblers).

AVAILABLE: Department stores and glass shops.

20th – China

Delicate, beautifully made Limoges boxes in the shape of fruits and vegetables.

PRICE: £62.

AVAILABLE: The General Trading Company, 144 Sloane Street, Sloane Square, London SW1X 9Bl Tel: 071-730 0411.

25th – Silver

Table adornments for very splendid occasions. A very special frippery.

PRICE: Sets of six name holders from £50.

AVAILABLE: Silverware departments, specialist jewellers and antique dealers.

40th – Ruby

A ruby-red scented rosebush (best bought in November) may be more appreciated than a Siam ruby at about £7000. Alternatively, a diamond and ruby eternity ring costing . . .

PRICE: £1500; roses from £3.

AVAILABLE: Garrard & Co Ltd, 112 Regent Street, London W1A 2JJ Tel: 071-734 7020. All garden centres.

50th – Gold

Three different coloured golds woven into a 'Russian wedding ring' style – which is inseparable.

PRICE: From £100.

AVAILABLE: All good jewellers.

60th – Diamond

A diamond ring is not just for engagements, but given on special family occasions like the birth of a child or an anniversary. In the simplest possible, famous Tiffany setting a ring will cost £700 upwards according to the size and quality of the stone. Cheaper rings are available from traditional outlets like Hatton Garden – but a Tiffany diamond …?

PRICE: See above.

AVAILABLE: Tiffany & Co, 25 Old Bond Street, London W1X 3AA Tel: 071-409 2790 and all good jewellers.

Weekend at L'Hotel de Crillon

Owned by the Tattinger family, this hotel is the epitome of luxury in what is considered to be the most romantic city in the world. Enjoy.

PRICE: From 3600FF per person (standard double room).

AVAILABLE: Hotel de Crillon, 10 place de la Concorde, Paris 75008 Tel: 010 33 4471 1500 or contact Leading Hotels of the World Tel: 0800 181123.

18TH BIRTHDAY

Plant a Tree

Environmentally friendly – the Woodland Trust will plant a tree for you (and send you the certificate to prove it) and for a slightly greater investment they will plant it in the woodland of your choice.

PRICE: From £10; £25 for woodland of your choice; £75 to sponsor creation of an entire area of woodland.

AVAILABLE: The Woodland Trust, Autumn Park, Dysart Road, Grantham, Lincolnshire NG31 6IL Tel: 0476 74297.

Jelly Bean Dispenser

Designed like the old fashioned bubblegum dispensers; drop in a penny and turn the handle to release a mouthful.

PRICE: £34.50.

AVAILABLE: The Conran Shop, Michelin House, 81 Fulham Road, London SW3 6RD Tel: 071-589 7401 (Mail Order available).

Membership to a Club

A sports club, a nightclub, a gentlemen's club. Membership requires certain years and often a first or a second proposal from established members.

PRICE: Membership may be nominal – it's just the getting in that counts.

AVAILABLE: Club of their choice.

Watch

Now is the time to discard that Scuba Swatch and turn from childish things. A new watch given for an eighteenth or twenty-first need not cost a fortune – it will always have more sentimental than mercenary value (although a Rolex or a Breitling would always be welcome).

PRICE: Depending on make.

AVAILABLE: Jewellers and specialist watch shops.

Unicycle

Hoping for a set of wheels? Well here's one to get you going – if nothing else, it will guarantee success at parties when it comes to tricks time.

PRICE: From £40.

AVAILABLE: The Juggling Shop, 56 Islington Park, London N1.

Vintage Port/Wine

This may be a case that was layed down for them at birth that has been lovingly, and recently enviously, guarded during its maturity; or may be just one bottle of very drinkable port.

PRICE: e.g. Talbot '89 £20 per bottle, £250 per case; Talbot '77 £45 per bottle, £513 per case.

AVAILABLE: Good wine merchants. Ask them for advice.

Objets – China/Silver/Paintings

Investments for the future – but choose something they will appreciate at present; heavy silver candlesticks and photoframes are popular, or a limited edition print from a contemporary artist.

PRICE: Silver frames from £25; pair of silver candlesticks £175; candelabra £2100; Persian carpet from £500.

AVAILABLE: Antique shops, specialist shops and galleries.

Car

Serious object of desire and privilege of a very few.

PRICE: From a couple of hundred pounds.

AVAILABLE: Local car dealers, classified columns, *Exchange & Mart*, etc.

Round-the-World Ticket

Wanderlust is usually at its peak and a ticket to a faraway place or all the way round may sate urges that would prove destructive in later life.

PRICE: Tickets to NYC are available from £199; Around the world ticket from £1000 (Australia, Pacific, USA, Far East).

AVAILABLE: Local travel agent; Trailfinders, 194 Kensington High Street, London W8 7RG Tel: 071-938 3939.

A Party

Organize one yourself or organize someone else to organize one. Marking the day ranges from hiring the top room of the pub, erecting a marquee in the garden or hiring the Dinosaur Room at the Natural History Museum – in whichever situation, father's speech is guaranteed to be drunken and someone will be sick in the flowerbed.

PRICE: An arm and a leg.

AVAILABLE: Contact local venues for room hire; Party organizers include Juliana's Tel: 071-937 1555; Zino's Tel: 071-385 3438; London Zoo (where you might like to hire The Reptile House) Tel: 071-722 3333.

Jewellery

Signet ring with family crest, pearls, diamond earrings and a charm-bracelet are all traditional, acceptable, and will be treasured for a lifetime.

PRICE: Charm bracelets from about £150 plus charms; Diamond studs around £600; Signet ring with seal from £150.

AVAILABLE: Jewellers.

Family Heirlooms

Now is the time for them to come into that rather ungainly wooden dining table and Regency commode – as well as Aunt Agatha's exquisite diamond bracelet.

PRICE: Priceless.

AVAILABLE: Your own cache of goodies.

FATHER'S DAY

Patum Peperium

Men actually seem to love Gentleman's Anchovy Relish that tastes rather like fishy marmite. If you buy the ordinary black-and-white plastic pots (rather than the jazzed-up hunting scene gift pots) – you get twice as much for your money.

PRICE: £2.65 for 71g; £7.50 for 85g.

AVAILABLE: Sainsburys, delicatessens.

James Bond Theme Tunes

To assure him that he really is man amongst men.

PRICE: £4.50.

AVAILABLE: Selected record shops.

Floating Bath Plugs

A replacement for the rubber duck, these fun plugs float, squeak and squirt water. Made from brightly-coloured latex, they come as bombs, frogs, hippos, crocs.

PRICE: From £6.99 (ugly monsters).

AVAILABLE: The Reject Shop, most gift shops and department stores.

Letter Tray Set

Desk tray accessory that will separate the 'in' and 'out' or rather the 'paid' and 'to be paid' piles.

PRICE: From £8.49.

AVAILABLE: Branches of WH Smith and Ikea.

Nasal Hair Tweaker

For those with a sense of humour, this little device prunes bushy noses, ears and eyebrows.

PRICE: e.g. £9.75. (Remington Hygienic Clipper).

AVAILABLE: Boots, most other chemists and large department stores.

BOOK CHOICE
Fathers and Sons

Eight men talk about their relationships with their fathers and the effect this has had on their lives. Particularly interesting when one considers how they have turned out.

PRICE: £10.99 [Serpent's Tail].

AVAILABLE: Most good bookshops.

Bottle of Favourite Tipple

You know what it is and you know he doesn't always buy it for himself.

PRICE: Whatever it costs.

AVAILABLE: Wine merchants or off-licences.

Subscription to Fortean Times

From the bizarre to the ridiculous – *Fortean Times* is a magazine dedicated to continuing the work of Charles Fort, a nineteenth-century philosopher, investigating corn circles and other phenomena.

PRICE: £12 p.a. (6 issues).

AVAILABLE: *Fortean Times*, John Brown Publishing Ltd, 20 Paul Street, Frome, Somerset, BA11 1DX Tel: 0373 451777.

D R Harris Pick-Me-Up

The gentleman's hangover cure.

PRICE: £15.90 for 600 ml.

AVAILABLE: D R Harris, 29 St James's Street, London SW1 Tel: 071-930 3915 (Mail Order available).

Pub Games

Traditional pub games with illuminating names like Shove Ha'penny and Shut the Box can bring that pub atmosphere right into your own front room.

PRICE: From £3.95 (poker dice); Shove Ha'penny £29.95; Shut the Box £11.95.

AVAILABLE: Just Games, 71 Brewer Street, London W1R 3FB Tel: 071-734 6124 (Mail Order available).

Traveller's Tales

Useful not only for keeping kids quiet on interminably long journeys, but also for fathers who may frequently have to travel long journeys or spend a large part of their day in static traffic jams. More than 2000 titles.

PRICE: Four tapes can be hired for one week for £6.50; Annual Membership £20; Lifetime Membership £100.

AVAILABLE: Traveller's Tales, Great Weddington, Ash, Canterbury, Kent CT3 2AR Tel: 0304 812531.

Monogrammed Bookmarks

Terribly distinguished leather bookmarks with monogrammed brass ends which would look horribly out of place around Ludlum's latest paperback.

PRICE: £24.95 (including monogram).

AVAILABLE: Barclay and Bodie, 7-9 Blenheim Terrace, London NW8 0EH Tel: 071-372 5705 (Mail Order available).

Membership of Attend-a-Lock

The service designed for people with a bad track record with keys. A network of professional locksmiths (registered with the police) can reach you within a hour if keys have been lost or stolen and get you into your office/house, etc, and fit new locks if required.

PRICE: From £25 p.a.

AVAILABLE: Membership Services, Attend-a-Lock, 1 Saville Row, Bath BA1 2QD Tel: 0225 311252.

Train Set

The dedication to detail in some of the more sophisticated versions will be fully appreciated by train fanatics. Lima trains are so exquisitely detailed that even train spotters will be satisfied as the serial number of the same model varies.

PRICE: From £19.99.

AVAILABLE: Branches of Beatties nationwide; 10 The Broadway, Southgate, London N14 6PN Tel: 081-886 4258 (Mail Order).

Monogrammed Slippers

Give that crumbly old pair to Bingo and replace them with a spanking new (monogrammed) pair.

PRICE: Around £54.95 [Church's].

AVAILABLE: Church's, 58 Burlington Arcade, London W1 Tel: 071-493 8307 (Mail Order available).

Survival Weekend

A get-back-to-nature weekend should appeal to the Neanderthal in him – learning how to trap rabbits, pheasants and fish, how to fashion weapons and how to make shelter.

PRICE: From £59.

AVAILABLE: Red Letter Days, 8/12 Woodhouse Road, North Finchley, London N12 0RG Tel: 081-343 8822.

Weekend at Gleneagles

Not much fun unless he plays golf – in which case he will find plenty to do and will particularly enjoy the short trip to the nineteenth hole!

PRICE: From £119.50 (winter) plus green fees – prices rise in summer.

AVAILABLE: Gleneagles Hotel, Auchterarder, Perthshire PH3 1NF Tel: 0764 662231.

Silk Dressing Gown

Stylish, sophisticated, and oh so sexy against the skin.

PRICE: £295.

AVAILABLE: Hackett, 137/138 Sloane Street, London SW1X 9AY Tel: 071-730 3331, most gentlemen's outfitters.

Fountain Pen

A Mont Blanc Solitaire is as opulent as you can get without being solid gold and jewel encrusted. With a ribbed silver stem and smooth writing 18ct gold nib, it is not only a joy to behold, it is also (more importantly) a joy to write with.

PRICE: £540.

AVAILABLE: Good department stores and stationers; Pencraft Ltd, 281 Regent Street, London W1 Tel: 071-493 2125 (Mail Order available).

Fax Machine

The friendly face of technology – letters can now be sent down phone lines and therefore completely revolutionize the home office system.

PRICE: Approximately £900.

AVAILABLE: For information contact: Canon (UK) Ltd, Freepost BM1 489, Birmingham B1 1BR Tel: 0800 252223 for information.

GOING TO SCHOOL

Address Book

For all the letters they will never write and to compile all the addresses of the friends they are about to make.

PRICE: From £6.95.

AVAILABLE: Stationers.

Pocket Edition Board Games

Cluedo, Mastermind, etc, are available by Waddingtons in pocket editions.

PRICE: £7.99.

AVAILABLE: Department stores, larger toy shops.

A Fruitcake

Food to share is a sure way to ensure a new bug's popularity. Cut no corners – this has to be the biggest, stickiest and fruitiest you can bake. Their future depends on it.

PRICE: Make it yourself – or have it sent mail order from Meg Rivers (prices from about £11).

AVAILABLE: Meg Rivers Cakes, Middle Tysoe, Warwickshire CV35 0SE Tel: 0295 688101 (Mail Order).

Foreign Language Dictionary

A heavy English/French or German or Latin Dictionary.

PRICE: e.g. Collins dictionaries from £4 to £20; *Collins Complete English Dictionary* £19.99.

AVAILABLE: All good bookshops.

Notepaper Headed with School House Address

Just in case – families always hope for letters home from school; in more cases than not, a two-minute reverse charge phone call is all they hear for weeks.

PRICE: From £21.99 to £41.99 (for 100 sheets).

AVAILABLE: All good stationers.

Sports Equipment

A spanking new racquet, bat or stick – perhaps just the grown-up version of their junior size.

PRICE: £19.99 (Slazenger tennis racquet)–£300 (Prince Vortex); £15–£170 (cricket bat); £15–£95 (hockey stick).

AVAILABLE: All good sports shops.

Folding Photoframes

Travels closed, but opens to reveal up to six pictures of our home, our dog and our mum.

PRICE: Around £24.

AVAILABLE: Branchs of John Lewis Partnership.

Hot Water Bottle Cover

Many schools will not allow electric blankets, especially for its younger pupils. Those big dorms can get awfully draughty – so get equipped with a hot water bottle cover with thermal lining that is 'snuggle safe' and keeps the water warm until the early hours.

PRICE: £24.99 including bottle.

AVAILABLE: Hot water bottles from most chemists and department stores; covers from, Cally & Co, 130 Walham Green Court, Moore Park Road, London SW6 2DG Tel: 071-385 8404.

Dressing Gown

Will probably be on the uniform list anyway; but any young lady or young gent would like to cut a dash at brushing teeth time.

PRICE: £29–£39 (coloured).

AVAILABLE: Branches of Habitat, Marks & Spencer.

Spellmaster

Creditcard-size spelling aid to bamboozle the teacher.

PRICE: £34.99.

AVAILABLE: Electrical and department stores.

Trunk

Their whole life is about to packed into one box, so it had better be sturdy.

PRICE: Around £120.

AVAILABLE: Luggage shops, department stores.

GOING TO UNIVERSITY

Photos of the Family

It may be some time before Dave and Sue see the family again, especially if the college is some distance from home, and if they are sporty, with fixtures every weekend. More of a comfort than many care to admit.

PRICE: Reprints from Boots are 49p each.

AVAILABLE: Any shop which offers a photo developing service.

Condoms

We all know that going to college is not just about getting a degree – it's about finding yourself, learning to live with independence, and making new friends.

PRICE: Mates from £1.19; Ultra Safe from £1.39.

AVAILABLE: All chemists.

Hangover Cure

If the new student is 'unused to wine' then he may well risk missing all his morning lectures trying to recover from the night before. Pack him off with a good supply of Resolve and he should recover his equilibrium enough to do it all over again the following evening.

PRICE: From £1.58 for five sachets [Resolve].

AVAILABLE: All good chemists.

Lever Arch Files

Many colleges sell files emblazoned with a crest or motto. Will or will this not instil an enormous rush of pride and intellectual zeal? Also silver-dipped bic biros and silver sharpener covers.

PRICE: Lever Arch files from £3.29 (ring binders from £1.30); silver-dipped Bic £14, sharpener cover £35.

AVAILABLE: Try the College stationers; Links, 27 Broadgate Circle, London EC2M 2QS Tel: 071-628 9668 (Mail Order available).

Phonecard

A phonecard packed with units may give you a fighting chance of hearing some news in their first term. An outside chance.

PRICE: From £1 to £20.

AVAILABLE: All Post Offices; a large number of shops and newsagents which display the phonecard sign.

BOOK CHOICE
Grub on a Grant

This plus a new title, *Peckish but Poor* by Cas Clarke.

PRICE: £5.99 each [Headline].

AVAILABLE: All good bookshops.

Catering Pack of Coffee/Tea

You hope this is what they stay up all night drinking whilst sorting out the problems of the world. A large cannister of instant coffee will ensure popularity.

PRICE: From £6.39 [Nescafé].

AVAILABLE: Cash-and-carry superstores; some large supermarkets.

Money Belt

When travelling among the light-fingered, a money belt is essential, but often so bulky it actually invites attention. One of the neatest and most inconspicuous is from Travelling Light, made from 100% cotton webbing with a zip that travels the whole length of the belt.

PRICE: £6.95.

AVAILABLE: Travelling Light, Freepost, Morland House, Morland, Penrith, Cumbria CA10 1BR Tel: 0931 7144 (Mail Order).

Frying Pan

If he or she has to fend for themselves in digs or self-catering halls of residence then some cooking implement is essential. Many students live by dictum that 'if it ain't fried then it ain't food' – if they don't, a wok is a more versatile option.

PRICE: From £14 (standard size); from £18.50 (wok).

AVAILABLE: All good kitchen shops, department stores.

Sandwich Maker

Toasted sandwiches have been the staple diet of generations of students – having a personal toaster is a sure way of making friends.

PRICE: From £14.99 [Morphy Richards].

AVAILABLE: All good electrical appliance and department stores.

Mail Order Beer

A selection of unusual beers, gift-packed and sent right to the address where they are needed most.

PRICE: From £14.99 for 11 bottles.

AVAILABLE: The Beer Shop, 8 Pitfield Street, London N1 6HA Tel: 071-739 3701.

Self-Hypnosis Video

Tease them with a self-hypnosis video on Accelerated Learning. Designed as a self-help tape, you pop it on the telly and induce a state of open-eyed dreamy state of consciousness in which you are receptive to properly phrased suggestions! Worth a try?

PRICE: £19.95.

AVAILABLE: New World, Paradise Farm, Westhall, Halesworth, Suffolk, IP19 8RH Tel: 098681 682 (Mail Order).

Student Rail Card

A Young Persons' Railcard allows the holder to travel anywhere in the country with a third off the standard fare.

PRICE: £16.

AVAILABLE: All BR stations.

A Daily Newspaper

Arrange delivery of a quality daily newspaper to ensure they are hot on current economic, political and social affairs – as well as the hot-blooded variety.

PRICE: Around £25 per term.

AVAILABLE: Contact a newsagent in the area.

A Heavy Tome

Gray's Anatomy, Jansen or any of the other weighty tomes that form the basis of a subject and which will constantly be referred to, not just for the next few years but for the rest of their lives. They are expensive, but essential, and any student will appreciate the outlay being made by someone other than themselves.

PRICE: e.g. *Gray's Anatomy* £95!

AVAILABLE: All good bookshops.

Bicycle

If they haven't got an Alfa Spider, then one of these will have to do for wheels.

PRICE: From £160; Alfa Romeo Spider £16,720.

AVAILABLE: Cycle shops.

Money

Couldn't be simpler – couldn't be more welcome.

PRICE: The more the better.

AVAILABLE: From your pocket.

MOTHER'S DAY

A Day Off

Start with breakfast in bed, and carry on with coffee, lunch, tea and dinner in bed if that's what she wants – just as long as she doesn't have to lift a finger all day.

PRICE: It doesn't cost a penny!

AVAILABLE: From her grateful family.

Herbal Cure for Shopping

Herbal and Medieval cures for Uncontrolled Shopping and also For the Fear of Spiders, Creepy Crawlies and Daddy-Long Legs – all in one little sachet. If only it was this easy!

PRICE: £2.50.

AVAILABLE: The Master Herbalist, Broomhill Herb Farm, Great Brickhill, Buckinghamshire Tel: 0525 261720 (Mail Order).

Plant Minder

A water-retaining tray which can keep up to four pot plants moist for a week.

PRICE: £3.99 [Humex].

AVAILABLE: Gardening centres.

Handbag Mirror

Slim case to slip into the bag in brass or silver finish.

PRICE: £7.50.

AVAILABLE: Hairdressers, department stores.

Tapes of Gregorian Chant

Simple medieval compositions that have a calming and stilling effect on the mind, body and spirit.

PRICE: From £4.

AVAILABLE: Record stores.

Spider Catcher

Spiders and other creepy crawlies can be scooped up and deposited safely outside without squashing them and without severely jangling your nerves. The scooper is operated by a finger trigger and a 36″ long handle allows you to reach up to high corners and also keep the creatures at arm's length.

PRICE: £4.95.

AVAILABLE: Innovations (Mail Order) Ltd, Euroway Business Park, Swindon SN5 8SN Tel: 0793 514666.

Beeswax Candles

Beeswax candles last twice as long as paraffin wax and neither drip nor smoke – they also have a warm aroma of beeswax and retain their honey cell markings.

PRICE: From £4.95 (small fat candle) to £16.80 (large, extra fat); Boxed set of three small fat candles £13.80 (honey or cream colour).

AVAILABLE: Kirker, Greer & Co, 85 High Street, Burnham-on-Crouch, Essex CM0 8AH Tel: 0621 784657 (Mail Order).

Chocolates

Handmade chocolates that taste tremendous. A small box with ten chocolates or the 1½ lb mixed box with 60. You can even spell out a name inside, in chocolate!

PRICE: £5.75 (¼ lb) – £33 (1½ lb).

AVAILABLE: Charbonnel et Walker, 28 Old Bond Street, London W1 Tel: 071-491 0939 (Mail Order available).

Old Cottage Garden Roses

Mother is sent a catalogue showing all the different types of roses available with a greetings card showing the value of the gift. Alternatively send your choice of favourite direct.

PRICE: From £6.

AVAILABLE: Roses Du Temps Passé, Woodlands House, Stretton, Nr Stafford, ST19 9LG Tel: 0785 840217 (Mail Order).

A Beauty Treatment

A pampering session of any description will allow her to just sit/lie with no-one to think about but herself.

PRICE: Manicures start at about £7; Facials from £15.

AVAILABLE: Contact local beauty salons and health clubs.

Send-a-Shrub

Cut flowers are beautiful for a very short time, a characteristic which is their charm as well as their downfall. For a beautiful flower that lasts just a little longer, Send-a-Shrub will send a boxed shrub with a personal message and planting instructions.

PRICE: From £10 + £2 p&p (list includes roses, camellias and viburnums).

AVAILABLE: Send-a-Shrub, Broome Lodge, Bungay, Suffolk, NR35 2HX Tel: 050845 432.

Photos of the Family

Family groups are set off a treat in a watercolour print frame printed 'Love Thy Family'.

PRICE: £10.95.

AVAILABLE: Barclay and Bodie, 7-9 Blenheim Terrace, London NW8 0EH Tel: 071-372 5705 (Mail Order available).

Aromatic Oil Burners/Vaporizing Ring

Pottery burners which can be used for burning aromatherapy oils to give you a bit of get up and go, or any aromatic oil to disperse the smell of decorating or spicy food. Vaporizing rings are an alternative – a few drops in the ring and pop the whole thing over a lightbulb and the oils will vaporize.

PRICE: £11.20 (burner); £3.10 (vaporizing ring); £23.70 (electric burner and oils).

AVAILABLE: Aromatherapy Products Ltd, The Knoll Business Centre, Old Shoreham Road, Hove, Sussex BN3 7GS Tel: 0273 412139 (Mail Order).

Extra Large Bathtowel

A bathtowel as big as the bathroom is a luxury to wrap up in.

PRICE: e.g. £15.95 (90 cm × 180 cm).

AVAILABLE: Habitat branches.

Message Recording Clock

If your mother promises faithfully to record *Omnibus* on the video and then forgets, or loves the cat to death but rarely remembers to feed it, then a message-recording clock could act as a handy reminder. A 20-second message can be recorded and then replayed by pulling a cord.

PRICE: £19.99.

AVAILABLE: Argos stores nationwide.

Ansaphone

If mother has become the friendly telephone operator as well as the family taxi service, then this will allow her to perform one task without neglecting the other.

PRICE: From £28.99 [Binatone].

AVAILABLE: Electrical appliance shops, department stores.

A Day at the Sanctuary

The Sanctuary really does offer a haven from the trials and tribulations of everyday life. Steambaths and saunas are all part of the package which includes use of all the facilities (and one sunbed session). Extras include a whole range of health and beauty treatments, from massages and body wraps to reflexology or a make-up lesson.

PRICE: Daily membership £37.50 (extra treatments from £4 to £82); Annual membership £1370.

AVAILABLE: The Sanctuary, 12 Floral Street, London WC2E 9DH Tel: 071-240 9635.

Pamper Hamper

Filled with unlimited luxury from Champagne Bath Salts to Coconut Milk Wash so mum can spend all day in the tub.

PRICE: About £40.

AVAILABLE: Cosmetics To Go, Freepost BH15 1BR Tel: 0800 373366 (Mail Order).

In and Out Board

Are they 'out' or 'in'? Large families in rambling houses may find this useful when disciplined to use it, and mother will know whether it's worth bellowing upstairs to get the phone. A family version of the sliding-in and out boards reminiscent of college stairwells and doctors' surgeries.

PRICE: £48.

AVAILABLE: Barclay and Bodie, 7-9 Blenheim Terrace, London NW8 0EH Tel: 071-372 5705 (Mail Order available).

Bath Tray with Bookrest

The bath is the most luxurious place to read but it is a hazardous undertaking, risking soggy or sodden pages. A bath tray with bookrest is based on the conventional design of a bath tidy with a special rest to secure the book.

PRICE: £113 (comes in antique gold, chrome and brass finishes and fits most baths).

AVAILABLE: Samuel Heath Tel: 021-772 2303.

Cream Jars

English crystal jars with silver lids are beautiful dressing-table accessories which make you FEEL beautiful as you're putting on and taking off your face.

PRICE: £120–£250 (antique silver).

AVAILABLE: Department stores; Bruford and Heming Ltd, 28 Conduit Street, London W1R 9TA Tel: 071-629 4289 (Mail Order available).

CHAPTER SEVENTEEN

WEDDINGS

Tʜᴇʀᴇ's something about a wedding that cheers everyone up – not least of all the party! We are obviously all hopelessly optimistic and old-fashioned at heart. Over a third of all weddings today are remarriages (which makes present-giving just a little tricky) and divorce rates are still rising. So choose a present that adds to the delight of the occasion and the memory.

UNDER £5

Glass – Duralex

This strengthened French glassware takes you right back to the school refectory – another affordable design classic. These glasses now have rather a cult status and, as we all know, are virtually indestructible.

Pʀɪᴄᴇ: Small glasses from 75p.

Aᴠᴀɪʟᴀʙʟᴇ: The Design Museum, Shad Thames, London SE1 2YD Tel: 071-403 6933 (Mail Order available).

Preserving Jars

In various sizes from Le Parfait – a whole collection for larder supplies looks wonderful.

Pʀɪᴄᴇ: £1.45 for 0.5 litre – £3.35 for 3 litre.

Aᴠᴀɪʟᴀʙʟᴇ: Most good kitchen shops, large department stores.

Set of Stain Devils

To make sure the new residence keeps its shine. Stain Devils will remove milk, coffee, sauce, blood, ballpoint pen, etc.

PRICE: £1.75.

AVAILABLE: DIY, hardware stores.

Set of Wooden Coathangers

Wouldn't everyone like to get rid of those wire ones from the drycleaners and admire the genuine wood model?

PRICE: From approximately £3.50.

AVAILABLE: Haberdashery depts, hardware stores.

Silk Flowers

Some of these flowers are incredibly realistic. All have the advantage of being able to be washed of dust every so often so they look as good as new.

PRICE: £1.35–£6.95 per head (allow £25 plus for an arrangement).

AVAILABLE: Branches of John Lewis Partnership.

────────────────────

BETWEEN £5–£10

Book/Video Camouflage

Who would have thought that what looks like a first edition of *Byron's Poems* actually contains a tape of *Terminator II*? CDs are likewise tastefully camouflaged by the equally historic looking covers.

PRICE: £8.50 (video box); £13.95 (CD box – holds 10 CDs).

AVAILABLE: Barclay and Bodie, 7-9 Blenheim Terrace, London NW8 0EH Tel: 071-372 5705 (Mail Order available).

Candlesticks

Dartington produce slim elegant glass ones, or choose the rustic look with pewter or the antique silver variety.

PRICE: From £9.99.

AVAILABLE: Silverware, glassware and gift shops, craft shops, department stores.

Chopping Board

Should be in very hard timber – beech or sycamore – to survive the rigours of day-to-day abuse. The more substantial the better. Melamine ones are OK, but wear quickly – the ceramic-topped 'Tuf Top' claims to unscratchable and unbreakable.

PRICE: From £6.95 (wood); £24 (Tuf Top 20″ × 16″).

AVAILABLE: All cookery shops, branches of John Lewis Partnership.

Instant Round Table

A chipboard table which comes flat packed and can be erected in moments. A snip at under £10 – but it does need covering with a round cloth.

PRICE: From £8.95 (small) to £16.95 (large); £5.99 (Homebase – 20″ diameter).

AVAILABLE: Branches of Laura Ashley nationwide; Laura Ashley by Post, PO Box 19, 19 Newtown, Powys SY16 1DZ Tel: 0800 868100 (Mail Order); Branches of Homebase, Do It All, etc.

Picnic and Patio Glasses and Bowls

Everyone's fooled by clear acrylic glasses and bowls until they pick them up – they're light as a feather.

PRICE: From £7.99 (four tumblers), £16.99 (four long stemmed glasses), £11.99 (lidded pitcher), £12.99 (large sealed bowl).

AVAILABLE: Selfridges and all department stores and good gift shops.

Sconces

Wall-mounted tin candle holders in traditional Shaker design i.e. simple and functional. Punched tin reflects candle light beautifully.

PRICE: From £8.95 (holds tiny candles) to £23.95.

AVAILABLE: Shaker Ltd, 25 Harcourt Street, London W1H 1DT Tel: 071-724 7672 (Mail Order available).

Wedding Bouquet Pressing

Sylvia Pepper's main line is inscribed paperweights for special occasions. Names, dates and places are embellished with flowers. A glorious sideline are her framed, pressed flowers, the components of which can be taken from a wedding bouquet.

PRICE: From £7.50.

AVAILABLE: Sylvia Pepper, 35 Chantry Lane, Hatfield, AL10 9HS Tel: 0707 266688.

BETWEEN £10–£20

Cocktail Plate

Wondering where to display the nuts, crisps and Roka biscuits? The answer is in one divided and very tasteful glass plate.

PRICE: £15.45 [J G Durant].

AVAILABLE: Selfridges and all large department stores.

Door mats

From a standard to giant size, thick coir doormats, hand-stencilled with country-style cow, pig, duck, etc, motifs. Plain or decorated, woven for very heavy-duty wear.

PRICE: From £15.50.

AVAILABLE: Happy Mats, Land House Farm, Lanchester, County Durham CH7 0TA Tel: 0388 730744.

Dummy Books

Create an instant library and solve the problem of looking illiterate because of empty shelves by cheating! Dummy books – available either tired and shabby or neat and well-preserved – are sold by the foot and can be used to hide space or unsightly paperbacks. Titles include Shakespeare (ten books), Ruskin (nine books), The Law Times Reports.

PRICE: From £14 a foot.

AVAILABLE: For stockist contact: The Dummy Book Company Ltd, No 1 Cow Shed, Upton Grove, Tetbury, Glos GL8 8LR Tel: 0666 503376 (Mail Order).

Glass – Bristol Blue

Blue glass goblets to quaff, quaff and quaff yet more in Bachanalian fashion. Cobalt became fashionable in glass-making at the end of the nineteenth century as a means of tax evasion but afterwards remained popular because of its striking appearance.

PRICE: e.g. £15.75 (sherry glass); £19.95 (reproduction goblet).

AVAILABLE: Handmade in Britain, 10 Conlan Street, London W10 5AR Tel: 081-964 3807 (Mail Order).

Hot Plates

Invaluable for those who entertain. From a simple tray, to a tray with a compartment for dishes, to a sophisticated Hostess trolley with integral veg dishes and large, enclosed heated compartment.

PRICE: From £11.99.

AVAILABLE: All large department stores, electrical shops.

Ice Cooler

Ice buckets are now known as coolers and come in every conceivable finish.

PRICE: From £12.

AVAILABLE: Department stores, hardware shops.

Kitchen Starter Set

From Addis, the starter kit of bin, bowl, plate rack, cutlery tray and drainer – all matching.

PRICE: £12.99.

AVAILABLE: Hardware shops and department stores.

Knife Block

Knife storage block keeps knives safe, is convenient and doesn't ruin the blades.

PRICE: £11.95 (holds six 10″ knives and a steel).

AVAILABLE: Kitchen shops, department stores and hardware stores.

Magazine Rack

The antique versions known as 'Canterburys' are so elegant they cost upwards of £500. Equally useful modern versions are a lot less.

PRICE: From £19.

AVAILABLE: Branches of John Lewis Partnership; furniture retailers.

Relationship Compatibility Chart

Do you dare? Chris Marshall (the regular astrologer for *Marie Claire*) can analyse the relationship by focusing on each person, their date, time and place of birth. From this he can interpret how they relate to each other, highlighting the differences and similarities between them.

PRICE: £15.

AVAILABLE: Chris Marshall, c/o Mysteries Ltd, 9-11 Monmouth Street, London WC2H 9DA Tel: 071-240 3688 (Mail Order).

Sabatier Knife Set

Don't be fooled by the name 'Sabatier' – now that no one company holds an exclusive licence over the use of the name, the quality of knives vary from brand to brand. There is also no need to buy the whole set – four basic knives should cover all cutting eventualities – a cook's knife, filleting knife, a paring and a carving knife. Available either in carbon steel (which discolours) or stainless steel – excellent to use, practical to care for and retains its cutting edge – the only disadvantage is its relatively high cost.

PRICE: e.g. Cook's knife 18 cm stainless steel £17.57; carbon steel £15.26. Prices in stainless steel vary from £10.95 to £28.95.

AVAILABLE: All kitchenware departments and specialist stores.

Slick Pewterware

Orb salt and pepper grinders, spiral egg cups and napkin rings are part of Nick Munro's extremely chic range of goods.

PRICE: e.g. Four egg cups £16.99; four napkin rings £16.99.

AVAILABLE: Nick Munro, c/o Handmade in Britain, 10 Conlan Street, London W10 5AR Tel: 081-964 3807 (Mail Order).

Tandoori Cooking Pot

A clay pot which can be used inside household ovens and is true to the cooking methods of India and Pakistan. You too can enjoy the tenderest and juiciest tandoori chicken and nan bread without having to go to the takeaway.

PRICE: £19.95.

AVAILABLE: Scotts of Stow, Admail 222, The Square, Stow-on-the-Wold, Glos GL54 1AF Tel: 0249 449111 (Mail Order).

Trays

Think about it. Small trays for cups of tea; large trays for TV suppers. Can anyone find a use for the not quite large enough tray? (See also: Lap Trays – Oldies and Goldies chapter).

PRICE: About £15 for good-sized tray.

AVAILABLE: Kitchen shops, hardware and department stores.

Wastepaper Bins

There are some you'd be proud to display as 'objects' but would probably feel extravagent investing in yourself.

PRICE: From £14.

AVAILABLE: Department stores.

Windchimes

Remarkably soothing, close to nature chimes, which clang melodiously as the wind takes them.

PRICE: £18.80–£33.50.

AVAILABLE: Flora & Fauna, Orchard House, Patmore End, Ugley, Bishop's Stortford, Hertfordshire CM22 6JA Tel: 0799 88289 (Mail Order available).

BETWEEN £20–50

Bed Throws

Not just thrown on beds these days; drape them over chairs and sofas, hang them across windows and down walls. Stunning woollen throws are available from Melin Tregwynt; cheaper versions from most furniture stores.

PRICE: From £40 (fringed throw from Melin Tregwynt).

AVAILABLE: Melin Tregwynt, Castle Morris, Haverfordwest, Dyfed SA62 5UX Tel; 0345 644 (Mail Order); department stores, branches of Ikea.

Cast-Iron Cookware

Like copper it will last a lifetime, but unlike copper it is not prohibitively expensive. The Victor Cast Ware range is about as authentic as you can get – it comes from the Ironbridge Gorge.

PRICE: From £11.95 (11″ skillet) to £64.95 (traditional kitchen scales).

AVAILABLE: The Victor Cast Iron Ware range, c/o Handmade in Britain, 14 Conlan Street, London W10 5AR Tel: 081-964 3807 (Mail Order).

Document Safe

Where do you put passports, birth and marriage certificates? This is a sensible protection against fire, and stores most sizes of document without folding.

PRICE: £44.99 [Sentry].

AVAILABLE: Security firms, large department stores.

Fondue Set

Methylated spirit burner keeps either oil or cheese bubbling to cook meat or dip bread, and makes original chocolate puddings as well. Metal for meat and oil, pottery for cheese.

PRICE: £45 for Le Creuset version (including forks).

AVAILABLE: Department stores and kitchen shops.

Glass – Hand-Blown Lead Crystal

Tim Casey produces stunning free-blown glass from his refuge on the Isle of Sark. All pieces, including glasses, decanters and scent bottles, have subtle purple, gold, blue or clear rims. Their contours are smooth, they look substantial – and are exquisite.

PRICE: From £15 for a tumbler to £17.50 (red wine, white wine, sherry, and water glasses).

AVAILABLE: Tim Casey, c/o Handmade in Britain, 14 Conlan Street, London W10 5AR Tel: 081-964 3807 (Mail Order).

Handmade Photo Albums

Bound in leather and handtooled on the spine (plus optional gold embossing) these albums are fit only for the finest photos.

PRICE: From £48 (10″ × 12″).

AVAILABLE: Lydden Albums, 7 Salisbury Street, Blandford Forum, Dorset DT11 7AU Tel: 0258 459537 (Mail Order).

House Sign

Weatherproof aluminium – the range starts in black with numbers and expands to include pictures in colour.

PRICE: £33–£89.

AVAILABLE: Branches of John Lewis Partnership.

Key Rack

Boards covered in green baize, grey flannel or tweed with fleur-de-lys hooks make an elegant place to hang a key, and, more to the point, prevent them getting lost.

PRICE: £29.95.

AVAILABLE: Barclay and Bodie, 7-9 Blenheim Terrace, London NW8 0EH Tel: 071-372 5705 (Mail Order available).

Linen Chest

If you're determined to give the biggest present they've ever seen – see if you can get a piece of wrapping paper to cover this one. A rattan linen chest – where many children will find their favourite hiding spot.

PRICE: £48 [Habitat]; cheaper versions (from £8) from hardware stores.

AVAILABLE: Habitat branches nationwide.

Marble Pastry Slab

Marble's chilliness counteracts the natural warmth of the cook's hands and keeps the pastry light.

PRICE: £29.50 for 51 cm × 38 cm slab.

AVAILABLE: Kitchen shops.

Nutmeg Mill

After the salt and pepper mill, the nutmeg mill will save grated fingers.

PRICE: £21.99.

AVAILABLE: Selfridges, also kitchen shops and department stores.

Rugs/Durries/Kilims

Woven floor rugs and runners which are a fraction of the price of carpets and often come from exotic places to brighten up a room.

PRICE: From £11 to £200 upwards.

AVAILABLE: Branches of Habitat, interior-design shops and department stores.

Shaker Oval Boxes

Epitomize the Shaker appeal – simple and beautiful. Boxes with no particular purpose which can be used for various storage or display purposes around the house. Available in plain cherrywood or painted.

PRICE: From £21 to £63.

AVAILABLE: Shaker Ltd, 25 Harcourt Street, London W1H 1DT Tel: 071-724 7672 (Mail Order available).

Soda Stream

Some people are terribly fussy about their mixers and refuse to drink anything but 'real' coke and 'real' tonic. In which case at they will at least appreciate a soda stream for its soda-making capabilities.

PRICE: Around £29.

AVAILABLE: Most hardware and department stores.

Sundial

Armillary and vertical versions are available as well as horizontal sundials (the vertical must be mounted on a south-facing wall). Very traditional garden ornamentation, these are available in 'aged' bronze and copper.

PRICE: £22.50–£475 (plus delivery).

AVAILABLE: Good Directions Ltd, Unit 15, Talisman Business Centre, Duncan Road, Park Gate, Southampton, Hants SO3 7BX Tel: 0489 577828 (Mail Order); department stores.

The Elmley Airer

In the days before tumbledriers there were contraptions of wooden slats, ropes and pulleys over which you draped washing and then raised them to the ceiling. Reliable and economical use of space and more convenient than draping damp washing over the shower rail. From 4 to 8 ft.

PRICE: From £35.

AVAILABLE: Elmley Heritage, Stone House, Elmley Lovett, Nr Droitwich, Worcs WR9 0PS Tel: 0299 23447 (Mail Order).

Towel Rail

A freestanding beechwood towel rail with waxed pine finish is as elegant as it is useful.

PRICE: £27.50.

AVAILABLE: Country Furniture, 2 Chapel Court, Hospital Street, Nantwich, Cheshire CW5 5RP Tel: 0270 610453 (Mail Order available).

Victorian Storage Boxes

Wonderfully decorative storage boxes in the Discovery Collection range which would also double up as tables, stands, etc, without disgracing anyone.

PRICE: From £39 to £99.

AVAILABLE: Selfridges Household Department.

Visitors' Book

A slim or a fat one (depending on their popularity) or a beautiful one for which you can buy refills from The Italian Paper Shop. A smart ring-binder of Italian marbled paper and leather-bound.

PRICE: £43.

AVAILABLE: The Italian Paper Shop, 11 Brompton Arcade, London SW3 1DY Tel: 071-589 1668.

Wooden Loo Seat

Warm landings are happy landings!

PRICE: £40.

AVAILABLE: Bathroom specialists, department stores.

£50 AND ABOVE

A Serious Safe

Safes can reduce insurance premiums. Small free-standing models or versions that Fort Knox would be proud of, which have to be installed by crane.

PRICE: From £350.

AVAILABLE: Check with local Police for reliable security firms.

A Wine Cellar

Most people believe that vast sums of money are involved in this sort of behaviour and only the rarest wines suitable. With sensible help it's possible to buy good wines that will mature over the years and give spectacular drinking for a very modest outlay.

PRICE: From £250 to £30,000 upwards.

AVAILABLE: Corney & Barrow Ltd, 12 Helmet Row, London EC1V 3QJ Tel: 071-251 4051.

Address Book

A substantial phoneside book to gather friends and then cross them out over the next 50 years.

PRICE: eg. £59 (8″ × 10″); £180 (12″ × 10″ – buckskin).

AVAILABLE: Smythsons, 44 New Bond Street, London W1Y 0DE Tel: 071-629 8558 (Mail Order available).

Aga

If they have mastered cake-baking in an Aga before marriage, it's not going to be one of those skills they will drop lightly (it is a rare and treasured skill).

PRICE: From £3600 (solid-fuel-fired, two-oven – no water heating) – £5975 (electric four-oven, with water-heating).

AVAILABLE: For nearest stockist contact: Aga-Rayburn, Headland House, New Coventry Road, Sheldon, Birmingham B26 3AZ.

Audio Unit

An attactive furniture unit which accommodates the high-tech stereo deck, CDs, etc, and blends it in with more traditional furniture.

PRICE: £165 [New Leif].

AVAILABLE: Branches of John Lewis Partnership.

Bakelite Phones

Something of a collector's item now – genuine ex-Post Office telephone designed in 1936 by Jean Heiberg. Wonderful to use but although every phone has been reconditioned it still sounds like the incoming call is being made from the bottom of a deep hole.

PRICE: £85.

AVAILABLE: The V&A Museum Catalogue, Freepost SU361, Dept 5316, Hendon Road, Sunderland SR9 9AD Tel: 091-514 2999.

Bed Linen

Peter Reed's bed linen is woven in Lancashire, the textile heart of Britain, although the linen naturally hails from Ireland. Crisp sheets that stay crispy rather than become bobbly like a polyester mix.

PRICE: From £78.95 (pair of 100% cotton flat sheets) to £189 (100% linen); Double duvet covers start at £99.99 (100% cotton).

AVAILABLE: Branches of John Lewis Partnership.

Colonial Shade

Large square umbrellas of hardwood and canvas which produce enough shade for cool tea parties on hot summer days.

PRICE: £500.

AVAILABLE: Oryx Trading Ltd, 33 Cornwall Gardens, London SW7 4AP Tel: 071-938 2045.

Conservatory Furniture

Traditional twill furniture that is ideal for conservatory, terrace or outdoor use. It is light enough to be moved around easily but sturdy enough to withstand the vagaries of the British summer. Marston & Langinger offer their range in up to 600 colours. 'Chubb' chairs from Habitat only come in four colours but are very reasonably priced.

PRICE: From £125 (footstool) to £1013 (three-seater sofa including cushions) [Martson & Langinger]; £75 [Chubb chairs from Habitat].

AVAILABLE: Marston & Langinger Ltd, 192 Ebury Street, London SW1W 8UP Tel: 071-824 8818; branches of Habitat; larger garden centres.

Croquet Set

Flat lawns beg for England's favourite garden game.

PRICE: £89 (full size version includes four wooden mallets, six steel hoops, wooden winning post, four balls, storage box and a full set of rules).

AVAILABLE: Branches of John Lewis Partnership.

Crystal Bowl

Don't even think of making trifle or displaying fruit without one. Lead crystal bowls should last a lifetime.

PRICE: £60 upwards.

AVAILABLE: China and glass specialists, department stores.

Dinner Service

The backbone of most wedding lists – can't eat off it (too scared of breaking it) but can't get by without it. Glorious services from Doulton, Wedgwood, etc, which vary from the plain to the ostentatious. Do check before you launch into making large purchases – your taste may not be to their taste.

PRICE: e.g. Royal Doulton (Clarendon design) – plates from £12, soup bowls £23.50, vegetable dish £129.

AVAILABLE: China specialists and large department stores.

Double Deckchair

A two-seater version of the traditional stripey deckchair.

PRICE: £89.

AVAILABLE: The Conran Shop, 81 Fulham Road, London SW3 Tel: 071-589 7401.

Dualit Toaster

Industrial American retro-style toaster that has become a modern classic. Combines durability with design; available for all widths of bread.

PRICE: £85 for two-slice toaster.

AVAILABLE: Large department stores, ironmongers and kitchen shops.

Espresso Machine

A home espresso machine that operates on the same principle as the gurglers and splurters in nearly every restaurant and bistro.

Heated water is forced through the ground coffee for perfect espresso – froth the milk with the integral milk frother for capuccino.

PRICE: From £54.50 [Gaggia].

AVAILABLE: Most good department stores, Boots.

Fireplace Fender Seats

Fender seats custom-made to fit any fireplace. Made from a variety of materials including brass, steel, copper and wood, the seats are padded and covered with leather or fabric of your choice.

PRICE: From £350.

AVAILABLE: Brian Stapleton, Elmley Heritage, Stone House, Elmley Lovett, Nr Droitwich, Worcs WR9 0PS Tel: 0299 23447.

Food Processor

Magimix is still widely honoured as the most efficient and reliable of the bunch. Chops, blends, liquidizes, mixes, kneads, beats, slices, grates, and cuts.

PRICE: From £99.50.

AVAILABLE: All good electrical shops and department stores.

Garden Temple

The ultimate in garden ornaments. A Roman-style temple – statues of Venus are extra!

PRICE: From £3688 (no roof); (fibreglass domed roof £1540; wrought iron domed roof £2200).

AVAILABLE: Chilstone Garden Ornaments, Sprivers Estate, Lamberhurst Road, Horsmonden, Kent TN12 8DR Tel: 089272 3266.

Glass Tie-Backs

Ravishing tie-backs that can only be used on the plainest curtains. Inspired by Venetian glass they combine glass and bead flowers in rainbow colours. Produced to order enabling you to choose specific colour combinations.

PRICE: £235 a pair.

AVAILABLE: Tessa Kennedy Designs, Studio 5, 91-97 Freston Road, London W11 Tel: 071-221 4546.

His and Hers Towelling Robes

These sound like a prize on *Sale of the Century*. They are luxurious to wear and wonderful to snuggle up to. Monogrammed matching his and hers sets are available.

PRICE: e.g. £139 and £135 (shawl collars); £120 and £120 (suit collars); or go to M&S (£29.95 each!).

AVAILABLE: The Monogrammed Linen Shop, 168 Walton Street, London SW3 Tel; 071-589 4033.

Intertwining Initials Door Knocker

In the style of Henry VIII and Anne Boleyn, mark all property with intertwining initials as a statement of love and belonging.

PRICE: £85.

AVAILABLE: Cyphers of Cheltenham, 16 Ryleworth Road, Charlton Kings, Cheltenham, Glos GL52 6LH Tel: 0242 512879 (Mail Order).

Kingsize Bed

Beds for big people or those who just like to move around a lot are available from the Big Bed Co. Built to any size required, you could have a bed as big as the bedroom – the largest they have made so far is 12' across.

PRICE: eg. 6' × 6'6" £680 + VAT; 10' × 6'6" £1200 + VAT.

AVAILABLE: Big Bed Co, Freepost London E18 1BR Tel: 081-530 1000.

Leather-Bound Books

Lavishly bound versions of *The Concise Oxford Dictionary*, *Roget's Thesaurus* and *The Complete Works of Shakespeare* that add weight to any library. Bound in chieftain goatskin, hand-tooled in 23-carat gold, gilt-edged and with marbled endpapers.

PRICE: £150 each.

AVAILABLE: Mappin & Webb, branches nationwide.

Letterbox

A trompe d'oeil simulated parchment stationery box which is handpainted with the recipient's name and address and also a postmark to commemorate a special date.

PRICE: £54.

AVAILABLE: Barclay and Bodie, 7-9 Blenheim Terrace, London NW8 0EH Tel: 071-372 5705 (Mail Order available).

Luggage

Smart and sturdy buckgrain luggage (in tan, olive or navy) with a saddle leather trim by The Regent Bag Co comes in weekend right through to continental travel sizes.

PRICE: Kitbags around £110.

AVAILABLE: The Regent Belt Company, 85 Station Road, Long Buckby, Northampton NN6 7QB Tel: 0327 842434.

Picnic Hamper

Wonderful for al fresco occasions – Henley, Ascot, a picnic at the bottom of the garden. They come in various shapes and sizes with a choice of crockery.

PRICE: £65–£300.

AVAILABLE: Most department stores, and Posh Picnics, 61 Mansfield Road, Selston, Notts NG16 6EE Tel: 0773 581704.

Sofa Bed

Give a new meaning to sleeping on the sofa – no-one would guess that the sofas are anything other than what they seem (a sofa) until the cushions are removed and the bed frame is revealed. Some versions are more suited than others to everyday use, while all are brilliant for the occasional visitor.

PRICE: From: £198.

AVAILABLE: Branches of Ikea.

Table Linen

There are only about three mills left in Ireland producing the much coveted linen – but you can go to The Irish Shop to get it. Plain white handstitched tablecloths are available, and also a slightly cheaper damask range (with shamrock, chrysanthemum or satin band design). All are 100% linen and 100% the real McCoy.

PRICE: From £69 (54" × 72" damask cloth – napkins from £7.50); Plain white from £112 (72" × 108" – napkins from £9.95).

AVAILABLE: The Irish Shop, 11 Duke Street, London W1 Tel: 071-935 1366; 14 King Street, London WC2 Tel: 071-379 3625 (Mail Order available).

Vacuum-Packed Wedding Dress

The most effective way of preserving the most treasured and perhaps the most expensive garment in a girl's life. Vacuum packing the dress places it in an air-free plastic bag which should preserve it in its original condition for at least 25 years, although once the seal is broken the preservation process is destroyed.

PRICE: £65.

AVAILABLE: Jeeves of Belgravia Tel: 081-809 3232.

CHAPTER EIGHTEEN

OTHER SPECIAL OCCASIONS

THE notable exception to the list of occasions we've chosen here is Christmas. With the vast majority of present-giving happening between September and December it seemed hardly appropriate to encourage more spending! However, we hope that when the shops aren't so loaded the discerning buyer will find ideas in this section which will be a cut above the latest range in the shop window – and, as such, proof of the thought that's gone into the giving.

HOSPITAL VISITS

Eye Shades/Ear Plugs

Avoid disturbances during the night, and catch a nap at whim.

PRICE: From £1.

AVAILABLE: Boots, chemists.

The Glossies

A big pile of glossy magazines is a luxury at any time, but particularly when you've actually got time to read them.

PRICE: From about £1.50 each.

AVAILABLE: All newsagents, the hospital shop.

Writing Paper

They probably won't want to write epistles, just jot a few lines – so make the quality, not quantity count. Also give stamped envelopes, because they won't be nipping out to the Post Office.

PRICE: £2.50 (five sheets of paper and five envelopes from Smythsons) + stamps.

AVAILABLE: Smythsons, 44 New Bond Street, London W1Y 0DE Tel: 071-629 8558 (Mail Order available).

Badedas Bubble Bath

A pick-me-up in the fairly clinical surroundings of the hospital bathroom: the most luxurious bubblebath we know.

PRICE: £2.99.

AVAILABLE: Chemists.

Water Aerosol

Cool mineral water spray (recommended for refreshing women in labour) is also bliss for instant cooling while laid up for any old reason. Also very useful for restyling hair.

PRICE: From £3.60 [Evian].

AVAILABLE: All chemists and department stores.

BOOK CHOICE
Life's Little Instruction Book

With time for contemplation, read this book which lists 511 suggestions, observations and reminders on how to live a happy and rewarding life. Rule no. 511 is Ring Your Mother.

PRICE: £3.95.

AVAILABLE: WH Smith, and bookshops.

Dried Flowers/Pot Plants

Guaranteed to last as long as the patient is in hospital, and then can be taken home!

PRICE: From about £4.50.

AVAILABLE: Most florists; baskets of flowers from Forever Flowering, Orchard House, Mortlake Road, Kew Gardens, Surrey TW9 4AS Tel: 081-392 9929 (Mail Order).

Patience Cards

It's a crazy old thing, but those bed tables in hospital are just the right width for a good game of patience, if the ward sister can't be tempted to game of poker.

PRICE: From £4.50 (two decks).

AVAILABLE: Stationers, department stores.

Miniature Cakes

A 3″ cake which can be nibbled between hospital meals.

PRICE: £8.

AVAILABLE: Harrods; Fiona Cairns, PO Box 24, Market Harborough, Leicestershire LE16 7GQ Tel; 085883 781.

Lambswool Heel Protectors

Lambswool pads with velcro straps protect heels from friction and rubbing and prevent pressure sores.

PRICE: £9.10 per pair.

AVAILABLE: Chester-Care, Low Moor Estate, Kirkby-in-Ashfield, Notts NG17 7JZ Tel: 0623 757955 (Mail Order).

Sinus Pillow

For cold sufferers, this is a therepeutic pillow which clears the nose and isn't like a log to sleep on. It contains a mixture of aromatic herbs, and menthol crystals that help relieve nasal congestion while sleeping. Filled with non-allergenic duck feathers.

PRICE: £19.95.

AVAILABLE: Innovations (Mail Order) Ltd, Euroway Business Park, Swindon SN5 8SN Tel: 0793 514666.

Personal Radio/Cassette

Keep up-to-date with the news and *The Archers* and enjoy Van Halen at any time of the day or night.

PRICE: From £22 [Sony].

AVAILABLE: All electrical appliance shops, department stores.

PASSING DRIVING TEST

Furry Dice/Nodding Dog

Add style and panache to any vehicle but are illegal.

PRICE: From £1.99.

AVAILABLE: Halfords, driving accessory shops.

Atlas/Road Maps

Maps of 'My Home Town' may be a good place to start because it's surprising how quickly you can lose your sense of direction when used to being a passenger or travelling on foot.

PRICE: *Ordnance Survey* from £3.95; *A-Z* from £1.50; *National Atlas* from £4.50.

AVAILABLE: Bookshops, garages.

Initialled Key Ring

Remember the joy of placing the car keys on the bar in full view! Personally initialled, there's more likelihood they won't be left behind.

PRICE: From £4.99.

AVAILABLE: Hardware shops, leather goods, department stores.

Driving Gloves

Leather driving gloves help maintain a firm grip on the wheel (if palms tend to go clammy at roundabouts).

PRICE: From £9.99.

AVAILABLE: Halfords, driving accessory shops.

Car Vacuum

Works from the cigarette lighter to speed around the car removing dried mud, sweet papers and all the other amazing things you wish weren't there.

PRICE: £10–£35.

AVAILABLE: Branches of John Lewis Partnership; department and hardware stores.

Vouchers for Advanced Driving Test

You don't actually learn anything new for an Advanced Driving Test (if they were hoping to perfect a hand-brake turn or the art of heel and toeing!), but the standard of driving must be higher to pass. Many insurance companies offer cheaper premiums as a result.

PRICE: Lessons around £19.50; first lesson £35 (two hours); (vouchers available up to any value).

AVAILABLE: British School of Motoring nationwide. Check *Yellow Pages* for nearest driving school.

AA/RAC Membership

More than sensible precaution to take especially as most 'first cars' are far from top-of-the range reliable models. Home Start will get her going in the morning and Relay will bring her home from the layby.

PRICE: AA from £48; RAC from £60.

AVAILABLE: AA Tel: 0800 919595; RAC Tel: 081-686 2314.

Car Stereo

Young drivers often consider this as essential for travel as insurance.

PRICE: From about £40 to £300.

AVAILABLE: Halfords, electrical equipment shops, large department stores.

Pay Insurance for a Year

Quite an undertaking in the first year – especially if the driver is young and aspires to a turbo engine (and a go-faster stripe)! To pay for, or offer assistance with insurance may make driving affordable rather than impossible.

PRICE: From £600.

AVAILABLE: Contact local insurance companies; Call RAC 0800 678000 (Ext 142) or AA: 0800 919595 for insurance advice.

PASSING EXAMS

Badge of Success

'Not just a pretty face', 'Genius' and such like are available as badges to be worn with pride.

PRICE: From 50p.

AVAILABLE: Card shops, gift and stationery shops.

MENSA IQ Test

The society for superbrains may or may not open its portals to the newly confirmed genius. Having passed the home IQ test, a supervised test must be taken before being invited to join. Members of MENSA all have IQs of 148 and above.

PRICE: Home IQ test £9.75; supervised IQ test £9.75; yearly membership £25.

AVAILABLE: For details contact: MENSA, Bond House, St Johns Square, Wolverhampton Tel: 0902 772771.

Premium Bonds

Incredible as it may seem you cannot buy Premium Bonds for a friend, only for a child under 16 in that child's name if you're a parent, guardian or grandparent. You can buy them for children in units of £10, otherwise the minimum purchase is £100!

PRICE: From £10.

AVAILABLE: Tel: 0253 66151.

Champagne

The bubbles will turn relief into euphoria – a magnum probably to hysteria.

PRICE: From £12.99.

AVAILABLE: All wine merchants, off-licences and supermarkets.

Financial Reward

An apposite amount of financial reward – say £8 for eighth position in class; £70 for seven GCSEs; £210 for a 2:1?

PRICE: Depends on success.

AVAILABLE: Your pocket!

353

RELIGIOUS OCCASIONS

Bar Mitzvah (Boys)/Bat Mitzvah (Girls)

In the Jewish faith boys come of age at 13, girls at 12. *The Bar Mitzvah Book* is for boys and is an illustrated patchwork of Jewish life and history. Candlesticks for girls so that they can start lighting their own candles on Friday nights.

PRICE: £22 *The Bar Mitzvah Book*; from £15 upwards for candlesticks.

AVAILABLE: The Blue and White Shop, No 6 Beehive Lane, Ilford, Essex Tel: 081-518 1982.

Christening – A Bottle of Wine per Year

A bottle or case per year? Berry Brothers will start a cellar for the child and call you every year to discuss each addition. The child receives a letter informing them of their accumulating fortune.

PRICE: £4.59 charge per year (plus wine).

AVAILABLE: Berry Bros & Rudd, 3 St James St, London SW1A 1EG Tel: 071-396 9600.

Christening – Christening Robe

There's something quite wonderful about a long, lacy, embroidered christening robe which is good enough to be handed down from babe to babe from generation to generation.

PRICE: £58 (4' christening robe with pintucking, lace and embroidery); £18 (matching cotton petticoat).

AVAILABLE: Lunn Antiques Ltd, 86 New Kings Road, London SW6 4LU Tel: 071-736 4638 (Mail Order available).

Christening – Engraved Silver Frames

Baby pictures with a difference, because engraved around the side are the smiler's vital statistics – name, time and place of arrival and birth weight.

PRICE: £58–£66.

AVAILABLE: Bruford and Heming Ltd, 28 Conduit Street, London W1R 9TA Tel: 071-629 4289 (Mail Order available).

Christening – One Hundred Pounds

One hundred pounds invested at an annual return of 5% per annum will be worth £239.46 by the time the child is 18 years old. What it will actually buy in in the year 2011 is another matter. National Savings Certificates are one of the best buys as all interest is gross.

PRICE: £100.

AVAILABLE: Your pocket.

Confirmation – Bible

Not everyone gets confirmed but for those who are, a first bible of their own is a present that will be kept for life.

PRICE: £7.99 *Good News Bible* [Collins].

AVAILABLE: Bookshops.

Eid

Two Islamic festivals; the first day after the month of Ramadam, the second two-and-a-half months later, at the end of the pilgrimmage to Mecca. Presents to children only – toys, sweets, books with stories about the prophets, etc.

PRICE: From under £2.

AVAILABLE: Muslim Information Centre/Bookshop, 233 Seven Sisters Road, London N4 2DA.

Hindu

The big Hindu festival is the Feeding Ceremony when the child is six months and being weaned – presents surround eating and include silver plates and spoons etc as well as gold chains and money. Books and statues are also very good news.

PRICE: Books from £1.

AVAILABLE: Contact: The Institute of Indian Culture, 4a Castletown Road, London W14 9HP Tel: 071-381 4608 (Mail Order available).

RETIREMENT

Chef's Hat and Apron

White, as the professionals wear them, and in men's sizes.

PRICE: Hat £4.99, apron £8.99, oven gloves £6.99.

AVAILABLE: Selfridges, Oxford Street, London W1 Tel: 071-629 1234; department stores, kitchen shops.

Yoga Classes

Buddhist exercises combined with relaxation and meditation, which practitioners swear was the best thing they ever started and which enhances mental as well as physical wellbeing.

PRICE: Star at £2–£3 for one hour.

AVAILABLE: Local evening classes.

BOOK CHOICE
Superwoman

Shirley Conran's book from which comes the ubiquitous expression 'Life's too short to stuff a mushroom' – encouragement to get on with the better things life has to offer.

PRICE: £5.99 [Penguin].

AVAILABLE: Bookshops.

Details of Open University

If they've always wanted to learn more about the history of art, the habits of the Romans, or quantum mechanics, then now's the time to do it. Up to 200 courses offered.

PRICE: Details of courses sent free. Each course costs around £400.

AVAILABLE: Open University, Walton Hall, Milton Keynes, Bucks MK7 6AA Tel: 0908 274066.

Homebaking Book

A taste for homebaked bread can be nurtured now there's time to let the dough prove. Perhaps send them on a three-day baking course at the Cordon Bleu School to learn how to do it the French way.

PRICE: e.g. *Mrs Beeton's Book of Bakery* £14.95 [Ward Lock];
Baking course £290.

AVAILABLE: Bookshops; Cordon Bleu, 114 Marylebone Lane,
London W1M 6HH Tel: 071-935 3503.

Bookclub Membership

It's now time to read all those books that were too heavy to lug
around in a briefcase – biographies, memoirs and histories of the
world are renowned for their weight.

PRICE: Starting offers usually feature 'Four books for 50p' etc.

AVAILABLE: Contact 0793 512666 for details of 12 different
specialist bookclubs.

World's Most Difficult Jigsaw Puzzle

529 pieces but printed both sides of each piece. A double brain-
teaser.

PRICE: £11.50.

AVAILABLE: Department stores, larger toy shops.

Sportswear

Tight cycling shorts are perhaps a little de trop, but golfing
jumpers, sailing wellies or a fisherman's jumper may be just the
ticket for new or established hobbies.

PRICE: eg. Golf sweater £39.99 [Pringle]; Goretex sailing jacket
£100.

AVAILABLE: Sportwear shops, gentlemen's outfitters and department stores.

Amstrad Notepad

A very reasonably-priced laptop wordprocessor which can be
used as an address book and diary as well as dashing off a letter to
The Times and working out the savings guaranteed by a pension
book.

PRICE: £198.58.

AVAILABLE: All good electrical appliance shops and department
stores.

A Dog

There's no need to worry about leaving him cooped up during the day – he can be a constant companion as well as the excuse for hearty walks.

PRICE: e.g. Pedigree Cavalier £380.

AVAILABLE: For reputable breeders contact The Dog Breeders' Assocation Tel: 081-742 7447. Contact the RSPCA who can put you in touch with local animal centres which have rescued all types of animals and will give them away to very good homes.

Mantel Clock

Retirement wouldn't be complete without one – an antique carriage clock or a modern copy.

PRICE: £49.99–£450.

AVAILABLE: Jewellers.

Mountain Bike(s)

They say you never forget how – but sometimes rusty riders find cornering a little precarious. A little practice and you can be well and truly on yer bike.

PRICE: From £250.

AVAILABLE: Cycle shops, Halfords.

Weather Detector

The Ultra-Pro Weather Station is practically a personal meteorological station measuring wind direction, wind speed, barometric pressure, dew point, rainfall, hours of sunshine. So it's easy to make a decision about booking a round on the golf course or setting off to the coast.

PRICE: From £189.

AVAILABLE: Ultra-Pro, Unit 3, Wharf Street, Warwick CV34 5LB Tel: 0926 408006 (Mail Order).

World Cruise

Time to lie back and let it all hang out. The world is there to be discovered – it's not going to go anywhere so the pace can be leisurely.

PRICE: On the QEII – from £11,495 (full 95 day cruise); (Luxury A1 Grade: £72,000).

AVAILABLE: Cunard, 30 Pall Mall, London SW1 TEl: 071-491 3930.

VALENTINE'S DAY

Forget-Me-Not Seeds

Delightful tiny blue blooms which are nearly as charming as the gesture itself.

PRICE: 95p.

AVAILABLE: Some large supermarkets; all garden centres; Hollington Nurseries, Woolton Hill, Newbury, Berkshire RG15 9XT Tel: 0635 253908 (Mail Order).

Aphrodisiac Bombs

Phials containing the natural aphrodisiacs of ginseng, guarana and royal jelly should make the day go with a bang.

PRICE: £2.45.

AVAILABLE: Wong Singh Jones, 19 All Saints Road, London W11 1HE Tel: 071-792 2001 (Mail Order).

Love and Kisses Bathsalts

Kiss-shaped fizzy bathsalt and two soaps that together make a heart.

PRICE: £3.60.

AVAILABLE: Cosmetics To Go, Freepost, Poole, Dorset BH15 1BR Tel: 0800 373366 (Mail Order).

BOOK CHOICE
Love Sonnets

Forty-four of Shakespeare's love sonnets published in miniature – small enough to slip into a pocket next to your heart.

PRICE: £4.99.

AVAILABLE: The Museum Store, 37 The Piazza, Covent Garden, London WC2 Tel: 071-240 5760.

Neon Lightbulb

'I Love You' in neon with pink hearts – if you want to take the subtle approach.

PRICE: £8.45.

AVAILABLE: Wong Singh Jones, 19 All Saints Road, London W11 1HE Tel: 071-792 2001 (Mail Order).

BOOK CHOICE
Sensual Massage

A practical guide by Mitya Lacroix to the art of touch.

PRICE: £8.99.

AVAILABLE: Most good bookshops.

BOOK CHOICE
The Foods of Love

Max de Roche's guide to all manner of secret love potions.

PRICE: £8.99.

AVAILABLE: Good bookshops; The Pathetic Club, 14 Windermere Way, Thatcham, Berkshire RG13 4UL Tel: 0635 865774 (Mail Order).

Original Victorian Valentine

Achingly or cloyingly sentimental.

PRICE: £15–£60+.

AVAILABLE: Pleasures of Past Times, 11 Cecil Court, Charing Cross Road, London WC2 Tel: 071-836 1142.

Pink Champagne

Say 'I Luv You' with a blush.

PRICE: £17.49 [Laurent Perrier].

AVAILABLE: Wine merchants.

A Basket of Flowers

Dried white flowers – which will last the week out – arranged in a basket with a heart of red roses.

PRICE: £24.50 and £3 p&p.

AVAILABLE: Forever Flowering, Orchard House, Mortlake Road, Kew Gardens, Surrey TW9 4AS Tel: 081-392 9929 (Mail Order).

Aphrodisiac Hamper

The Pathetic Club is a mail order service specifically for people who are 'hopelessly, completely, pathetically gaga' and besides themselves with love. You can make up a hamper from any of the suggested morsels – many of which are potent aphrodisiacs and guaranteed to titillate not only the tastebuds. Delivered either in a wicker basket (costs) or cardboard carton (does not cost).

PRICE: e.g. £29.95 bottle of Bollinger champagne; £1.95 smoked oysters; heart-shaped biscuits 75p; small wicker hamper £29.95.

AVAILABLE: The Pathetic Club, 14 Windermere Way, Thatcham, Berkshire RG13 4UL Tel: 0635 865774 (Mail Order).

Name a Star After the One You Love

The International Star Registry will register a real star in the sky in the name of your choice and send out a gift pack including an expanded sky chart pinpointing the exact star and a constellation chart to help locate it.

PRICE: £40.

AVAILABLE: International Star Registry, Freepost, 24 Highbury Grove, London N5 2BR Tel: 0800 212493.

Double Hammock

Handwoven Mexican hammock in vibrant colours – made for two. Includes sturdy bolt hooks and bolts.

PRICE: Double Hammock £59.95.

AVAILABLE: The Pathetic Club, 14 Windermere Way, Thatcham, Berkshire RG13 4UL Tel: 0635 865774 (Mail Order).

Daytrip on the Orient Express

A romantic fantasy for all but the stony-hearted. Day trips through the countryside to visit historic places such as Hever Castle or just 'Lunch in the Garden of England'. Dinners are generally five courses and include champagne.

PRICE: £65–£165; London–Venice (two nights at The Capriani) £1645.

AVAILABLE: Venice Simplon-Orient Express, Sea Containers House, 20 Upper Ground, London SE1 9PF Tel: 071-928 6000.

Loving Cup

Eximious specialize in personalized presents – and their loving cup with two handles has room for two names (handpainted in gold). Traditionally a bride and groom drank from such a cup to celebrate their marriage.

PRICE: £87.50.

AVAILABLE: Eximious, 10 West Halkin Street, London SW1 Tel: 071-235 7828 (Mail Order available).

Romantic Break – Unromantic Breaks

Test your love in the face of adversity with a weekend that is designed to dampen even the ardent desire – twin beds five feet apart, a four-pack of lager and two bottles of brown ale, dinner at opposite ends of a six-foot table, tickets for a local football, rugby or cricket match, cassette of snoring and woolly bedsocks – just a few of the obstacles thrown in the path of romance.

PRICE: £120 per person.

AVAILABLE: Fairfield Manor Hotel, Skipton Road, Skelton YO3 6XW Tel: 0904 670222.

Poesy Ring

Poesy rings were widely given in the sixteenth and seventeenth centuries as tokens of love or regard. An example in the V&A has the inscription *Vous et Nut Autre* – You and No Other – and this has been reproduced in 14 carat gold.

PRICE: £150.

AVAILABLE: Past-Times, Witney, Oxford, OX8 6BH Tel: 0993 779444 (Mail Order).

Romantic Break – Tring Fling

Trips specifically tailored for romantics which feature dawn horseriding through forests to spot deer, a canal cruise and drinks in a windmill.

PRICE: £199 per person for two nights' half board and all extras.

AVAILABLE: The Pendley Manor Country House Hotel, Tring, Hertfordshire Tel: 0442 891891.

Concorde to Paris

It hardly seems worth going to Paris on a daytrip but with Concorde you can be there and back in the wink of an eye with bags of shopping and postcards from the Louvre to prove it. A supersonic weekend would be much more appropriate, especially staying overnight in a first class hotel which is all part of the deal.

PRICE: From £565 for one-day trip; £690 two-day trip (Concorde one way; Boeing the other); (trips on Concorde both ways start at £1010).

AVAILABLE: Goodwood Travel Ltd, Concorde House, Stour Street, Canterbury CT1 2NZ Tel: 0227 763336.

CHAPTER NINETEEN

OFFICE & BUSINESS OCCASIONS

Business gifts clearly divide into two categories. The lightweight, packable, non-breakable, quintessentially English ones to impress your foreign hosts and hostesses as you whisk them out of the overnight bag, and the large, impressive presentation ones (usually breakable, heavy and virtually guaranteed to get you stopped in Customs) which they give you to take home. To get your own back try giving the latter category to visiting dignitaries in the UK – or to business colleagues on special occasions.

UNDER £5

A Message in a Bottle

Whether you want to reward a special client or just make somebody happy, few presents go down as well as nice wine. Help and advice on everything from a single bottle to a case of good claret or serious amounts of champagne from this first class wine merchant.

PRICE: From £3.70 a bottle plus carriage.

AVAILABLE: Corney & Barrow Ltd, 12 Helmet Row, London EC1V 3QJ Tel: 071-251 4051.

BETWEEN £5-£10

Flower Holders

A perfect present to take to a host, these beautiful small crystal vases will hold a single bud or a small display.

PRICE: From £9.95.

AVAILABLE: Stuart & Sons Ltd, Redhouse Glassworks, Wordsley, Stourbridge, West Midlands DY8 4AA Tel: 0384 71161.

Victorian Street Map

Street maps of Dickensian London, which would have been used by Hansom cabs to find their way around the city. Drawn in minute detail, the maps shows street names, workhouses, etc, and also the undeveloped market gardens of Chelsea and Southwark and villages of Earls Court and Kentish Town.

PRICE: From £6.99 (folded in a wallet) to £12.99 (rolled ready for framing).

AVAILABLE: Old House Books, Freepost, 30 Sutton Mead, Moretonhampstead, Newton Abbot, Devon TQ13 8BR Tel: 0647 40296 (Mail Order).

Vouchers

They're not boring. Almost every major retailer in the country provides them for incentive programmes including Tesco, Sainsbury, M&S, Thomas Cook, B&Q, Oddbins, and so on. All are enthusiastically received, especially the holiday ones.

PRICE: All values.

AVAILABLE: The retailer of choice.

Wedgewood Jasper

This is the pale blue-and-white design famous throughout the world. Apart from the ubiquitous small ashtrays there are a variety of bowls, useful little boxes and vases. All make excellent presents for travellers.

PRICE: Trays from £8.95.

AVAILABLE: Department stores and good china shops.

BETWEEN £10–£20

Basket of Fruit

There isn't a fruit equivalent of Interflora but with a little imagination and a friendly fruiterer you can make up delicious colourful and attractive baskets of fruit. A good present for the healthy and hungry.

PRICE: According to size from about £10 upwards.

AVAILABLE: Local fruiterers.

Business Card Case

So that they're not carried in the wallet or lie around in the pocket getting dirty.

PRICE: £12 (silver plate); £75 (silver – to order).

AVAILABLE: Links of London, 27 Broadgate Circle, London EC2M 2QS Tel: 071-628 9668 (Mail Order available).

Organizer Mirror

A thoughtful, useful present for women. This mirror clips into any organizer.

PRICE: £14.

AVAILABLE: David Hayward, 123 Leckhampton Road, Cheltenham, Glos GL53 0DQ Tel: 0242 570314.

Paintball

Cowboys and Indians for grown-ups. A day out in the deepest, darkest forest armed with a gun that shoots paint pellets. Split into teams to take each other's flags, plot ambushes, etc. Very good fun and when rounded off with a good dinner, a very good way to reward a star sales team?

PRICE: £19.95 per player plus cost of paintball.

AVAILABLE: Campaign Paintball Sports, 198 Bellevue Road, London SW17 7EG Tel: 081-672 7711.

Personal Walkman Speakers

Literally a pair of speakers to make your little Walkman burst into life. Good news on holiday.

PRICE: From £10.99 a pair to £79.99.

AVAILABLE: Sony centres throughout the UK.

Roulette Wheel

Full roulette set containing wheel, cloth, rake, chips and instructions.

PRICE: From £19.95 (8″ wheel) to £39.95 (12″ wheel).

AVAILABLE: Department stores; Just Games, 71 Brewer Street, London W1R 3FB Tel: 071-734 6124 (Mail Order available).

Tartan Scarf and Tie Set

Available in 300 tartans representing every family.

PRICE: Around £20.

AVAILABLE: Locharron of Scotland, Waverley Mill, Galashiels, TD1 3AY Tel: 0896 3671.

Travel Iron

Essential, unless the entire wardrobe is drip-dry and crease-resistant.

PRICE: £12.75 [Philips].

AVAILABLE: Branches of John Lewis Partnership, other department stores and electrical retailers.

Wine Pourer

Pops onto the end of bottles of house red and class clarets to ease the flow into the glass. Over the top perhaps, but comes in its own little Asprey box.

PRICE: £18.50.

AVAILABLE: Asprey, 165-169 New Bond Street, London W1Y 0AR Tel: 071-493 6767.

BETWEEN £20–£50

A Night at the Theatre

Unoriginal perhaps, but few people fail to enjoy a 'good show and a meal afterwards'. Choose a show that they haven't seen, make sure the seats are good ones and book a suitable restaurant nearby for supper (eating before is more sensible, but less jolly).

PRICE: Theatre approx £30 for two; dinner dependent on restaurant.

AVAILABLE: The theatre or Ticketmaster Tel: 071-413 1453.

Champagne and Smoked Salmon

A bottle of non-vintage champagne and 12 oz of Scottish smoked salmon in a Fortnum & Mason box. A perfect personal indulgence.

PRICE: Price £35.

AVAILABLE: Fortnum & Mason, 181 Piccadilly, London W1A 1ER Tel: 071-734 8040.

China Figure

It's easy to forget how stunning some of these figures are. Royal Doulton have produced 2500 different figures over the past 100 years: character figures, pretty ladies (given popular Christian names), child figures and the beautifully modern 'images' range. Also a range of horse and dog figures.

PRICE: From £25 to £200 upwards.

AVAILABLE: Royal Doulton (UK) Ltd, Hobson Street, Burslem, Stoke-on-Trent, England ST6 2AQ Tel: 0782 577997.

Crystal Glasses

Real crystal is a) lovely b) deeply expensive. For both these reasons it makes a wonderful present, though before purchase check what make and design the recipient has, if any. Stuart Crystal is one of the famous and desired makes and their catalogue is excellent.

PRICE: eg. sherry glass £17.50; wine goblet £20.50; tumbler £12.50 (examples from the Glencoe range).

AVAILABLE: Stuart & Sons Ltd, Red House Glassworks, Stourbridge, West Midlands DY8 4AA Tel: 0384 71161.

Decanter

Another obvious corporate gift but a welcome one (puts an end to the horrible habit of pouring straight from the bottle!). Available in modern and traditional designs (in either plain glass or crystal). Burrowing around in antique shops is a sound alternative to normal outlets.

PRICE: From £40.

AVAILABLE: Branches of John Lewis and other department stores.

Engraved Glass Bowls

From the same company that made the Mastermind Trophy. Anniversary bowls, vases and rose bowls in both traditional and modern designs.

PRICE: Anniversary bowls from £28.95.

AVAILABLE: Caithness Glass Plc, Inveralmond, Perth PH1 3TZ Tel; 0738 37373.

Organizer Flask

Totally original and award-winning flask that is slim and light enough to fit into any standard personal organizer.

PRICE: £36.

AVAILABLE: David Hayward, 123 Leckhampton Road, Cheltenham, Glos GL53 0DQ Tel: 0247 570314.

Personalized File Paper

Put an end to the frequent loss or borrowing of file pads which is the excuse for lack of reports.

PRICE: £50 (five A5 pads with holes).

AVAILABLE: Smythsons, 44 New Bond Street, London W1Y 0DE Tel: 071-629 8558 (Mail Order available).

Silver Money Clip

For the remaining notes in your life, these are available in plain and a dollar sign version – just the job for visits to the USA.

PRICE: £43.

AVAILABLE: Links of London, 27 Broadgate Circle, London EC2M 2QS Tel: 071-628 9668 (Mail Order available).

Silver Plate Paperweight

The fun thing about these plain paperweights is the ability to engrave anything on their flat surface. Words to commemorate a particular deal, a copy of someone's signature or a single word like 'Urgent'.

PRICE: £24 (engraving extra).

AVAILABLE: Links of London, 27 Broadgate Circle, London EC2M 2QS Tel: 071-628 9668 (Mail Order available).

Travel Clock

Well designed, smart, slim alarm clock with an FM radio, foldaway aerial and a 'time in other parts of the world' chart.

PRICE: £23.99 [Braun].

AVAILABLE: Department stores.

Travel Shaving Brush

For real shavers, a badger brush with a nickel-plated brass base. The bristles are stored inside the base when travelling.

PRICE: Price £48.

AVAILABLE: David Hayward, 123 Leckhampton Road, Cheltenham, Glos GL53 0DQ Tel: 0242 570314.

Travelling Pepper Mill

A member of the family carried one of these all over the world to add a touch of home to various foreign dishes.

PRICE: £28 (gold-plated with its own leather pouch).

AVAILABLE: Asprey, 165-169 New Bond Street, London W1Y 0AR Tel: 071-493 6767.

Vibrating Pager

A pager with a difference – rather than the shrill and embarrassing alarm alert, this one either has a musical tone or a vibrating option for silent messaging. The pager is pocket-sized and is available in orange, blue, and green, with a holster that can be clipped onto a belt.

PRICE: £49.98.

AVAILABLE: Mercury Paging 081-528 9003 or Freephone 0500 505505.

£50 AND ABOVE

A Mini Hi-Fi System

All the components necessary to provide sound for a large living room in an attractively designed mini system. Saves space and all further discussions about hi-fis.

PRICE: From £279.99 to £749.

AVAILABLE: Sony centres throughout the UK.

A Negotiating Course

Essential for anyone operating at a senior level in any commercial capacity, be it business or the arts. If you think brainpower and streetsense are enough, the chances are the other people are enjoying themselves at your expense. Literally.

PRICE: £499 + VAT (two days).

AVAILABLE: Andis International Ltd, Kingfisher House, North Poulner Road, Ringwood, Hants BH24 1SN Tel: 0425 479048.

A Painting

An extremely satisfying present but a difficult one to buy. Try to discover if the potential recipient is interested in a particular subject, artist or style (or even take note of the paintings on their wall!). Research should unearth a suitable local gallery where the prices of oils and watercolours are usually very affordable.

PRICE: According to budget – £50 upwards.

AVAILABLE: Galleries nationwide.

A Portrait

Commissioning a portrait of someone needs care. The Royal Society of Portrait Painters give sensible and free advice on such issues as style, the budget you have, etc. They prefer you to visit their offices where you can look through photographs of various members' work and discuss your requirements.

PRICE: £700 (pencil drawing); £2500 (oil painting, head and shoulder).

AVAILABLE: Emma Davis, Federation of British Artists, 17 Carlton House Terrace, London SW1Y 5BD Tel: 071-930 6844.

A Sabbatical

If someone who works for you needs a break or deserves one after a period of especially pressurized work, long service, etc, consider sending them on a sabbatical. ... Some firms insist on these every few years and find that the recipient returns with their batteries thoroughly recharged.

PRICE: According to time taken.

AVAILABLE: Director or Personnel Director.

Box of Havana Cigars

Tycoons and film directors are not the only lovers of cigars. Ordinary mortals will grin with appreciation when presented with a box. Buy the ones they smoke regularly or, with a little secret research, the ones they aspire to.

PRICE: According to size brand – from £70 for box of 25 to £200.

AVAILABLE: The Cigar Club, 151 Harrow Road, Wembley, Middlesex HA9 6DN Tel; 081-902 2656 (Mail Order).

Camcorder

You might not believe this but 'this feature stabilizes the picture you record, even if your hand is shaking or if you are on a boat or a plane which is moving'. Exactly. Amazing. Will someone please give me one?

PRICE: £1199.99.

AVAILABLE: Sony centres.

Cigarette Lighter

The 'sylphide' is a smart, slim silver lighter that is claimed to light every time. It's also a Dunhill, statement in itself.

PRICE: £135.

AVAILABLE: Alfred Dunhill Ltd, 30 Duke Street, St James, London SW1Y 6DL Tel; 071-499 9566.

Colour Video Printer

Listen carefully, I will write this only once. You video a family occasion – put the tape in the video machine, press a button and out comes a high quality print of what appears on screen. P.S. If you can't afford the machine you can take your tape to a Sony centre and they'll do the pictures you want.

PRICE: £1099.99.

AVAILABLE: Sony centres.

Corporate Hospitality

Corporate hospitality at popular sporting events has become very grizzly over the past few years. A day-out can resemble a school outing and the food may be horrible too. Plan It do many of the main events, in a slightly more personal and original way. Cricket at Lords with a hamper; overnight in Ireland playing golf; Windsor evening racing up the river in a boat, afterwards to dinner at Eton.

PRICE: According to treat – Windsor evening from £139 per person.

AVAILABLE: Plan It Events Ltd, 15 Nottingham Road, London SW17 7EA Tel: 081 680 4900.

Desk Set

Stately, but make sure he or she uses ink first. Two lead crystal inkwells set onto a specially lacquered base.

PRICE: £115.

AVAILABLE: David Hayward, 123 Leckhampton Road, Cheltenham, Glos GL53 0DQ Tel: 0242 570314.

Emerald Diamond Necklace

23 cts of exceptionally clean emeralds set amidst 259 diamonds weighing 68 cts. If you'd like to know more please phone Tiffany who are, not unnaturally, very helpful, gentle and reassuring folk.

PRICE: £252,000.

AVAILABLE: Tiffany & Co, 25 Old Bond Street, London W1X 3AA Tel: 071-409 2790.

Fine Bone China

Good news. Glorious patterns, stylish and classical shapes, elegant dinner parties. Bad news – awesomely expensive and serious sadness when broken. If you're giving a whole service discuss with the recipient. Additions/replacements to an existing set will also be very welcome.

PRICE: e.g. dinner plates average £20 each.

AVAILABLE: Wedgewood, Barlaston, Stoke-on-Trent, ST12 9ES TEl: 0782 204141.

Full Highland Kilt

Is he/she Scottish? The widest collection of tartans in the world, over 500, are available from Peter Anderson. They'll make a kilt or skirt to measure after you've supplied the relevant information.

PRICE: £250 (gentleman's kilt); £79 (lady's kilted skirt).

AVAILABLE: Peter Anderson, Nethermill, Galashiels, Scotland Tel: 0896 2091.

Globe

A magnificent 32″ illuminated globe which claims to the 'world's most detailed globe' – let's hope they're fast workers! Cradle is solid mahogany and globe available in blue ocean map only; or choose the nearly as magnificent 20″ illuminated globe which is in 'antique'-style ie. parchment-like oceans.

PRICE: e.g. Diplomat £7800 (32″); President £2500 (20″).

AVAILABLE: Thanet Globe Emporium, Orange Street, Canterbury, Kent CT1 2JA Tel: 0227 450055 (Mail Order – to order).

Handmade Attaché Case

Swaine Adeney are specialists in handmade attaché cases and also stock a wide variety of ready-mades.

PRICE: From £325.

AVAILABLE: Swaine Adeney, 185 Piccadilly, London W1 Tel: 071-734 4277 (Mail Order available).

Headscarf

Gucci floral headscarves have achieved such a following because they're quite simply stunning. Made in Italy from 100% pure silk twill, some have up to 36 colours; a wonder hug for a woman.

PRICE: £120.

AVAILABLE: Gucci, 32-33 Old Bond Street, London W1X 3AD Tel: 071-629 2716.

Humidor

'A good cigar deserves a humidor. A bad cigar needs one'. Offer the ideal storing conditions for the biggest and best cigars.

PRICE: From £117 (holds 25 × 6″ cigars) to £425 (holds 100 × 7″ cigars).

AVAILABLE: The Cigar Club, 151 Harrow Road, Wembley, Middlesex HA9 6BR Tel: 081-902 2656 (Mail Order).

Leather Personal Binders

The slimmest of the 'personal organizers' fits comfortably into a jacket pocket. Holds diary, telephone numbers, notepaper, credit cards and cash. Perfect and smart.

PRICE: £62.75.

AVAILABLE: Lefax Publishing Ltd, 179 Forest Road, Ilford, Essex IG6 3HP Tel: 081-501 3911.

Macintosh Powerbook

Macintosh computers – 'Apple Macs' are one of the most popular and easy-to-use machines in the world (we know – this book was written on one!) The powerbook is a portable computer that's small, light and as powerful as most desktops.

PRICE: £1199.

AVAILABLE: Selected computer outlets; Mac Warehouse, Queens Road, Barnet, Herts, EN5 4DL Tel: 0800 181332 (Mail Order).

Membership of the Institute of Directors

The Institute has 28 regional branches and members in more than 100 countries across the world. Benefits include a monthly magazine, a strong conference and seminar programme, annual convention, etc. Probably the most useful benefits are the information and advisory service and the HQ itself, full of meeting rooms, workstations and business back-up facilities.

PRICE: Election fee (once off) £160; annual subscription £170.

AVAILABLE: Membership details and rules: Institute of Directors, 116 Pall Mall, London SW1Y 5ED Tel: 071-839 1233.

Non-Executive Directorship

Ask someone you respect to become one. A present to you because everyone needs helpful experience. A present to them because you'll have to pay them. Make sure each party knows the legal requirements of such a role – it can be a serious responsibility in bad times.

PRICE: According to age and experience, etc.

AVAILABLE: Register at: The Institute of Directors, 116 Pall Mall, London SW1Y 5ED Tel: 071-839 1233.

Open Heart Pendant

One of Tiffany's most popular gifts – a small heart-shaped pendant designed by Elsa Peretti. Good news because they cover most budgets according to whether they're silver or gold and the quality of the accompanying chain.

PRICE: £40–£100 (silver); £150–£3,500 (gold, with or without diamonds).

AVAILABLE: Tiffany & Co, 25 Old Bond Street, London W1X 3AA Tel: 071-409 2790.

Organizer (Electronic)

Telephone directory memos, a schedule facility, secret files, plus a 64K memory and the ability to communicate with a personal computer. All in a small grey calculator-size wallet!

PRICE: £74.99 [Casio].

AVAILABLE: WH Smith, Boots and electrical retailers.

Original Telephone Box

The proper red one is now becoming rarer. Lots of them are exported; other find their way into hotels and restaurants, boutiques, gardens, even embassies and military bases.

PRICE: £895.

AVAILABLE: Heritage Trading Company, PO Box 1107, Marlow, Bucks SL7 2YJ Tel: 0628 485841.

Paperknife

The more refined way to open invitations, bills, premium bond winnings and mailshots.

PRICE: £95 (silver).

AVAILABLE: Aspreys, 165-169 New Bond Street, London W1Y 0AR Tel: 071-493 6767.

Party 1

A good party must be planned well in advance. The venue, the food, the drink and the music (if any) are all important. All this can be bought in or arranged yourself using local contacts, word of mouth, the back pages of *The Tatler*, etc. Better a smaller affordable one that a large do that runs out of wine, etc.

PRICE: Variable.

AVAILABLE: The Personnel Department.

Party 2

A party can take place anywhere, doing anything. Mask Entertainments have served lunch for ten in the middle of the River Severn, arranged Prohibition Casino, and Hollywood theme parties, the Mad Hatter's Ball and dinner plus opera at Kensington Palace. Nobody pretends that this sort of behaviour is cheap, but the recipient(s) will never forget the day.

PRICE: According to plan.

AVAILABLE: Mask Entertainments, 130 Leslie Road, London E11 4HG Tel: 081-532 8001.

Personal Paintings

Seascapes, a home, a boat, landscapes, in fact anything you like, can be commissioned using the same procedure as that for a portrait. Again, carefully done, this can be a very special present for anyone.

PRICE: Depending on commission.

AVAILABLE: Emma Davis Federation of British Artists, 17 Carlton House, Terrace, London SW1Y 5BD Tel: 071-930 6844.

Portable 14″ Television

One of the most popular corporate gifts, especially used in incentive packages. This model has remote control, teletext and can be tilted to change the viewing angle.

PRICE: £249.99.

AVAILABLE: Sony centres.

Propelling Pencil and Ballpoint Pen Set

These sets are extremely simple and elegant – in fact, it's hard to imagine anyone not coveting one. Each instrument is individually numbered and made from silver. Fountain pens also available.

PRICE: From £125.

AVAILABLE: Yard-o-Led Pencil Company Ltd, 179 Forest Road, Ilford, Essex IG6 3HP.

Rent a Racehorse

For one year you can be the proud owner of a racehorse – trained, maintained and raced throughout the country. It includes your own colours, visits to the yard – you might even be able to name the horse after an individual or a leading sales team.

PRICE: £15,000.

AVAILABLE: The Market Racing Agency, Phoenix House, 86 Fulham High Street, London SW6 3LF Tel: 071-371 5639.

Sculpture

Tom Greenshields started sculpture late in his life and then produced 40 bronze figures that have now gained a great following – including 'Chrissie Drying Hair' and 'The Girl and the Boy' bookend set.

PRICE: From £130.

AVAILABLE: Through Thompsons Gallery, 38 Albemarle Street, London W1X 3FB Tel: 071-499 1314.

Set of Leather Luggage

There's luggage. Then there's this type of luggage; the sort that shouldn't be put in the aircraft's hold, and should be carried through customs for you. Three rigid suitcases and a proper trunk beautifully made in Cambridge leather.

PRICE: From £860 for one case; £5095 for the set of four.

AVAILABLE: Alfred Dunhill Ltd, 30 Duke Street, London SW1Y 6DL Tel: 071-499 9566.

Shaving Bowl, Mirror and Soap

The soap comes in a small pewter bowl and the mirror is cunningly fixed inside the lid.

PRICE: £58.

AVAILABLE: David Hayward, 123 Leckhampton Road, Cheltenham, Glos GL53 0DQ Tel: 0242 570314.

Specially Commissioned Enamel Box

Not just boxes, but any of the objects in the Halcyon Days range can be specially decorated to commemorate a specific occasion – the secession of a company, the retirement of a star player, etc. A handpainted box can be complete within about three months, a specially designed edition may take more than six months to produce.

PRICE: £82.50.

AVAILABLE: Halcyon Days, 14 Brook Street, London W1Y 1AA Tel: 071-629 8811.

Sports Cufflinks

Unique silver cufflinks that are great fun. Gun and cartridge, golfball and bag, wellie and fish, tennis racquet and ball, racing car, skier and more.

PRICE: £55–£58.

AVAILABLE: Links of London, 27 Broadgate Circle, London EC2M 2QS Tel: 071-628 9668 (Mail Order available).

Subscription to the Hambro Company Guide

An invaluable source of information, this quarterly updated publication gives you details on all UK stock market companies. Includes five years of summarized profit and loss and balance sheets and details of directors and advisers.

PRICE: £99 (four issues).

AVAILABLE: Hemmington Scott Publishing Ltd, City Innovation Centre, 25-31 Whiskin Street, London EC1R 0BP Tel: 071-278 7769.

The English Folio Case

An extraordinary story centring on a supply of reindeer leather over 200 years old recently found in a shipwreck. From this leather a number of wonderful items have been created including this elegant folio case. It takes several A4 files and has an external pocket.

PRICE: £385.

AVAILABLE: English Leather Company, Mortimer House, Castle Street, Hay-on-Wye, Herefordshire HR3 5DF Tel: 0497 821205.

Tie

Mock not. There are ties that mother might give you and then there are Chanel ties. Fun motifs like racing cars and toys are instilling them with increasing cult status.

PRICE: From £55.

AVAILABLE: Chanel, 26 Old Bond Street, London W1X 3AA Tel: 071-493 5040.

Travel Radio

Very small (wallet-sized) very popular, very punchy little radio. Listen to The World Service in Bombay, music and commentary from all over the world in the comfort of your own home.

PRICE: £180.

AVAILABLE: Sony centres throughout the UK.

Trouser Press

Not only confined to hotel rooms, a Corby Trouser Press may be a byword for straightlaced, but they also mean straight creased trousers.

PRICE: From £75.99.

AVAILABLE: Department, electrical and menswear stores. Call 0800 220351 for nearest stockist.

CHAPTER TWENTY

SPECIAL NEEDS

I~N~ his book *Under the Eye of the Clock* Christie Nolan speaks for all disabled people when he writes 'Accept me for what I am and I'll accept you for what you're accepted as'. Special needs can be so slight that we don't want to admit to them (that's directed at the 10% of people who can't hear well, but don't wear a hearing aid!), or rather more severe, but life need not be as restricted as others suppose. Here are just a few ideas to get you started.

UNDER £5

Capscrew

Wall-mounted help for those impossible-to-budge lids. Push the jar into the funnel and twist.

PRICE: £4.10.

AVAILABLE: Keep Able (Arthritis Care), Freepost, Fleming Close, Park Farm, Wellingborough, Northants NN8 3BR Tel: 0933 679426 (Mail Order).

Directory Magnifier

8″ plastic magnifier ruler which enlarges small print, for reading directories, etc.

PRICE: £2.99 (+45p p&p).

AVAILABLE: Chester Care, Low Moor Estate, Kirkby-in-Ashfield, Notts NG17 7JZ Tel: 0623 757955 (Mail Order).

Disabled Magazine

Product news, features on sport, travel and cars. Even if the magazine does seem full of ads, it's a very interesting barometer of issues and equipment of interest to disabled people.

PRICE: £4 (quarterly for two years).

AVAILABLE: CGB Publishing, Newspaper Publishing, Tannery Lane, Penketh, Cheshire WA5 2UD Tel: 0925 724234.

Free Hand Tray

A small tray with a clip-on handle and a non-slip surface, that means you can carry it and contents safely in one hand.

PRICE: £4.79.

AVAILABLE: Chester Care, Low Moor Estate, Kirkby-in-Ashfield, Notts NG17 7JZ Tel: 0623 757955 (Mail Order).

Guide to British Rail for Disabled People

Covers information on over 500 main stations, including access and useful telephone numbers. It's a good idea to phone ahead to make sure that assistance can be available at both stations.

PRICE: £4.50.

AVAILABLE: Published by RADAR, 25 Mortimer Street, London W1N 8AB Tel: 071-637 5400.

Holiday Information Leaflets

You will not be surprised to learn that any form of disablement has no bearing on a person's holiday/travel-the-world aspirations. Planning is the key. The Holiday Care Service provides factsheets for many countries together with excellent accommodation details and travel insurance.

PRICE: Free/18p stamps or donation.

AVAILABLE: The Holiday Care Service, 2 Old Bank Chambers, Station Road, Horley, Surrey RH69 9HW Tel: 0293 774535.

Key Turner

A keyring that includes a handle, giving better leverage when opening doors.

PRICE: £2.75.

AVAILABLE: Keep Able Ltd (Arthritis Care), Freepost, Fleming Close, Park Farm, Wellingborough, Northants NN8 3BR Tel: 0933 679426 (Mail Order).

Large Print and Brailled Playing Cards

As the title says, slightly wider than standard playing cards.

PRICE: £1.75.

AVAILABLE: RNIB, P O Box 173, Peterborough PE2 6WS Tel: 0345 023153.

Learning Development Aids Catalogue

Another non-present, but good source of 100s of ideas. The emphasis here is on learning and LDA supply these learning aids to almost all of the special needs schools in the country plus some of the 25,000 primary schools.

PRICE: Free.

AVAILABLE: LDA, Duke Street, Wisbeck, Cambridgeshire PE13 2AE Tel: 0945 63441.

Liquid Level Indicator

Imagine making a cup of tea if you're blind. This simple aid gives out beeps when the milk reaches a certain level. Turned round it then beeps when the hot liquid gets near the top of the cup/mug.

PRICE: £4.25.

AVAILABLE: RNIB, P O Box 173, Peterborough PE2 6WS Tel: 0345 023153.

Medicine Dispenser

A dispenser that pours liquid into a chamber opened and closed by a key. Then into a cup. Result? Known quantities of medicine taken without spilling.

PRICE: £1.50.

AVAILABLE: RNIB, P O Box 173, Peterborough PE2 6WS Tel: 0345 023153.

Needle Threader

Everyone needs one of these. An ingenious gadget that threads needles at the push of a lever.

PRICE: £1.80.

AVAILABLE: Keep Able Ltd (Arthritis Care), Freepost, Fleming Close, Park Farm, Wellingborough, Northants NN8 3BR Tel: 0933 679426 (Mail Order).

Non-Slip Pads

Hold plates and other items in place while they're being used. Especially useful for people who only have the use of one hand.

PRICE: From £3.79 according to size.

AVAILABLE: Boots Stores or Tel: 0602 506111 for catalogue, 'Independence in the Home'.

Pat Saunders Straws

People who drink regularly through a straw should get one of these. The straw has a small non-return valve in the base which limits the ingestion of air.

PRICE: £3.19 (pack of two).

AVAILABLE: Boots Stores or Tel: 0602 506111 for catalogue, 'Independence in the Home'.

Special Cutlery

A well thought-out range of knives, forks and spoons for people with limited wrist movement or the use of one hand. Specially designed handles and dishwasher-safe.

PRICE: From £4 per item.

AVAILABLE: Chester Care, Low Moor Estate, Kirkby-in-Ashfield, Notts NG17 7JZ Tel: 0623 757955 (Mail Order).

Stocking/Sock Aid

Sounds complicated, but is very effective. Feed the sock or stocking over a polythene gutter and pull up over the foot using attached tapes. There's also a version to help pull on tights.

PRICE: £2.65; £4.75 (tights version).

AVAILABLE: Boots Stores or Tel: 0602 506111 for catalogue, 'Independence in the Home'.

Tap Turners

Taps can be difficult to turn on and off at the best of times. These extensions act like a handle to provide easier leverage, and fit most taps.

PRICE: £4.75.

AVAILABLE: Boots Stores or Tel: 0602 506111 for catalogue, Independence in the Home.

TFH Fun and Achievement Catalogue

Not strictly a present in itself, but a wonderful source of presents for children and young people with special needs. 100s of ideas from multi-sensory rooms, soft play toys and music, to electric rewards, computing, games and active play products.

PRICE: Free.

AVAILABLE: 76 Barracks Road, Sandy Lane Industrial Estate, Stowport-on- Severn, Worcestershire DY13 9QB Tel: 0299 827820.

BETWEEN £5–£10

Backgammon

Specially designed for the blind, this set includes rubbed and smooth coloured playing counters and raised lines to indicate where each point is.

PRICE: £9.20.

AVAILABLE: RNIB, P O Box 173, Peterborough PE2 6WS Tel: 0345 023153.

Bed Table

Perfect for eating and reading in bed, this plastic tray has side storage for newspapers, books, pens, etc.

PRICE: £9.50.

AVAILABLE: Boots stores or Tel: 0602 506111 for catalogue, 'Independence in the Home'.

BOOK CHOICE

Nothing Ventured

A collection of over 100 tales by disabled travellers describing their adventures, setbacks and more often triumphs. An inspirational book as well as giving sensible details on key issues like choosing an airline, discovering hotels, etc.

PRICE: £7.99 [Harrap Columbus].

AVAILABLE: Larger bookshops.

Bottle Holder

No more bending down to pick up the milk. A nylon bottle-holder with a long detachable handle like a walking stick. Takes two pints of milk.

PRICE: £8.60 + 95 p&p.

AVAILABLE: Chester Care, Low Moor Estate, Kirky-in-Ashfield, Notts NG17 7JZ Tel: 0623 757955 (Mail Order).

British Sports Association for the Disabled Membership

This excellent organization creates opportunities to compete in more than 20 different sports at local, regional and national levels. Now has approximately 50,000 individual members and 550 clubs, schools and associations in ten regions of England.

PRICE: £9.

AVAILABLE: British Sports Association for the Disabled, Solecast House, 13/27 Brunswick Place, London N1 6DX Tel: 071-490 4919.

Chair Mate

A handy small tray that clips onto the arms of sofas, wheelchairs and armchairs. Useful for TV snacks or writing letters.

PRICE: £6.99.

AVAILABLE: The Special Collection, P O Box 123, 53 Dale Street, Manchester M60 6ES Tel: 061-228 0626 (Mail Order).

Handiplug

Standard 13 amp three pin plug with a large moulded handle that makes it much easier to pull out (or put in).

PRICE: £6.50 (+70p p&p).

AVAILABLE: Chester Care, Low Moor Estate, Kirkby-in-Ashfield, Notts NG17 7JZ Tel: 0623 757955 (Mail Order).

Holidays in the British Isles/Abroad 1993

RADAR's Guide to the British Isles has been published for the last 18 years and includes detailed information on over 1000 places to stay in the UK and Ireland; includes hotels, guesthouses, self-catering and special centres. *The Guide to Holidays Abroad* includes information on over 100 countries from Algeria to Zimbabwe.

PRICE: £5 (British Isles); £3.50 (Abroad).

AVAILABLE: RADAR, 25 Mortimer Street, London W1N 8AB Tel: 071-637 5400.

Long Handreachers

Extra-long lightweight arms, with strong plastic jaws and a trigger. Makes picking things up, like newspapers, from the floor much easier. This model even has a magnet at the tip for picking up pins and needles!

PRICE: £6.89 (+70p p&p).

AVAILABLE: Chester Care, Low Moor Estate, Kirkby-in-Ashfield, Notts, NG17 7JZ Tel: 0623 757955 (Mail Order).

Long Reach Nail Scissors

Forgotten what it was like to touch your toes? These 6.5″ long handled nail scissors are designed to exert powerful leverage when short-scale clippers are tricky.

PRICE: £6.95.

AVAILABLE: Chester Care, Low Moor Estate, Kirkby-in-Ashfield, Notts, NG17 7JZ Tel: 0623 757955 (Mail Order).

Riding for the Disabled

Over 700 groups throughout the country, some in purpose-built centres, some attached to riding schools. Rates for lessons may vary from the full hourly rate to free depending on the fundraising/funding situation of each individual school.

PRICE: Variable.

AVAILABLE: Details of schools from: Riding for the Disabled Association, Avenue R, NAC, Kenilworth, Warwickshire CV8 2LY Tel: 0203 696510.

Shoe and Boot Remover

Simple beechwood frame to help remove shoes and boots without bending.

PRICE: £5.05.

AVAILABLE: Chester Care, Low Moor Estate, Kirkby-in-Ashfield, Notts NG17 7JZ Tel: 0623 757955 (Mail Order).

Tall Dustpan and Brush

A very useful three-foot handle allows sweeping up with a minimum of bending.

PRICE: £7.35.

AVAILABLE: Boots stores or Tel: 0602 506111 for catalogue, 'Independence in the Home'.

Two-Handed Mug

Sensibly designed with two large easy-to-grip and adjustable handles. A drinking spout and/or an antispill lid which can be added to control any possible spillage.

PRICE: £6.30.

AVAILABLE: Boots Stores or Tel: 0602 506111 for catalogue, 'Independence in the Home'.

Warmers

Warmers provide gentle heat to relieve all manner of aches and pains. Available for hands, backs, and other limbs.

PRICE: From £5.99.

AVAILABLE: Boots Stores or Tel: 0602 506111 for catalogue, 'Independence in the Home'.

Waterskiing

The British Disabled Water Ski Association do wonders. They've developed teaching techniques and training devices that can enable almost everyone to take up this sport including amputees, the blind, deaf, those suffering from partial paralysis and those confined to a wheelchair.

PRICE: Beginners: day £6, then £3 every 10 minutes.

AVAILABLE: The British Disabled Waterski Assocation, The Tony Edge Centre, Heron Lake, Hythe End, Wraysbury, Middlesex TW19 6HW Tel: 0784 483664.

BETWEEN £10–£20

BOOK CHOICE
Gardening Equipment for Disabled People

Describes and illustrates an immense range of tools and equipment that can make gardening possible for those who might otherwise have to abandon this hobby.

PRICE: £11.50.

AVAILABLE: Disability Information Trust, Mary Marlborough Lodge, Nuffield Orthopaedic Centre, Headington, Oxford OX3 7LD Tel: 0865 741155 (Mail Order).

Clothes for Women

'The Special Collection' is a mail order catalogue that caters especially for those with dressing difficulties. Full of bright, pretty and practical clothes and chosen with advice from the Disabled Living Foundation. Includes clothes with such features such as 'step-in' styles, long front zip fastenings and special loops for pulling on skirts.

PRICE: e.g. plain knit dress with front button fastening £19.95.

AVAILABLE: The Special Collection, P O Box 123, 53 Dale Street, Manchester M60 6ES Tel: 061 228 0626.

Easy Slice Knife

An adjustable blade lets the user cut meat, cheese, bread and other foods to different thicknesses.

PRICE: £12.25.

AVAILABLE: RNIB, PO Box 173, Peterborough PE2 6WS Tel: 0345 023153.

Horticultural Therapy Membership

Staffed mainly by horticulturalists with expertise in gardening with special needs. Offer an information service, advice and courses for blind gardeners, training days and a magazine published four times a year, plus books and leaflets.

PRICE: £15 annual membership.

AVAILABLE: Horticultural Therapy, Goulds Ground, Vallis Way, Frome, Somerset BA11 3DW Tel: 0373 464782.

Kettle Tipper

Platform that holds a kettle firmly in place allowing it to be tipped gently to pour out hot water. Jug kettle versions also available.

PRICE: £13.99.

AVAILABLE: Boots Stores or Tel: 0602 506111 for catalogue, 'Independence in the Home'.

Monopoly

A special tactile board with money, title deeds, chance and community chest cards in large print and braille.

PRICE: £14.95.

AVAILABLE: RNIB, P O Box 173, Peterborough PE2 6WS Tel: 0345 023153.

Scrabble/Large Size Scrabble

The large print version features a bigger board with the letters and values in large print. Another version has them in braille and the tiles fit into embossed squares on the board. The large size has grabbable size bits that save giving up the game because scrabbling's no fun anymore.

PRICE: £15.75/£16.50 (large print); £23.44 (large size).

AVAILABLE: RNIB, P O Box 173, Peterborough PE2 6WS Tel: 0345 023153; Notting Rehabilitation, Ludlow Hill Road, West Bridgford, Nottingham, NG2 6HD Tel: 0602 452345 (Mail Order).

MAGAZINE SUBSCRIPTION
See Hear!

A monthly magazine for the deaf and hard-of-hearing published in association with the BBC. Product previews, consumer advice column and a 'what's on' section plus the latest news and stories.

PRICE: £11 p.a.

AVAILABLE: *See Hear!* Subscriptions, RNID, 105 Gower Street, London WC1E 6AH Tel: 071-387 8033.

Slimline Talking Clock/Talking Clock

Very neat creditcard-size talking clock. Ideal for pockets or handbags. The talking clock speaks the time at the push of a button and has an alarm function and an hourly time announcement setting.

PRICE: £14.95 (Slimline); £14.95 (talking clock).

AVAILABLE: RNIB, P O Box 173, Peterborough PE2 6WS Tel: 0345 023153.

Snuggler

Hot-waterless hot water bottles! Fitted with a special gel pack which can be heated in a microwave or in boiling water.

PRICE: £10.20.

AVAILABLE: RNIB, P O Box 173, Peterborough PE2 6WS Tel: 0345 023153.

Spill Not

This base firmly holds jars and bottles upright so that the top can be twisted with one or both hands.

PRICE: £11.50.

AVAILABLE: Boots Stores or Tel: 0602 506111 for catalogue, 'Independence in the Home'.

Talking Newspapers

A great scheme whereby newspapers and magazines are available on cassette. Publications cover the whole range, from *The Observer* and *The Economist* to *Farmers Weekly*, *Private Eye* and *Just Seventeen*.

PRICE: Annual membership fee £10 for three titles.

AVAILABLE: The Talking Newspaper Association, Heathfield, East Sussex TN21 8DB Tel; 0435 866102.

Washing and Grooming Products

All these aids are well designed with long, easy-to-hold handles and adjustable articulated joints.

PRICE: comb £13.75; hairbrush £21.80; flannel £17.80; extra-long bathbrush £20.50.

AVAILABLE: Keep Able (Arthritis Care), Freepost, Fleming Close, Park Farm, Wellingborough, Northants NN8 3BR Tel: 0933 679426 (Mail Order).

Wedge Pillow

The most comfortable way to read or watch telly in bed, this wedge-shaped pillow with a gentle 30 degree slope allows the spine to rest in a natural, stress-free position.

PRICE: £19.99.

AVAILABLE: Chester Care, Low Moor Estate, Kirkby-in-Ashfield, Notts, NG17 7JZ Tel: 0623 757955 (Mail Order).

BETWEEN £20–£50

Bath Seat

Designed specifically for people who find it tricky to get in or out of the bath. The seat fits inside the bath and has non-slip non-scratch plastic rests. (It is advisable to check with the occupational therapist or DSS to ensure correct fitting.)

PRICE: £29.95.

AVAILABLE: Boots; Pam's Shopping Service, Help the Aged, P O Box 28, London N18 3HG Tel: 081-803 6861 (Mail Order).

Clarity Telephones

No more shouting down the phone. This phone is designed to make incoming calls louder and clearer. Also lights up so you can see an incoming call.

PRICE: £49.99.

AVAILABLE: Sound Advantage, 1 Metro Centre, Welbeck Way, Peterborough, PE2 7UH Tel: 0733 361199 (Mail Order).

Cutting Guide

If you can't cut bread, meat or vegetables straight, this simple piece of equipment will help enormously. Vertical pillars guide the knife through the item until it hits the base.

PRICE: £21.99.

AVAILABLE: Boots stores or Tel: 0602 506111 for catalogue, 'Independence in the Home'.

Electric Can Opener

Opens cans, removes bottle tops, and slices open plastic bags quickly and simply.

PRICE: £28.99 [Kenwood].

AVAILABLE: Boots stores or Tel: 0602 506111 for catalogue, 'Independence in the Home', department stores, kitchen depts.

Flower Picker/Pruner

Cuts and holds so that you can pick flowers without bending; or prune roses at arm's length.

PRICE: £24.95.

AVAILABLE: Keep Able Ltd (Arthritis Care), Freepost, Fleming Close, Park Farm, Wellingborough, Northants NN8 3BR Tel: 0933 679426 (Mail Order).

Folding Chair Stick

Good news for race meetings, picnics or just 'taking a breather', this is a smart, lightweight, rustproof, instant seat.

PRICE: £31.50.

AVAILABLE: Boots stores or Tel: 0602 506111 for catalogue, 'Independence in the Home'.

Handisocket Extensions

Extension sockets for electric plugs that raise them from the skirting board to an accessible height. Not a stunningly attractive idea but very practical.

PRICE: £22.75 (single) plus £1.95 p&p; £26.25 (double) plus £1.95 p&p.

AVAILABLE: Chester Care, Low Moor Estate, Kirkby-in-Ashfield, Notts NG17 7JZ Tel: 0623 757955 (Mail Order).

Long Handled Weeder

Do the weeding without bending down.

PRICE: £22.60.

AVAILABLE: Keep Able Ltd (Arthritis Care), Freepost, Fleming Close, Park Farm, Wellingborough, Northants NN8 3BR Tel: 0933 679426 (Mail Order).

Personal Listening System

Directional radar for ears. A microphone directed at a person or TV picks up the sound and amplifies it into a loop hanging round the neck.

PRICE: From £31.60 [Crescendo].

AVAILABLE: Sound Advantage, 1 Metro Centre, Welbeck Way, Peterborough, PE2 7UH Tel: 0733 361199 (Mail Order).

Shopping Trolley

The ultimate shopping trolley. Wheels, a detachable bag AND a full size seat that folds down so that you can take a rest.

PRICE: £48.85.

AVAILABLE: Keep Able Ltd (Arthritis Care), Freepost, Fleming Close, Park Farm, Wellingborough, Northants NN8 3BR Tel: 0933 679426 (Mail Order).

Sound Beacon

A humming device. If you're in the garden when the phone goes, put on the beacon and it will guide you back to the area of work when the conversation's finished.

PRICE: £22.25.

AVAILABLE: RNIB, P O Box 173, Peterborough PE2 6WS Tel: 0345 023153.

Talking Bathroom Scales

Good news, even if the voice is North American. Fitted with memory buttons so that they can tell you how much weight you've lost since you last stood on them.

PRICE: £35.

AVAILABLE: RNIB, P O Box 173, Peterborough PE2 6WS Tel: 0345 023153.

Talking Clock Barometer

Tells you the time and the weather forecast 6-7 hours in advance. Seems incredible but the agents claim the forecast are 80% accurate.

PRICE: £24.50.

AVAILABLE: RNIB, P O Box 173, Peterborough PE2 6WS Tel: 0345 023153.

Talking Kitchen Scales

Easy-to-use with a choice of imperial or metric weights. Accurate to within 10g (1 oz). Not suitable for diabetics or anyone else requiring exact food.

PRICE: £29.95.

AVAILABLE: RNIB, P O Box 173, Peterborough PE2 6WS Tel: 0345 023153.

Vibrating Pillow Alarm

A pad linked to a modified bedside clock. When the alarm goes off the vibrator unit is activated giving a gentle persistent signal. Wake Up.

PRICE: £39.90.

AVAILABLE: Sound Advantage, 1 Metro Centre, Welbeck Way, Peterborough PE2 7UH Tel: 0733 361199 (Mail Order).

£50 AND ABOVE

Adjustable Bed

This bed can be electrically adjusted to raise your head (to help with emphysema, asthma and other breathing problems) or your feet (to help with circulation problems, rheumatic pains, etc). It also has a built-in massage unit with different intensities to choose from.

PRICE: £2173.

AVAILABLE: Keep Able Ltd, Capital Interchange Way, Brentford, Middlesex TW8 0EX Tel: 081-742 2181.

Bathability

Perfect for people who have little strength in their arms and legs. A bathseat that literally lowers you to the bottom of the bath; and it is powerful enough to return you to the top again.

PRICE: From £272.50; £490 (Battery powered model).

AVAILABLE: Keep Able Ltd (Arthritis Care), Freepost, Fleming Close, Park Farm, Wellingborough, Northants NN8 3BR Tel: 0933 679426 (Mail Order).

Bracelet for People with Diabetes

These bracelets can be made out of silver or gold and are a much nicer way of carrying necessary information than the plain stainless steel. On each bracelet is the telephone number of

Medicalert – a 24-hour support system – together with your lifetime membership number and the condition i.e. diabetes. Full record of the type of insulin, etc, is kept on their computer.

PRICE: £70 silver bracelet; £90 gold plate.

AVAILABLE: Medicalert, 12 Bridge Wharf, 156 Caledonian Road, London N1 9UU Tel: 071-323 1531.

Domestic Loop System

A loop system round a room lets a person with a hearing aid listen to the TV or a hi-fi using his/her own volume controls without affecting others.

PRICE: £69.95.

AVAILABLE: Sound Advantage, 1 Metro Centre, Welbeck Way, Peterborough, PE2 7UH Tel: 0733 361199 (Mail Order).

Eezee Reader

A portable hand-held camera that plugs into a TV set and greatly magnifies the print from newspapers, magazines and books – the football score becomes enormous!

PRICE: £280.

AVAILABLE: The Force Ten Co Ltd, 183 Boundary Road, Woking, Surrey GU21 5BU Tel; 0483 762711.

Holiday for Children with Diabetes

Reports of huge amounts of fun and excellent organization on these holidays. Split into age groups ranging from 8 to 18, the children take over various schools and outdoor centres. Complete with a full team of nurses, doctors and dieticians. Then off on tour of country houses, all sorts of sport and so on. Even morning and evening blood tests become bearable.

PRICE: From £200 for one week.

AVAILABLE: Youth Dept, British Diabetes Association, 10 Queen Anne Street, London W1M 0BD Tel: 071-323 1531.

Holidays

The Seychelles, Disneyworld, Holland, Devon and Cornwall are some of the destinations offered by Chalfont. They offer three levels of care option on each holiday – basic for the client who feels able to manage on his own; share care designed for someone who wants to go in a wheelchair and be looked after; finally, individual helper, a one-to-one carer system.

PRICE: According to holiday and service level: e.g. a basic week holiday in a four-star hotel in Devon £456; an individual care fortnight in The Canadian Rockies £5945 (both include excursions).

AVAILABLE: The Chalfont Line Ltd, 4 Medway Parade, Perivale, Middlesex UB6 8HA Tel: 081-997 3799.

Scootas

The sheer freedom these machines give a person is invaluable. Whether going round the garden or down to the shops, these models go up to 8 mph with a range of 25 miles. They'll go up kerbs and can be dismantled to go in car boots etc. Four-wheels gives extra stability.

PRICE: £2295 (Sterling four 3 wheels); £2395 (Sterling XL four wheels).

AVAILABLE: Sterling Medical Ltd, Fens Pool Avenue, Brierly Hill, West Midlands DY51 1QA Tel: 0384 480480.

Sports Wheelchair

Practical, lightweight sports wheelchairs in a range of bright fashionable colours. Racing chairs, chairs specially adapted for basketball, even 'all terrain' four-wheel chairs for going off-road.

PRICE: Basic chair from £895.

AVAILABLE: Marshall Sports Chairs, Cherry Orchard Farm, Hawks Hill, Leatherhead, Surrey KT22 DS Tel: 0372 372731.

Stairlift

Only if you've experienced the difficulties involved in going up and down stairs will you appreciate the difference this apparatus can make to life. A simple chair that automatically carries you up and down stairs at the push of a button and doesn't matter what shape your stairs are. Now you don't have to move to a flat or bungalow.

PRICE: From £1900 to around £3900.

AVAILABLE: Stannah Stairlifts Ltd, Dept 6630, Freepost, Andover, Hants SP10 3BR Tel: 0800 378386.